THE SEX LIFE

HERBERT WENDT

OF THE ANIMALS

Translated from the German by Richard and Clara Winston

SIMON AND SCHUSTER / NEW YORK

■

ACKNOWLEDGMENTS

I am deeply indebted to the scholars and writers of past and present whose names I have listed in the bibliography, as well as to many institutions and persons who have aided me with valuable advice and supplied me with information and illustrations. I should like especially to mention the Senckenberg Library in Frankfurt am Main and the Baden State Library in Karlsruhe, to which I have turned for years with my literary projects; also Dr. Gerhart Heberer in Berlin, Dr. Adolf Portmann in Basel, Dr. Gottfried Koller in Saarbrücken and Dr. Jean Rostand in Ville d'Avray. In addition, the zoological institutions of Frankfurt, Cologne, Paris, Basel, and Rio de Janeiro have allowed me the privilege of studying the behavior of animals in captivity.

I am particularly grateful to my wife Ingeborg Wendt for her active assistance in libraries, on several overseas voyages, and in the preparation of the manuscript. Without her help, extending over many years, this book could never have been sent out into the world. I express the same cordial thanks to my son Peter A. Wendt for obtaining and preparing the material for many of the illustrations.

—HERBERT WENDT

■

CONTENTS

6 CONTENTS

LIST OF ILLUSTRATIONS

INTRODUCTION

THE TREE OF KNOWLEDGE

The story of reproduction is the story of life itself: the most tremendous event that has ever taken place on our small planet. Biologists may point out that the most significant of the life processes is not increase but metabolism, and that life is quite conceivable without sexuality, offspring, and the endless succession of new generations. So it is, theoretically. But such sterile self-perpetuating life would have no future, no potentiality of evolving. It would be nothing but a monstrous growth, a cancer upon the face of the earth. It would be meaningless, parasitic life, living death, a violation of nature.

It is true that for thousands of years philosophers have dreamed of eternal life, of an escape from the cycle of death and rebirth. But scientists can only smile at this dream of a static life, and hope that it will never be realized upon earth. For although the individual may long for immortality, if he ceased to reproduce, the earth would be a dying planet.

As things are, two mighty, irresistible instincts dominate all living things. Hunger compels living things to preserve themselves by taking in food; sex compels them to couple and multiply. That has been recognized for ages, and it may be assumed that hunger and sex will continue to be the great motive forces that will preserve life and permit it to develop, spread, and advance.

Ever since man began to think and to raise himself above his fellow creatures he has struggled, usually in vain, to free himself from the decrees of nature. At times he has condemned hunger and sex as low

9

animal impulses, and has opposed to them an enormous variety of ethical values.

He has regulated his sex life, has tried to limit it by all manner of taboos and moral strictures. Behind all these efforts has lain the desire to dominate this all-powerful natural force, to secure a firm grip on it and possibly in the end to overcome it. The desire is understandable—for man is always seeking to make the forces of nature do his bidding. But it is precisely this one natural force that civilized man has failed to control. On the contrary, his attempts to deal with it have only exposed his helplessness. In this case he has learned that he is not the measure of all things but a part of nature, dominated by his instinctual life. In spite of all his intellect he is "more of an animal than any brute," as Goethe puts it in his *Faust*.

The long moral and cultural history of humanity has not, however, been entirely without effect. Animal standards and instinctive animal conduct have been replaced by different standards and rules of behavior. Man discovered love, faithfulness, family affection. And so he would like to think that he has also developed a higher, nobler form of sexuality, one less bound by instinct. But this flattering belief has been considerably shaken by the discoveries of two generations of scientists—the generation of Freud and the generation of Kinsey. Civilized man is, to use a favorite phrase of biologists, a creature who has domesticated himself. In doing that, he has placed himself outside the strict rules of the strugggle for existence. He has grown more independent of nature—which means that he has become more unnatural. This unnaturalness emerges especially in his sexual life.

The art, literature, and moral philosophies of all times and countries have dealt largely with the subject. Domesticated mankind has invariably pushed all its potentialities to extremes and has produced not only philosophers, poets, and founders of religions, but also tyrants, mass murderers, and sex criminals; not only moralities and religions, but also sexual psychoses, anomalies, and perversion. From time immemorial every generation has faced anew the problem of how to control these extremes.

If we call sexuality the "most animal of all the instincts," as some moralists do, we are in fact honoring it. For it is a moralistic fable to picture the sex life of animals as a realm of unrestrained promiscuity. Actually animals are bound by instincts which enforce a stricter code of behavior than any moral commandments can impose. In the higher vertebrates, it is true, deviations from the norm do occur. But such perversions, as we would call them, are exceptions and frequently outgrowths of unnatural conditions of life. On the whole they do not significantly influence the whole life of a species. Animals continue to live in a state of sexual innocence.

In the early days of animal psychology, when the trend was still to interpret animals in human terms, moralists held up the ethical and sexual lives of animals as a mirror to mankind. Some species of animals provided examples of gracious wooing, chivalric competition, tender love of offspring, and parental sacrifice. Others served as illustrations of lust, voluptuousness, sexual jealousy, polygamy, and deficient familial affection. Today it is generally agreed that no group of animals is more moral than any other. We recognize that our human conceptions of vice and virtue are irrelevant for passing judgment in the world of animals. It is as foolish to draw an analogy between a stupid, rough, violent human being and an animal as it is to contrast a brutal, excessive, or degenerate sex life with the sane sexuality of animals. Animals are neither good nor evil, neither moral nor immoral. Each species obeys its predetermined laws. But man departed from this pattern once he had tasted of the tree of knowledge.

The propagation of life is by no means always linked to the sex instinct. Lower plants and one-celled animals reproduce by asexual means, by division or budding. Asexual reproduction sometimes takes place in the higher, multicellular organisms as well, but such instances may be considered abnormal, a response to special conditions of life. Normally a multicellular plant or animal consists of a perishable body and a number of reproductive cells which separate off at maturity and grow into new organisms. The higher stages of life are characterized by that process which we call fertilization. Two unlike sexual cells, one male and one female, merge into a single fertilized cell which develops into a new living creature either outside or inside the body of the mother.

At these higher stages of evolution sexuality becomes a dominant force. An irresistible instinct which no organism can escape drives both sexes toward sexual union. The process is one that man observes with esthetic pleasure when it takes place in the plant world, but with a certain embarrassment when animals are involved. Until the end of the eighteenth century flowering plants were generally regarded as symbols of chastity, coupling animals as symbols of concupiscence.

In the year 1787 Christian Konrad Sprengel, assistant headmaster of a school in Spandau, Germany, published an essay bearing the somewhat pompous title of *The Newly Revealed Mystery of Nature in the Structure and Fertilization of Flowers.* The work disposed of the pretty illusion that flowers were free of sex. Sprengel presumed

The title page of Christian Conrad Sprengel's work, in which he was the first to describe accurately the sexual intercourse of plants. This boldness cost him his teaching job.

to compare the blossoms of plants with the sexual organs of animals. He also described precisely how the sexual intercourse of plants took place with the aid of various intermediaries, such as insects and the wind. Today, these details are commonplace to every school child, but Sprengel's contemporaries found them shocking. He was dismissed from his teaching post and his book was withdrawn from circulation. The discoverer of fertilization in plants would have been reduced to beggary but for a number of broad-minded citizens of Spandau who let him tutor their children.

One hundred and ten years after Sprengel's rash venture, a writer on popular science named Wilhelm Bölsche brought out a three volume chronicle of *Love Life in Nature*. His book was a typical product of the nineteenth century's enthusiasm for natural science. Bölsche's "Kaleidoscope of Love" covered all that was known of the processes of reproduction and sexuality in nature. It ran the whole gamut of creation, from one-celled plants to man. It discussed everything, from the origins of life to the absurdities of the human sex act, from the bewitchment of love to venereal diseases—which Bölsche poetically called "love's dance of death." Written in a smug, romanticizing Victorian style, the book is scarcely readable today. But the very complacency and euphemism of the style was, according to Bölsche himself, a matter of strategy. This tone permitted him to inform the general public of matters which had theretofore been considered disgusting.

Bölsche's evolutionary history of sex smashed innumerable taboos and prejudices. And it became a best seller. It was translated into every major language and became a standard item in the libraries of solid citizens seeking self-improvement. With wonderment the good bourgeois discovered that there was nothing repellent about the sexual processes, whether they took place in sponges, worms, fish, birds, monkeys, or men. In Bölsche's own words, these processes were miracles of nature, "eternal wonders of generation, eternal miracles of love . . . manifestations of the Creative Word that has built worlds and out of old worlds builds better ones. . . ."

In our far more sober, fact-hungry and fact-haunted age, we can only smile tolerantly at these sentimental effusions. Further taboos have fallen by the wayside. Men such as Sigmund Freud and Alfred C. Kinsey, and generations of physicians, psychologists, and biologists, have analyzed and tabulated, have compared animal with human sexual behavior. The study of reproduction, of genetics and of sexology has become a group of scientific disciplines of supreme importance. Man is trying to understand and manipulate the processes of procreation, fertilization, and heredity in order to exert some control over the future development of his domestic animals, his cultivated plants, and himself.

The time is ripe for a new, evolutionary history of reproduction. I am not being coy or circumspect when I deal chiefly with animals rather than with human beings. On the contrary, it seems to me that most histories of morals have far too little to say about sexuality in the animal world. The instinctual life of animals forms the natural and the scientific basis for our own sexual life, and we can properly interpret virtually all aspects of human sex only by examining its prehuman roots in the animal world. "To go to the animals means to go home," the Danish writer Johannes V. Jensen once said.

Wilhelm Bölsche. His smugly romanticized, three-volume chronicle, Love-Life in Nature, *published in 1902, covered all that was known about reproduction and sexuality in nature. It became a best seller.*

■

CHAPTER ONE

LIFE'S ORIGIN AND THE LEGEND

OF SPONTANEOUS GENERATION

BORN OF SLIME AND DECAY

How did the first life come into being? Who begot it? And when did this first act of generation take place? This is one of the key problems of biology, but in spite of innumerable fine-sounding hypotheses it has not yet been solved.

The early Greek philososophers, the first thinkers who seriously speculated about the origin of life, were by and large evolutionists. They believed in a gradual development of the earth and its living creatures. Of course they also considered how life might have come into the world. Whether they assumed that life had arisen first in the water, in the air, or on the dry land, they were all convinced that the primal origin could only be explained by *spontaneous generation*.

Some of these early theories of spontaneous generation sound like a report from a chamber of horrors. The democratic statesman and philosopher Empedocles of Acragas in Sicily, for example, conceived of a veritable pandemonium in which crude shapes and unmatched parts of bodies had come thrusting out of the moist, damp earth. Torsos without heads and limbs, detached arms and legs, isolated eyes, ears, and noses, sought and found additional parts that did not always suit them. Thus, according to Empedocles, there arose grotesque monsters: "Many creatures were created with a face and breast on both sides; and again there arose offspring of men with heads of cattle; and mixed creatures with male organs and with hair-covered genitals in the manner of women."

But nature, Empedocles argued, made a strict selection among

15

these monstrous experiments, destroying all the unfit and the freaks. There remained those organisms capable of surviving. With a bit of good will we might regard this theory as a vague foreshadowing of Darwin's principle of survival of the fittest.

"It is impossible for it to be as Empedocles says. . . . If it were so, it would be a matter of chance what comes up when you sow this seed or that." Such was the conclusion of the great philosopher who lived at the court of King Philip of Macedon and instructed young Prince Alexander in science and philosophy. Aristotle, the greatest scientist of antiquity, would not admit that Nature operates by hazard. "Nature does nothing without a reason."

On his own account Aristotle elaborated a theory of the origin of life which for two thousand years was accepted by most philosophers and scientists, and which sounds eminently reasonable to this day. He declared that Nature accomplished the transformation from dead matter to living substance so gradually that the boundary between the two must remain uncertain and difficult to recognize. He went further, however, and promulgated an idea which has found little favor with modern biologists. Nature, he maintained, had not only shaped and animated crude matter in the dim and nebulous past, but continued to do so and was constantly producing a variety of creatures by spontaneous generation.

Thus the Father of Science was also the originator of the popular superstition that mice arise from dirt, tapeworms from the contents of the intestines, and cheese maggots from ripe cheese. Such things did not seem strange to the Greeks, who drew no sharp line of distinction between organic and inorganic matter. They would rather have wondered at the contrary assertion. If Aphrodite, the goddess of love, had been born of the foam of the sea, why should there not be foam-born or slime-born organisms? Consequently no one found it odd when Aristotle asserted that a variety of creatures whose reproduction he had been unable to explain emerged naturally from mud, ferment, dampness, or decay: plants, snails, worms, sponges, crabs, many insects, and even a number of vertebrate animals.

"The hermit crab," Aristotle wrote in his *History of Animals,* "grows spontaneously out of soil and slime, and finds its way into untenanted shells. As it grows it shifts to a larger shell. . . . Some insects are not derived from living parentage, but are generated spontaneously; some out of dew falling on leaves, ordinarily in springtime, but often in winter when there has been a stretch of fair weather and southerly winds; others grow in decaying mud or dung; others in timber, green or dry; some in the hair of animals; some in the flesh of animals; some from excrement after it has been voided, and some from excrement yet within the living animal."

Since Aristotle was regarded as the highest authority on scientific questions among the Romans, the Arabs, the Scholastics, and down to the time of the Enlightenment, it became an axiom that frogs and mice were born of the Nile mud, that crabs rained from the sky and caterpillars spawned from humus and decay. The notion was hard to dislodge when Maria Sibylla Merian, the great investigator and painter of European and South American butterflies in the latter part of the eighteenth century, observed that caterpillars came from eggs and butterflies from pupated caterpillars. Her statements were generally regarded as fantasy or outright fraud. Yet a good deal was already known about the reproduction and metamorphoses of insects.

The favorite example of the believers in spontaneous generation was, however, the eel. There was a special reason for this. Aristotle had emphasized that no eel "was ever found supplied with either milt or spawn, nor are they when cut open found to have within them passages for spawn or for eggs." It was not suspected that river eels have an extremely complex reproductive history and do not reach sexual maturity until they set out on their spawning journey to the sea. In consequence, Aristotle made the eel the hero of a picturesque romance of spontaneous generation:

"Eels are not the issue of pairing, neither are they oviparous. . . . There can be no doubt about this. For in some standing pools, after the water has been drained off and the mud has been dredged away, the eels appear again after a fall of rain. In time of drought they do not appear even in stagnant ponds, for the simple reason that their existence and sustenance is derived from rain water. . . . Some writers, however, are of the opinion that they generate their kind, because in some eels little worms are found, from which they suppose that eels are derived. But this opinion is not founded on fact. Eels are derived from the so-called 'earth's guts' that grow spontaneously in mud and in humid ground; in fact, eels have at times been seen to emerge out of such earth guts, and on other occasions have been rendered visible when the earth guts were laid open by either scraping or cutting. Such earth guts are found both in the sea and in rivers, especially where there is decayed matter: in the sea in places where seaweed abounds, and in rivers and marshes near to the edge; for it is near to the water's edge that sun heat has its chief power and produces putrefaction."

Later writers amended some aspects of Aristotle's eel story. But their own contributions were equally quaint. One theory had it that young eels developed from horse hairs that had fallen into water; another that they originated out of scraps of skin cast or scraped off by the old eels. Izaak Walton, the "Father of Angling," mentions a third hypothesis: "And others say, that as pearls are made of gluti- nous dewdrops which are condensed by the sun's heat, . . . so Eels are bred of a particular dew, falling in the months of May or June on the banks of some particular ponds or rivers, apted by nature for that end; which in a few days are by the sun's heat turned into Eels."

Those who opposed *generatio aequivoca*, as spontaneous generation was called by the scholars of the time, proposed theories no less fan- tastic. It was an unusually cautious and sober person who suggested that eels were begotten by snakes.

ADAM'S TAPEWORMS

The seventeenth century delivered the first severe blows to the the- ory of spontaneous generation. The assault was led by two of the greatest scientific pioneers of the century: Jan Swammerdam and Antonij van Leeuwenhoek, the first microscopists.

"Mites, intestinal worms, and infusoria can no more arise without reproduction than an elephant can spring from the dust!" van Leeu- wenhoek declared. And Swammerdam emphatically supported him: "What folly it is to regard the larger animals as perfect while smaller creatures are seen as aberrations or chance products of putrefaction! Such views undermine the constant orderliness of nature."

Yet these challenging words might have gone unheeded had not a practical biologist set about confirming them by experiment. In 1674 Francesco Redi, a poet, biologist, and personal physician to the grand dukes of Tuscany, undertook a long-overdue experimental investiga- tion of the problem of spontaneous generation. He filled a number of vessels with fresh meat, cheese, and similar substances, wrapped some tightly with gauze and left others open, and placed them all in the hot sun.

After several days the contents of the jars turned putrescent. Redi examined them. The open vessels, he saw, were swarming with mag- gots; the closed ones were completely free of maggots. How had the maggots got into the open jars? Redi found out when he examined the gauze wrappings over the maggot-free jars more closely. Many tiny eggs were clinging to the gauze—eggs of blowflies laid by female flies attracted by the odor of decay. Fly maggots, Redi concluded, were not born from putrescent materials, but from eggs, just like fish, frogs, birds, and other higher animals.

Redi's experiment was a triumph of research over Aristotelian theories. Insects, all reasonable scholars had to admit, were begotten by parents who resembled them.

The case of intestinal worms, however, was somewhat more complicated. For there not only biology but also theology was involved. It was difficult to imagine that tapeworms and roundworms had existed to torment their hosts from the beginning of creation. For if Adam had been plagued by parasites even before the Fall, he could not have lived happily in Paradise.

Had intestinal worms arisen in later times, after the expulsion from Eden, by a special act of creation? Theologians found this untenable, for the Bible taught that God had done with his creation after the sixth day. In view of this, the only decent explanation was that these pests had arisen by spontaneous generation in the intestines of the host. Most naturalists fell in with this assumption; as late as the early years of the nineteenth century there were serious scientists who held that the tapeworm was a product of the intestines. As Bölsche wrote: "Whenever philosophy, whether materialistic or theological, found spontaneous generation useful, it trotted out the tapeworm; whenever it found spontaneous generation troublesome, it hacked away at it without mercy."

Redi, too, was inclined to exclude the tapeworm from his theory of reproduction and to regard spontaneous generation of this highly controversial creature as at least possible. Antonio Vallisneri, professor of medicine in Padua, at last disposed of the paradox by an ingenious kind of reasoning. As Vallisneri saw it, Adam had acquired his tapeworms at the time of creation, but because of the light, easily digestible food in Paradise the worms had held their peace until the Fall and had not in the least troubled the father of all mankind. They became a torment and punishment only after the Fall. As for Eve's tapeworms, Vallisneri reasoned, their germs had either already been contained in Adam's rib or had been transmitted by natural physical contact from man to woman, after the pair had lost their paradisiacal innocence.

The experimenters who followed in Redi's footsteps accepted Vallisneri's hypothesis—though somewhat doubtfully—for they were honest enough to admit that nothing was known about the origin of lower organisms. Nevertheless, they went on experimenting, with the result that they gradually had to exclude the possibility of spontaneous origin from dead matter in most classes of animals. There remained as a possibility only the microorganisms which had been discovered by van Leeuwenhoek, chief foe of the theory of spontaneous generation.

LOOKING THROUGH THE FLEA GLASS

On December 7, 1674, a bookkeeper employed in a textile firm in the Dutch city of Delft sent a letter to the Royal Society in London informing that celebrated group of scientists that he had taken a few drops of water from a pond near Delft and under the microscope seen in it "living little animals"—tiny creatures briskly swimming about in the water drops. A few months later this bookkeeper prepared the first *infusion*—a brew of hay, rain water, and ground pepper. Again, he looked at it under the magnifying lens and found to his astonishment that this infusion was swarming with living creatures.

This was the beginning of microzoology, and of new riddles concerning the origin of life. For the Delft bookkeeper, Antonij van Leeuwenhoek, and other early microscopists, subsequently moistened a great variety of lifeless materials with rain water. They tried dust, dirt from roof gutters, long-parched encrustations from moss-covered roofs, withered weeds, and dried mud. Each time their lenses showed that with the addition of moisture the dead matter suddenly came to life. Tiny oval or oblong animalcules writhed, swam, darted, and crawled around in the infusions—protozoa, as we would today call these one-celled animals. Very likely these early researchers were also seeing microscopically small members of higher classes of animals —rotifers, for example. But for the moment we shall concern ourselves only with the infusoria, the one-celled animals.

The art of microscopy was still new at the time. There had, it is true, been forerunners of the microscope in the sixteenth century, but the business of magnifying the world of small living creatures had not been taken very seriously. Itinerant showmen with a pair of lenses would go about from fair to fair amusing the public by placing fleas, lice, and other vermin under the glasses and thus converting them into huge monsters.

In the seventeenth century, however, the masterly glass polishers and spectacle-makers of Holland had transformed these "flea glasses" into useful scientific tools. The finest magnifying instruments were produced in Delft, the home of Leeuwenhoek. He occupies a place of honor in the pantheon of great biologists. The four hundred microscopes that he constructed in his long life of ninety-one years were instruments of amazing precision for the time. Some of them could magnify objects two and three hundred times. He guarded these superior products of his art with jealousy and suspicion, refusing even to permit Leibniz to use them, although the philosopher came to Delft for that very purpose.

In addition to the infusoria, Leeuwenhoek discovered many other small living creatures. He may even have seen bacteria through his wonderful microscopes. His curiosity was insatiable: everything that could possibly be viewed he placed under his lenses. Thus he was the first to see the red blood corpuscles, the channels of the teeth, the transverse striations of muscle fiber, the scales of the human epidermis, the eggs and larvae of fleas. He observed that the whitish things which theretofore had always been termed "ant eggs," and which are popularly called that even to this day, were actually ant pupae, and he obtained real eggs from ant nests. He placed tadpoles under the magnifying glass and followed the movement of the blood in the arteries of their transparent tails. Finally, he was the first to describe the virgin reproduction of plant lice (a subject which we shall deal with later), the budding of sweet-water polyps, and both human and animal spermatozoa.

This impressive achievement was all the more amazing in that Leeuwenhoek was entirely an amateur. He had had no professional training in science, had never attended a university. In an age in which Latin was the language of scholars, he spoke only his mother tongue. His microscopic studies were a hobby reserved for his leisure hours.

But the scientific community thought highly of this self-taught amateur's work. He was made a corresponding member of the London Royal Society, and communicated his discoveries, inventions, and theories in long, detailed and often touchingly modest letters to that body. He himself never wrote a book, but his letters, published first in the Royal Society's *Philosophical Transactions*, were collected and printed in Dutch and in Latin translations during his lifetime.

Those letters were basically a single endless monologue. For years they dealt almost exclusively with the mysterious infusoria seen under the microscope. Van Leeuwenhoek did not know how these animals arose, or how they reproduced, but he believed that he had observed a kind of copulation among them. And since he took the cilia of paramecia for feet, and furthermore saw microorganisms absorbing nourishment and reacting to stimuli, he could not accept the theory that they were merely living clots of slime, spontaneously arising out of inorganic matter. They must, he concluded, be complete living beings, equipped with all needful organs, begotten and born like other animals, despite the fact that they were so much smaller.

But how was it that infusoria developed as soon as hay, dust, or any other kind of dirt was moistened with water? To answer this question Leeuwenhoek developed a theory that sounds astonishingly modern. Germs of infusoria, he maintained, entered the atmosphere along with evaporating water, or clung to earth or to plants. If they were immersed in water again, the animalcules hatched out, grew, and produced new germs which once more filled the air and earth until fresh moisture stimulated their development.

Later microzoologists have confirmed this view—at least in principle. They have found that many tiny organisms can form spores which are virtually immune to drought, heat, and cold and which can often be awakened to new life by moisture after many years. But in Leeuwenhoek's day most scientists held other opinions. They clung stubbornly to the conviction that microscopic living creatures arose by spontaneous generation from dead matter.

LIFE FROM BOILED MEAT

In the eighteenth century the great age of biology began. First-rate intelligences appeared, men who were no longer satisfied to pursue their studies by pressing flowers, impaling beetles, collecting stuffed birds, and reading Aristotle. They wanted to know what really lay hidden in living creatures. It was the age of such men as Linnaeus (Carl von Linné), the great Swedish classifier; of Antoine Laurent de Jussieu, the French scientist who raised botany to the rank of a science; of Albrecht von Haller, the Swiss biologist who attempted to trace all life processes to a mysterious and as yet unexplained "vital force"; of the German J. G. Koelreuter, who discovered sexuality and the fertilization of plants even before the unfortunate Sprengel; and of the Italian Lazzaro Spallanzani, who first artificially fertilized female animals.

Paris, the intellectual capital of Europe, was also the mecca of natural scientists. This was due primarily to a man who for many decades was the superintendent of the Royal Gardens—the boldest, most farseeing zoologist of his time as well as a brilliant stylist whose books were loved by hundreds of thousands of readers: Georges Louis Leclerc, Comte de Buffon. This *grand seigneur* of the natural sciences became a demigod, a legendary figure, even in his lifetime.

Jean-Jacques Rousseau, the philosopher of nature, adored him as if he were an idol; once, when he visited Buffon in his modest tower room in the Jardin du Roi, he fell to the floor and kissed the threshold.

Count Buffon belonged among the avant-garde scientists of the Enlightenment. He anticipated Lamarck's and Darwin's theories of evolution, founded paleontology, trained a whole corps of capable scientists, and sent his collectors and explorers to all regions of the world. But even the greatest man can err. Buffon's errors were of the kind that command respect; they cannot be attributed to obstinate attachment to long-outmoded dogmas, but sprang from his lively imagination and his vigorous and daring mind, always ready to advance into new territory. Like his spiritual descendants Lamarck and Darwin, Buffon hit on the idea that all life must gradually have developed out of lower forms in the course of geologic time. "It may be assumed that all animals have descended from a single living being which in the course of time by steady improvement has brought forth all the forms of other animals." Thus Buffon hypothesized an uninterrupted succession from imperfect to perfect living creatures.

But which creatures were the most primitive, the lowest, the ones which must have been the beginning of all life? Buffon decided that they must be the infusoria, the microorganisms Leeuwenhoek had discovered. These organic molecules, as Buffon called them, must have arisen and must still be arising by spontaneous generation. Thus Buffon did not push the origin of life back to primordial times, as do modern biologists and biochemists. He fancied that microscopically small life could emerge from crude matter. "I suspect," he wrote,

> that close examination of nature would reveal to us intermediate creatures which do not have the strength to reproduce like animals and plants, but which nevertheless possess a kind of life and movement; and furthermore other creatures which without being animals or plants have nevertheless contributed something to the composition of both; and finally still lower creatures which are only a primary accumulation of organic molecules.

This was very cautiously expressed. Soon afterwards, however, the Danish zoologist Otto Frederik Müller came forth with the theory that after death all life dissolved into microscopically small molecules, similar to the infusoria, and that out of these molecules new living beings once more formed. Müller is responsible for the first useful classification of microorganisms. But in spite of many pretty descriptions and drawings by enthusiastic microscopists, the problem of how these organisms had arisen, how they lived and reproduced, remained unanswered.

Around the middle of the eighteenth century, when Buffon was at the height of his career, a scientific controversy over the spontaneous generation of small living creatures began. It went on for decades. The key event was an experiment undertaken by John Turberville Needham, an English partisan of Buffon's. Needham boiled meat, plants, and other organic substances, thus presumably destroying all life within them. But after he had let the boiled substance cool and prepared infusions to be examined under the microscope, he found that they were full of infusoria. This could only mean, Needham reasoned, that the infusoria had formed by spontaneous generation after the boiling.

A stubborn opponent of Buffon objected. He was René Antoine Ferchault de Réaumur, a scientist best known for his scale of temperature. Rejecting Buffon's evolutionism and his theory of spontaneous generation, Réaumur undertook to repeat Needham's experiment. His results were the same, but his conclusions were entirely different. The infusoria in the boiled substances, he asserted, had not been formed anew after cooling. They had come from the air and developed in the cooled substances—just as van Leeuwenhoek had maintained. The experiment therefore proved that the air was full of life, and that this life grew and multiplied as soon as it found congenial conditions.

Réaumur's theory went largely unnoticed—he was by now a very old man and lacked the drive to make himself heard. But an Italian abbé and professor undertook an experiment reminiscent of that epoch-making one performed by his fellow countryman, the Tuscan physician Francesco Redi. This man, Abbé Lazzaro Spallanzani of Pavia, proved to be one of the boldest and most resolute experimenters of early biology. He gave careful thought to Réaumur's argument, and recognized at once the mistake Needham had made. The air must not be allowed to enter the vessels of experimental substances. They must be kept sterile, as we would say today.

Spallanzani filled nineteen bottles with mixtures of various organic substances and water, melted the necks of the bottles to seal them, and then brought the contents to the boiling point. After being opened, the bottles showed no signs of microorganisms. A further series of experiments, this time with open bottles, produced the same results that Needham and Réaumur had already reported: the organic matter was swarming with microscopic creatures. This proved, Spallanzani concluded, that the eminent advocates of spontaneous generation from Aristotle to Buffon had been wrong. Infusoria did not form spontaneously out of dead matter; they had to arise out of germs traveling through the air. Consequently protozoa were genuine living creatures

Through his wonderful microscopes the
Dutchman Antonij van Leeuwenhoek
was the first to see the red blood corpuscles, the channels of teeth, the transverse striations of muscle fiber, the scale
of the human epidermis, the eggs and
larvae of fleas. He may even have seen
bacteria—in the 17th century.

Georges-Louis Leclerc, Count Buffon,
the avant-garde 18th-century scientist
who anticipated Darwin's theories of
evolution.

Lorenz Oken, enfant terrible of zoology.
At once a genius and a muddlehead, he
was the first—in 1833—to hint at the
existence of the cell.

like higher animals and plants, not vague, half-living, "organic molecules."

Spallanzani's experiments should finally have disposed of the theory of spontaneous generation. But people refused to believe him. Even into the nineteenth century some biologists continued to express the most fantastic ideas about the origin of one-celled organisms. The most prominent among them was Lorenz Oken, the *enfant terrible* of zoology in the first half of the nineteenth century. He was a man with a restless mind, much honored and much condemned, at once a genius and a muddlehead.

Infusoria, Oken maintained, arise from decaying, fermenting flesh. "The origin of infusoria," he wrote in his book on generation, "is not a development from eggs, but a liberation from the fetters of the larger animal, a disintegration of the animal into its components. . . . And if all flesh disintegrates into infusoria, the proposition may be reversed: all higher animals must consist of these creatures as their components. . . ." Oken continued, "I would assert that infusoria are primal animals which arose as generally and as indestructibly at the creation as earth, air, and water; like these other elements in their sphere, they are elements in the organic world and constitute the primal substance not only of animals, but also of plants. . . . In this sense, therefore, they may be called the original organic substances."

This biological mysticism contains a hint of the prime building block of life: the cell. Oken was still groping in darkness and therefore went astray. But once the cell was discovered, once it was determined that protozoa were one-celled animals, true investigation of sex and reproduction in these lowest organisms could begin. Only then was the final chapter written to the complex romance of spontaneous generation.

THE SEX LIFE OF THE PARAMECIUM

In the year 1815 a naturalist just past his twentieth year, Christian Gottfried Ehrenberg, on a commission from the Prussian government, set out to explore the coastline of the Red Sea. In the course of his travels Ehrenberg examined samples of the sea floor under the microscope and discovered that the layers of ooze deposited on the bottom consisted largely of the shells of primordial and recent microorganisms. As a result, we now know that diatoms, globigerina, foraminifera, and other one-celled creatures have contributed more to the building of our planet than all other living beings together. It was a revolutionary discovery.

Ehrenberg devoted the rest of his working life to the study of unicellular organisms. He was a sober, level-headed man, not given to rash speculations. His heroes were such accumulators of data as Leeuwenhoek, Redi, and Spallanzani. Theories of spontaneous generation held no charms for him. Infusoria were, he decided, *complete organisms;* therefore they must also have hearts, stomachs, glands, genuine circulatory systems, nerves, organs of digestion and reproduction, just like other animals. And he believed that he had observed such organs in the infusoria he studied. Moreover, these tiny living creatures seemed to copulate like the higher animals. For he had often seen under the microscope how the paramecia touched, merged, and then separated from one another again.

"No one among all previous observers," Ehrenberg pointed out, "has ever created a single infusorian by making infusians. All those who claim to have investigated the creatures have overlooked the organization of their bodies. In all my studies I have never come across a single instance which could convince me that organisms have arisen out of the infused substances. . . . Rather, the infusoria possess the same principles of organization as the higher animals, and reproduce by eggs, division, or budding."

Ehrenberg, then, converted the "organic molecules" into genuine animals capable of sexual reproduction. This was both a step forward and a step backward. It was a step forward because the protozoa are actually complete living organisms in their own fashion, with a complex pattern of reproduction—by no means the "primal substance of life." But it was a step backward because they neither lay eggs nor possess a system of organs like the higher animals. This Ehrenberg refused to believe. He really loved his amoebas and paramecia and would become quite furious when anyone tried to prove that they had neither hearts, stomachs, nor intestines and consequently could not be termed "real" organisms.

In 1838, the same year in which Ehrenberg published his theories, a botanist made certain observations through the microscope which were to topple all existing concepts. Matthias Jakob Schleiden of Hamburg, a former lawyer who had become an associate of the famous German physiologist Johannes Müller, subjected bits of a plant to microscopic analysis and came to an amazing conclusion: "Plants consist of an aggregate of individual, self-contained, organic molecules—*cells.* The cell is the elementary organ, the one essential constituent element of all plants, without which a plant does not exist."

Schleiden, however, took a cautious attitude toward his findings.

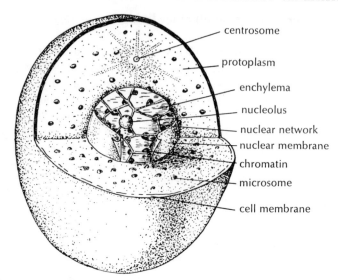

centrosome

protoplasm

enchylema

nucleolus

nuclear network

nuclear membrane

chromatin

microsome

cell membrane

The building block of life—the cell—has a complex structure.

He observed that every cell had a definite membrane and a nucleus, that it could divide as Ehrenberg's infusoria did, and that the growth of plants depended upon this cell division. But for some time he did not venture to reveal his discovery to the public. In naturalist circles he was in any case considered too imaginative and not really serious, because he read philosophy and wrote poems in his leisure time. For a year after his discovery he held his peace. Then, visiting a Berlin colleague and friend one day, he stammered a few words to the effect that the building block of all plants was, according to his observations, an alveolate (i.e., honeycombed) structure with a nucleus—*cellula*, a cell.

The colleague, Müller's assistant Theodor Schwann, gasped, led Schleiden to a microscope, and brought out slides which he, too, had been concealing from science out of caution. The slides contained animal tissue which revealed their structure under the lens. They, too, were made up of cells. The animal cells, to be sure, were not enclosed within a firm membrane like those of plants; but they too had a nucleus and other features similar to Schleiden's plant cells. This meant that the cell was not the "essential constituent element" of plants alone. It was the building block of all living organisms.

The discoveries of Schleiden and Schwann ushered in the glorious era of cytology—research into the structure and functions of the cell. All living things, it was found, are composed of millions upon millions of cells, from the alga to the tree, from the amoeba to the giant saurian and to man. Another pupil of Johannes Müller, the anatomist Max Schultze, demonstrated that the formerly mysterious life substance was a form of protein (protoplasm) which circulates incessantly in the cells. And the greatest medical scientist of the nineteenth century, Rudolf Virchow, flatly described the human body as a cell-state in which various groups of cells generated all the phenomena of life, from digestion and reproduction to the most refined expressions of the mind and the soul.

It took some time before the new generation of cytologists recognized that such microorganisms as infusoria and protozoa did not have genuine organs, as Ehrenberg had imagined, but that they indeed consisted of a single cell. That one cell was, nevertheless, capable of all the functions which we call *life:* motion, metabolism, sense reactions, propagation.

Once this had been determined, it was no longer difficult to discover the means of reproduction used by unicellular organisms. By then, to be sure, investigation had shown that propagation with them was really a matter of cell division. In nonsexual reproduction, the maternal cell can divide once or many times, so that two or more new daughter cells arise. However, a maternal cell can also preserve its individuality and produce small daughter cells by budding. In sexual reproduction cell division is preceded by the merging of two cells. In the course of time all the methods of reproduction which had been observed in higher organisms—division, budding, and copulation—were discovered among the protozoa.

Lower unicellular organisms—amoebas, for example—increase solely by the nonsexual methods of division and budding. "Immortal dwarfs," Bölsche called them, because they multiply and continue to live in their fragments, instead of begetting children and then dying. "Apparently this capacity is as intrinsic a necessity and as fundamental a property of unicellular life as eating and growing; it must be based upon fundamental forces of this life, forces whose nature we have not yet been able to discover, but whose existence must be assumed to be an absolute fact."

Division allows unicellular organisms to increase with tremendous rapidity and to attain to astronomically large numbers of individuals. If there were no natural obstacles to these avalanches of reproduction, a single culture of bacteria could—it has been calculated—fill all the seas of the world within a few days. The fastest reproduction is to be found among those microorganisms which split up into hundreds of lilliputian cells—spores—each of which can grow into a full-fledged individual in a matter of moments.

In 1865 the Augustinian monk Gregor Mendel discovered important laws of heredity, which were then lost sight of, to be rediscovered and made available to science in 1900. Genetics has taught us that organisms which multiply solely by asexual means can only reproduce the same hereditary stock as themselves; they have no potential for variation, for those many small changes which bring about evolution. Division and budding are the most extreme forms of inbreeding.

It is fortunate, therefore, that one-cell organisms are also capable of sexual reproduction. They practice three methods, which the biologist calls *autogamy*, *conjugation*, and *copulation*. Autogamy means "self-marriage." Certain types of amoebas, the sun animalcule, for example, pass through a maturation period in which they surround themselves with a firm membrane and divide into two cells. A complicated process then takes place in both partial cells: the cell nuclei break up, some of the nuclear substance is expelled, and a number of chromosomes disappear. Then the cells reunite, the chromosomes recombine—and the autogamous union has resulted in a changed inheritance.

Conjugation is a favored mode of union among that most familiar of the ciliate infusorians, the paramecium. It bears a surprising resemblance to the mating of higher animals and was mistaken for such by Ehrenberg and other early microzoologists. In reality, however, it is something entirely different. At certain times, especially under unfavorable environmental conditions, paramecia are seized by a reproductive impulse which spreads among them with epidemic speed. Pairs seek and find one another, touch, partially merge, and then separate again. Modern microzoologists have discovered what takes place in the course of such conjugation. When a pair of paramecia adhere together, they link their mouths and form a protoplasmic bridge. In each animal the nucleus breaks up and is gradually absorbed by the plasm. The nucleolus undergoes several divisions, the end product of which in each of the two partners is a "male" migratory nucleus and a "female" stationary nucleus. The migratory nucleus moves across the protoplasmic bridge into the partner's body and there unites with the stationary nucleus. After this exchange of migratory nuclei, the two animals separate again and each gradually resumes its original form, complete with nucleus and nucleolus.

The process is a rather complicated one, but it is clear that the conjugating paramecia do not copulate in the proper sense of the word; rather, they recombine their hereditary material. The effect, however, is the same as that of copulation: the heredities of the two animals are mingled. Paramecia which have conjugated can reproduce asexually by division for many generations, until bad water, unfavorable

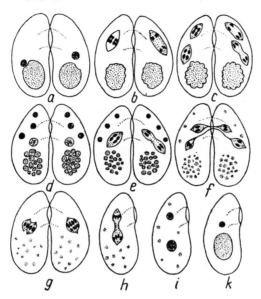

*Paramecia in conjugation. This mode of reproduction bears a striking re-
semblance to the mating of higher animals. In reality, it is something
quite different. (a) Beginning. (b–f) Division and exchange of cell nuclei.
(g–k) Separation and return to original stage.*

living conditions, or aging of the stock sets the stage for a new wave
of conjugation.

As we have seen, one-cell organisms utilize the most various methods of reproduction, from simple division, budding, and spore-forma-
tion through autogamy and conjugation. And even the ultimate
method—the one which has brought to the fore the dominant power
of sex—occurs in some protozoa. That method is copulation: the
union of a male and female germ cell. Thus, far down on the scale of
the animal kingdom, we encounter a division into two sexes.

The *Vorticella* or bell animalcules, which are ciliate infusorians
like the paramecia, live in colonies. Each member is attached to a
common base by a thin, pliant stem. These sessile animals are—if we
care to apply human categories—all "females." Now and then
smaller, stemless vorticels free themselves from the colony. These
"swarmers" as they are called swim away to visit other colonies.
There the "males" dance about the sessile "females," clamber up their
stems and slip into their bodies. Cell nuclei are exchanged, whereupon
the "swarmer" shrinks and dies, like so many male animals that have
fulfilled their function.

Certain forms of life practice a perplexing type of reproduction in which sexual and asexual propagation occur alternately. Plasmodium, the agent of malaria, is one of these. The plasmodia enter the red blood corpuscles of man. There they reproduce by dividing many times. They destroy the corpuscles they infest and infect others. This asexual reproduction takes place at fantastic speed and with devastating results. Alexander the Great, the Roman emperors Trajan and Marcus Aurelius, innumerable conquerors and colonizers in the tropics of the Old and the New World, the African explorer Livingstone, swarms of workers brought in to build the Panama Canal—all fell victim to plasmodium, the agent of malaria.

Now let a mosquito suck some of the blood of a man infected with malaria. Plasmodium promptly changes its method of reproduction. First, it divides itself in the mosquito's intestines into large female and smaller male organisms, called *macrogametes* and *microgametes*. The microgametes are attracted in swarms to the macrogametes, like sperm to the egg. A male germ cell penetrates into a female cell and unites with it. Thus the process is the same as that in all higher animals, including man, but for the fact that microgametes and macrogametes are not the sexual cells of an organism, but are independent organisms. The fertilized cell finally divides, like the fertilized ovum of the higher animals; the divided cells form a kind of chitinous shell, travel to the mosquito's salivary gland, and when the mosquito alights upon a man and bites him, enter the blood stream of the victim. This completes the life cycle of the plasmodium.

The protozoa, the "living animalcules" that Leeuwenhoek first saw under the microscope, are no longer regarded as rudimentary creatures midway between dead and living matter. Their methods of reproduction alone prove that in spite of their unicellular nature they have reached a rather high stage of organization and passed through a long, variegated evolution.

Nevertheless, the fable of spontaneous generation by unicellular organisms lingered on until it was finally banished a hundred years ago by the Father of Bacteriology, Louis Pasteur.

ON THE THRESHOLD OF LIFE

On April 1, 1864, Louis Pasteur stood before a group of noted scientists, philosophers, and writers assembled in the amphitheater of the Sorbonne and showed them a number of vessels containing infusions of hay and refuse. The vessels had been filled and sealed and then heated. All this, however, had been done years before. They had been kept sealed ever since. In principle this was a repeat performance of the famous experiment by Abbé Spallanzani to refute the theory of spontaneous generation. Pasteur, however, had developed his own method of "pasteurization" to exclude all possible sources of error.

He opened the vessels one by one and examined their contents in the presence of the entire group. In none of the pasteurized test tubes were the slightest traces of protozoans, bacteria, or fungi to be found. George Sand, Alexandre Dumas, and the other notables heard him conclude his demonstration by pronouncing, with great self-assurance, the death sentence upon a scientific theory twenty-two centuries old:

"There is no longer any reason whatsoever for us to believe that living organisms can arise except from germ cells, from parents that resemble them. The theory that maintains the opposite will never again recover from the fatal blow inflicted by this experiment."

There is every reason to believe that Pasteur's pronouncement will stand. The doctrine of spontaneous generation is dead—unless the virus researchers are someday to teach us otherwise. Nevertheless, the concept of spontaneous generation did not vanish from books on biology; it merely underwent a metamorphosis. After some spirited debate Pasteur's proofs were accepted even by his opponents. But, it was asked—especially by the evolutionists in the second half of the nineteenth century—did the principle apply to those primordial times in which the earth was without form and void, to use the words of Genesis? After all, life must somehow have appeared upon earth. And how could it have done so except by spontaneous generation?

Hitherto "spontaneous generation" had been generally understood as a miraculous process by which all sorts of living organisms arose spontaneously out of dead, decaying matter. Now it assumed a new meaning; the concept was transposed in time to the very beginning of creation. The most militant advocate of such a "natural history of creation" was the German zoologist Ernst Haeckel, a fervent adherent of the Darwinian theory of evolution which was then causing a great stir. Was it not conceivable, Haeckel suggested, that in the vast upheavals that accompanied the formation of the earth, certain changes, say, in terrestrial temperatures, caused carbon to enter into complex combinations which, in their turn, gave rise to protoplasm, the basic material of life?

Haeckel maintained that these intermediary forms were still to be found upon the earth—living clots of protoplasm without cell nuclei. He called them *Monera* and considered them the ancestors of all ani-

Ernst Haeckel, a German zoologist who early became a fervent adherent of Darwin's theories of evolution, but who speculated wrongly on the origin of protoplasm, the basic material of life.

mals and plants. "Spontaneous generation is the voluntary or spontaneous production of organisms of the simplest conceivable type. Such organisms are the *Monera*—perfectly simple microscopic clots of protoplasm without any structure and organization, which feed and reproduce by fission. One of these Monera, the primitive organism *Bathybius haeckeli* discovered by the famous English zoologist Huxley, covers the bottom of the ocean, at depths of between three and thirty thousand feet, in the form of a thick, coherent layer of slime. Granted that spontaneous generation of such Monera has not yet been observed, there is in itself nothing improbable about it. We may venture the assumption that the Monera represent the beginning of the living population of the earth, the starting point of the plant and the animal kingdoms."

But Haeckel had committed the scientific sin of placing theory before fact. His Monera, it turned out, were by no means structureless lumps of protein, for they possessed nuclei, and *Bathybius haeckeli* was simply a jellylike gypsum covering the ocean floor. Nevertheless, certain biologists obstinately clung to spontaneous generation as an alternative to a creation myth. "To reject abiogenesis," the botanist Karl Wilhelm Nägeli put it, "is to admit a miracle."

In the twentieth century the question of spontaneous generation became one of the central problems of biology—and a focal point of controversy. Two parties formed. One began to seek for "the primal slime"; the other condemned this search as ridiculous, exactly on a level with the belief that mice arise spontaneously out of old rags. One party dissected, ground up, liquefied, condensed, and analyzed protoplasm. It constructed innumerable theories about spontaneous generation, assigned names to innumerable hypothetical protoorganisms. The other party remained unimpressed by these efforts: it seemed that all the ideas advanced in proof of spontaneous generation invariably ended in a blind alley.

Spontaneous generation seemed to be unprovable. Apparently it had to be taken on faith, like the story of creation. Its opponents declared with ill-concealed sarcasm that it was biology's form of myth. Mechanistic biologists resorted to this myth for lack of any other answer to the problem of life's origin. A keen critic of mechanism, Jakob von Uexküll, summed up the alchemistic endeavors of the spontaneous-generation school as follows:

> Protoplasm is called living matter. But this term is inadmissible, for protoplasm is neither matter nor a mixture of matters, but a structure in which matter is constantly changing, undergoing metabolism. Protoplasm is the true *perpetuum mobile*, which no human art can produce. The candle flame, which since Helmholtz's day has been regarded as the symbol of life, is in truth only the symbol of dying, for it consumes itself without renewing itself. Those scientists who dream that man will some day succeed in bringing forth a living organism should apply themselves to the task of creating a compound capable of destroying and rebuilding itself. They would soon enough perceive the vanity of their efforts. But such a structure is the prerequisite for all life.

Another great naturalist, the French entomologist Jean Henri Fabre, declared with equal emphasis:

I hear that a learned scientist who regards life as merely an arrangement of chemical and physical forces believes that the time will come when science will be able to produce protoplasm, organic matter. Were it in my power, I would help this ambitious gentleman accomplish his purpose. Let me assume you have really produced protoplasm. By careful thought, searching studies, invincible patience, and the most precise attention to detail, your wish has been fulfilled: You have fabricated a protein slime, easily decaying stuff which after a few days stinks to high heaven. What are you going to do with it? Create something? Will you confer upon it the structure of a living organism? Will you inject it into two diaphanously thin foils in order to produce a fly's wing? Does your syringe contain the archetype, the organizer of forms, the primal regulator? No! Then throw the stuff into the garbage pail. Life will never arise out of this chemical trash.

Nevertheless, to this day biologists have refused to be dissuaded from their experiments. Hypotheses which can neither be proved nor refuted remain permanent challenges to them. Scientific inquirers must engage in scientific inquiry—that is their right, and no power in the world has ever been able to stop them. In spite of two thousand years of failure they have continued to seek the origin of life.

Today they are asking: Where is the boundary of life anyhow? Fifty years ago scientists thought they could draw a sharp borderline between animate and inanimate nature. That borderline has been obscured since medical and biochemical researchers have seen viruses under the electron microscope. Viruses are those mysterious parasites in the cells of higher organisms, which to the lay mind are associated almost exclusively with diseases. To the scientists, however, they are fascinating riddles which have reopened the whole question of spontaneous generation. For they seem to exist very close to the border between life and nonlife.

There are several groups of viruslike forms. Real, crystallizable viruses are, biochemists have determined, basically nothing but nucleic acids and protein molecules. They do not breathe and have no metabolism; by the strict standards of biologists, therefore, they do not qualify as living organisms. But they reproduce much as living organisms do. Other groups of viruses, on the other hand—the bacteriophages, for example—act almost like protozoans. They move with the aid of organellae, have a simple metabolism and a kind of sexual impulse, are divided into males and females and can therefore transmit their characteristics to their progeny. In other words, they are protein molecules which love, marry, and reproduce like the higher organisms.

Viruses and bacteriophages exist solely as parasites in host cells; hence they can scarcely have been the original ancestors of all animals and plants, at least in their present form. But a partisan of the modern doctrine of spontaneous generation is sorely tempted to believe that the earliest life may have appeared in the form of freely motile viruses. Along with this goes the hope that biochemistry will ultimately succeed in synthesizing such living, reproducing protein molecules.

Thus modern virus studies are not merely a branch of medical research. They may lead to some definite knowledge about the structure of the earliest life on earth. The virus of tobacco mosaic disease was the first virus whose structure was determined in the laboratory: it was found to consist of a single giant protein molecule. Professor Wendell M. Stanley of the virus laboratory of the University of California at Berkeley received the Nobel Prize for this triumph of research. The tobacco mosaic virus can be a crystal; it can also be a half-living organism. It has two aspects, partakes both of animate and inanimate nature. It grows, reproduces, has the capacity to pass on heredity; but on the other hand it also behaves exactly like inorganic substances.

There are viruses which are not only the bearers of hereditary characteristics but can also mutate, that is, spontaneously change their genetic material. In their chemical structure these curious molecules are surprisingly similar to genes, the hereditary factors in the chomosomes of reproductive cells. The question arises whether there may be some closer connection between viruses and genes. Does the similarity in structure between the agents of disease and the agents of heredity have a deeper significance which is still hidden from us?

Such possibilities are fascinating, though they may strike the serious scientist as perhaps too fanciful, at least for the time being. For we have not yet fathomed the true nature of viruses. Virus research is still in its earliest stages. And before there could be any thought of creating viruses in the laboratory, it would be necessary to synthesize certain proteins.

For a long time even this preliminary step seemed out of reach. But in the past ten years American and European laboratories have accomplished it. It has been perhaps the most exciting scientific feat of the modern age.

CREATION IN THE RETORT?

In 1953 Harold Clayton Urey, the American Nobel Prize winner who discovered "heavy water," which has proved so important for nuclear fission and for the making of the hydrogen bomb, proposed an unusual experiment to one of his pupils. The problem was to try to reproduce in the laboratory the origin of life.

The experiment took the following form: in a closed, sterile glass container, the pupil—Stanley Miller—created a hypothetical "primordial atmosphere" of methane, ammonia, and water vapor. It was an atmosphere such as the earth must have had in the Archean or oldest period of the earth's history. For a week Miller bombarded this mixture with electric discharges, for present-day theory holds that the Archean atmosphere was heavily subjected to such charges.

The result was sensational. In a week's time organic substances had formed out of the three gases. These substances were amino acids, which are among the fundamental building blocks of life. Certain amino acids may give rise, by fermentation and breakdown of the acids, to complicated giant protein molecules. The adherents of modern theories of spontaneous generation are convinced that such giant protein molecules at one time, in the remoteness of the Archean world, joined together to form the first—possibly viruslike—half-living organisms.

True, the quantity of amino acid produced was infinitesimal. Moreover, amino acids are scarcely equivalent to life in the biological sense. Thus, Miller was not really demonstrating "spontaneous generation"; he merely took a first step which might possibly lead in that direction. One skeptic, the anthropologist Loren Eiseley of the University of Pennsylvania, promptly contested the value of this and similar experiments. He remarked ironically:

> Someone has found a new chemical, vitamin, or similar necessary ingredient without which life will not flourish. By the time this reaches the more sensational press, it may have become "the secret of life." The only thing the inexperienced reader may not comprehend is the fact that no one of these items, even the most recently discovered, is *the* secret. Instead, the substance is probably a part, a very small part, of a larger enigma which is well-nigh as inscrutable as it ever was.

These words suggest how circumspect, how tentative, a majority of the specialists are to this day whenever there is any talk of producing life in the retort. Even now, as in the time of Ernst Haeckel, such experiments are highly controversial and science is still divided into two camps.

Miller's experiment has been repeated and varied many times in recent years by American and European scientists. Inorganic substances similar to those used by Miller have been bombarded with gamma rays, have been subjected to great heat and artificial thunderstorms. Again and again it has turned out that the atoms were regularly forced to form complex protein compounds. The experimenters have even succeeded in synthesizing proteins containing all eighteen of the amino acids necessary for life. It would seem that the scientists now have at their disposal all the raw materials of organic life, still chaotic and disordered, like a heap of blocks in box. Only the last, the most important and most fateful step remains: the step from synthetic protein to synthetic life.

Will these recent achievements some day lead us closer to the secret of life's origin? Or will this path also end in a blind alley, like microzoology's search for the primal slime? We do not know. The skeptics may, after all, prove right when they maintain that it is beyond the abilities of the imperfect mammal *Homo sapiens* to understand, direct, and re-create the fantastically complex chemophysical processes we call *life*.

We must wait for the verdict of the biologists of tomorrow.

■

CHAPTER TWO

EGG AND SPERM:

THE MYSTERY OF FECUNDATION

SEX AND MAGIC

On July 20, 1912, three enterprising boys were exploring the underground course of the river Volp in the department of Ariège in France. The three were brothers, sons of a Count Bégouen. In a boat built out of old crates they paddled into the sinister, gurgling blackness of the grotto. A few minutes' rowing brought them to a cave full of stalactites which they were able to explore on foot. The cave branched off into a series of passages and galleries.

The grotto is known today as Tuc d'Audoubert. In its passages the boys found a great number of cave paintings, and at the end of the last gallery the art work which has become one of the most significant items in any history of sex. This was a sculpture in clay depicting in the clearest fashion a male bison about to mount a female bison. Specialists in prehistory who came to the cave as soon as the discovery was reported saw at once that the underground labyrinth had been a place of worship for Paleolithic man. The hardened earth around the statue showed the imprint of many soles and heels. To judge by the size of the footprints, it must have been a group of adolescents who performed a solemn dance around the effigy. "We are led to think," wrote Abbé Henri Breuil, one of the greatest experts on Ice Age Art, "of the maturation ceremonies so important to tribal life, in which the youth, having become a man, is taken into the male community of the tribe."

Two years to the day after the discovery of Tuc d'Audoubert, the Bégouens stood in a second cave hollowed out by the river Volp, and

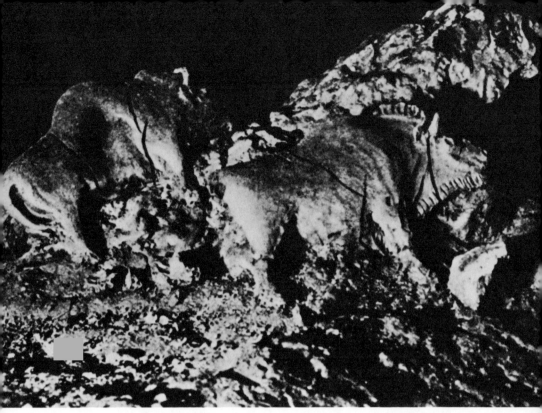

Sculptured bison pair in the cave of Tuc d'Audoubert, Ariège. This prehistoric artwork is early evidence of man's interest in the sex life of the animals.

A "magician" disguised as an animal pursues two female animals. That our earliest ancestors were familiar with the reproductive habits of mammals is clearly shown in this drawing scratched on the rock of the cave Les trois Frères, Ariège.

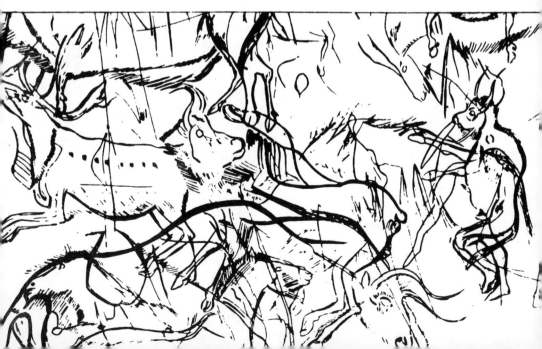

once again encountered evidences of early Stone Age sexual magic. The cave, named Trois Frères after the three adventurous brothers, is also known to archaeologists as the "Cave of the Great Magician." It contains several depictions of dancing men wearing animal masks and animal hides. In almost every drawing there is strong emphasis on the genitalia of the masked dancers.

One picture is of special interest. It shows a "magician" blowing a flute and following two female animals. One of the two animals—a chamois or reindeer—has turned its head toward the man and seems to be adopting the posture for copulation. Here was an authentic document of the Ice Age which lent strong confirmation to the theories of certain archaeologists. Those primeval animal dances, whether their purpose was to make magic for initiations, hunting, or fertility, must have had a close connection with sexuality. Apparently dance imitation of animal (and perhaps also human) habits of copulation were part of the rites of Ice Age religions.

In succeeding years a great many more artworks of the Ice Age have come to light: drawings, paintings, and sculptures of animals in rut and coupling; of animals pregnant, giving birth, and suckling young; of women with strongly stressed sexual characteristics, prominent breasts and vulvas. Dozens of caves have their walls covered with such sexual pictures. In some cases the figures of human beings and animals are connected in a curious way. Some are veritable puzzle pictures: pairs of lovers or women in childbirth are so represented that their outlines coincide with those of bears, stags, or other strong animals.

We may wonder whether all these diverse portrayals should be interpreted as magical and religious. All through the ages the human race has produced erotic graffiti; it is perhaps stretching a point to maintain that they are all aspects of fertility magic. But in any case, the art of the Ice Age proves that even cave man recognized the connection between copulation, fertilization, and birth—an amazing insight which ethnologists of only a few decades ago considered beyond the mental capacity of most primitive peoples. Not only that: Paleolithic man suspected that in regard to sexuality there existed no fundamental difference between animal and man. His descendant, civilized man, has long refused to bow to this bitter truth. Only after great resistance and in the face of growing biological knowledge, has he begun to admit that the mightiest of his instincts is also the most animal of instincts.

JACOB BREEDS SPOTTED LAMBS

Long after man left the caves, the chieftans and shamans of hunter tribes continued to dance before their warriors dressed in animal skins. Even up to the present day innumerable primitive and civilized peoples continue to practice certain rites which imitate the sexual behavior of animals. Ethnologists who have seen the Indian buffalo dances, the bird-of-paradise dances of the Papuans, the kangaroo and emu dances of the aborigines of Australia, report that these are among the most impressive and fascinating spectacles on earth.

Charles Darwin gave a vivid account of such a ceremony. When he was quite a young man, he witnessed an animal dance among the Australians in which the characteristic movements of certain animals were faithfully mimicked to the least detail. Darwin described the stamping and grunting of the dancers, the clashing of clubs and spears, the ecstatic twisting of body and limbs. "When both tribes mingled in the dance, the ground trembled with the heaviness of their steps, and the air resounded with their wild cries."

Animal dances and sexual magic dominated the religious life of ancient Greece. Animals and half-animals mingled with gods and men; the mythic landscapes of antiquity are full of sirens and centaurs, fauns, satyrs, and maenads. Significantly, the worship of Dionysus, which celebrated the power of animal generation, was the only Greek cult which spread triumphantly throughout the known world. The ethnologist Robert Lehmann-Nitsche once calculated that Dionysian orgies and bacchanalias were practiced by some twenty-eight peoples. In most cases the participants would deck themselves out in animal masks, horns, hoofs, skins, or tails—thus following the same pattern as the Australians, the Indians, and the cave men of the Ice Age.

Hunting peoples have a keen eye for the habits of game. The animal breeders of ancient times must have taken an even keener interest in animal reproduction. Once men ceasd to be nomads and became farmers and animal breeders, they faced a constant problem: if the fields of grain thrived, their domestic animals increased and they could live in ease and prosperity, but if the crop failed and the herds did not multiply, famine followed. Those early farmers, therefore looked closely into the reproductive habits of their domesticated plants and animals, and considered what they could do to further their increase.

Early man began to concern himself with genetic problems also. Science is inclined to look askance at some of the theories he constructed and the practices he adopted. Many superstitions born far back in the mists of time have not been eradicated, despite all the proofs of biologists.

One of these cherished concepts, known to scientists as *telegony*, probably arose shortly after the first breeds of domestic animals had been established. Telegony holds that the first conception stamps a female animal with a permanent, irrevocable brand. If, for example, a thoroughbred bitch is mated with a nondescript hybrid, she will be spoiled for all future breeding. Even if she subsequently mates with dogs of her own breed, she will go on having litters of ordinary mutts to the end of her days. This principle was naturally extended to the human race.

The story of Jacob in the Old Testament contains another common superstition of ancient genetics: prenatal influence upon pregnant animals. According to Genesis 30, Jacob had bargained with his father-in-law that he should have all the speckled and spotted sheep and goats for his hire; and since Laban attempted to cheat him of his wages, he resorted to a genetic trick:

> Jacob took him rods of green poplar, and of the hazel and chestnut tree; and pilled white strakes in them, and made the white appear which was in the rods. And he set the rods which he had pilled before the flocks in the gutters in the watering troughs when the flocks came to drink, that they should conceive when they came to drink. And the flocks conceived before the rods, and brought forth cattle ringstraked, speckled, and spotted.

The present-day geneticist, acquainted with Mendel's laws and Morgan's researches on mutation, can only shake his head at this. But to this day innumerable peasants, horse breeders, midwives, and quacks firmly believe that sudden and strong sense-impressions can physically influence the embryo of a pregnant female.

For thousands of years the people of ancient civilizations observed how seed germinated and fruits ripened, how birds laid and hatched eggs, how cattle coupled and after a definite, calculable period of time calved. It was only natural that these observations should be applied to man. But they left it at that. Farmers and animal breeders are sober, practical people. They do not care very much about the details of procreation; they are interested only in the results.

Consequently, when the first naturalists and natural philosophers appeared, they could talk only vaguely of impregnation, conception, fertilization and development. Not even the keenest thinkers had much notion of what lay behind those words.

BOY OR GIRL?

One of the first questions of sexual biology which preoccupied mankind was the determination of sex. It has remained a problem to this day. Couples desire an heir. Animal breeders may wish more male or more female progeny. Even in classical antiquity this problem was thought so important that virtually every natural philosopher discussed it and offered advice. In practice, this advice was not good for much. According to Empedocles, male children are begotten in a warmer womb, female children in a cooler one. Anaxagoras disagreed: boys grow on the right side of the womb, girls on the left. Aristotle tended to return to the notion of temperature: warmth means strength and masculinity; consequently young, hot-blooded. vigorous cocks, bulls, stallions, and men beget more masculine off spring, while older, cooler fathers produce chiefly daughters. Nevertheless, an aged husband need not, according to Aristotle, abandon all hope of a male heir. If the act of begetting takes place in a time of great heat, there are good prospects that a boy will result in spite of the father's cool temperature. On the other hand, a "hot" young man who has intercourse in cold weather must expect female offspring.

We would be doing an injustice to the three great Greeks if we were overly amused by these views. For in contrast to medical men and scientists of the intervening period, Aristotle and his two predecessors were at least working with scientific concepts. In the next two thousand years men turned their backs on science completely; they consulted astrologers, and relied on amulets, spells, or mysterious essences in order to conjure up the desired son or the desired sex in dogs or cattle.

Some primitives, among them the Swahili of East Africa, make their predictions in a more down-to-earth way. If a woman works hard during pregnancy, they believe a boy will be born; if she is lazy, a girl. It was a foolproof prescription. If the result was disappointing, the father could always claim that his wife had cheated him of the desired son by secret laziness.

How sex arises, what factors determine it, and to what extent it can be influenced, remained a mystery until the twentieth century.

Geneticists and biologists have learned that the sex of a child is determined at the moment of fertilization. Experiments with hormone injections have proved successful in reversing destiny in fish, frogs, and birds, but as yet not in man and other mammals.

TRIUMPH OF MASCULINITY

The great physicians of antiquity and the Middle Ages came by their anatomical knowledge through the dissection of animal cadavers. They had no other choice, for the human body, dead or alive, was sacred to Western peoples, and it was not until the year 1306 that the physician Mondino of Bologna ventured in secret, to dissect a human body. Up to the beginning of the Renaissance, therefore, the biology of reproduction was essentially animal biology. If man was discussed at all, concepts borrowed from the animal or even the vegetable kingdom were applied to him. Egg, seed, germ, fruit—these were the terms employed, terms which have lingered on in the vocabulary of physicians and scientists.

Historians more or less agree that the first biologist of the Occident was a physician of the Pythagorean school, Alcmaeon by name, who was active about 520 B.C. Alcmaeon is said to have dissected animals and to have discovered that all sense organs are connected with the brain by nerves. He also pronounced that the human fetus is nourished by the mother not only through the umbilical cord, but also through the pores of the skin.

A century and a half later the second great medical man appeared. To this day physicians speak his name with reverence and the professional oath they take bears his name: Hippocrates. This small, ugly genius of the island of Cos not only battled valiantly against sickness and death; he also explored the beginnings of life, the mysteries of generation and birth. And since, like Alcmaeon, he tried to draw conclusions about man from what he could see in animals, he undertook a highly modern experiment. He had a number of hen's eggs incubated and opened one egg each day in order to study the development of the embryo.

Hippocrates' demonstration of what takes place during the twenty-one day incubation period of a chicken embryo has remained a favorite example for embryologists and physiologists to this day. But it was only a partial explanation of the mystery of birth. The most important factor was still hidden: What is fertilization?

Some decades before Hippocrates two of the greatest of pre-Socratic philosophers had pondered this question—the same two who first theorized about the determination of sex: Empedocles and Anaxagoras. Their explanations sound extremely obscure, perhaps because their teachings have come down to us in fragmentary form. It seems clear, however, that both contended that the male and the female parents contributed something to the creation of the new living organism.

To their contemporaries and successors, that was not so obvious as it now sounds. How is it, the physicians and natural philosophers of classical antiquity asked, that children resemble not only the mother, in whose womb they grow, but also the father, who has really contributed nothing to their embryonic development? The followers of Hippocrates tried to answer this question. Semen, they decided, is formed not only in the genitals, but in the whole body of the man; it contains the quintessence of all the paternal organs and characteristics. And every germ which establishes the various traits of the father takes root in the womb at the time of impregnation and there independently reproduces itself.

Quaintly expressed as the theory is, modern geneticists can only be amazed at its insight. For the elements in the paternal seed according to that ancient theory bear an astonishing resemblance to the genes of the science of genetics.

Aristotle naturally had to have his say in this matter. He agreed with what the Hippocratians had to say about the male semen. But then what part did the woman play in reproduction? he asked. Nature, he pointed out, had created all living organisms according to a definite idea and for a definite purpose. Close observation and hard thinking about the nature of the sexes would disclose the special part played by each in the whole natural economy. The male principle is active; it is movement, creation, shaping. The female principle, on the other hand, is passive; it is matter waiting to be given form. Active movement is undoubtedly higher and more divine than passive matter. Consequently, everywhere in nature the male stands above the female; consequently he has the greatest share in the process of reproduction.

Advocates of feminine emancipation have a standing quarrel with Aristotle, for he was the first thinker to assert that male superiority was in keeping with the decrees of nature. According to Aristotle, male animals are larger, stronger, and more handsome than the females. They have ornate feathers, manes, antlers, or other adornments which the females lack. In the human race, also, man has numerous natural advantages over woman. It follows that the male

seed is the form-creating element in reproduction: it must be that
that gives meaning and shape to the maternal matter.

This creative seed consists, said Aristotle, not of mysterious essential germs, as the Hippocratians had taught, but quite simply of
"cooked blood." And the female substance which it shapes is, in all
egg-laying animals, naturally, the egg. In viviparous animals and
in man the menstrual blood takes the place of the egg. Higher animals thus beget a new organism by the mixture of sperm and menstrual blood.

That doctrine was scarcely any improvement upon the Hippocra-
tian version of the mechanics of reproduction. But the Romans, the
Arabs, and the Scholastics accepted it along with Aristotle's whole
intellectual picture of nature and man. For two thousand years it
was held to be established fact, until a number of fresh discoveries
overturned his whole authority.

THE EMBRYO AND THE EUNUCHS

"Wrongly do men cry out against experience and with bitter re-
proaches accuse her of deceitfulness. Let experience alone and rather
turn your complaints against your own ignorance, which causes you
to be so carried away by your vain and insensate desires as to expect
from experience things which are not within her power!

"Wrongly do men cry out against innocent experience, accusing
her of deceit and lying demonstrations!"

The above words were written in a diary which represents one of
the most interesting documents in the history of our civilization. The
man who made these notes in mirror writing was extraordinary even
among the extraordinary men of the Renaissance. He painted the
Mona Lisa, John the Baptist and *The Last Supper;* worked as a mili-
tary and civil engineer; sketched plans for canals and other water-
works; constructed a flying machine; offered a fairly correct interpretation of fossils; dissected human and animal cadavers; made
diagrams of bones, muscles, and organs; wrote tracts on anatomical,
zoological, mathematical, technical, and philosophical matters. It is
no surprise that this man, called Leonardo, son of the notary of Vinci,
a Tuscan village, also looked into the question of sexuality.

During the eighteen centuries from the time of Aristotle to that of
Leonardo da Vinci, naturalists had devoted themselves to reading and
writing commentaries upon Aristotle's writings, telling amusing

stories, and playing at system building. Throughout the Middle Ages, unbiased observation and recording of natural phenomena hardly took place. If anyone wanted to know what was going on inside an egg from the time it was laid to the time that it hatched, or how the stomach of a ruminant was constituted, he did not open an egg or dissect a cow—he looked into Aristotle's works on zoology to see what The Philosopher said about the matter.

Nevertheless, it occasionally happened that someone made a discovery which ran counter to Aristotle. Such persons were not hailed as scientific pioneers. On the contrary, they found themselves in trouble with the ecclesiastical or secular authorities. Even a hundred years after the time of Leonardo, the Jesuit astronomer Christoph Scheiner was severely reproved for his discovery of sunspots. The provincial of his order instructed him to keep quiet on the subject; since Aristotle had not mentioned sunspots, sunspots could not exist. Scheiner was allowed to discuss the matter again only after Galileo had published similar findings.

Even the greatest natural philosopher of the Middle Ages, Albertus Magnus, whose feats of alchemistic magic became a legend, did little to supplement or improve the work of Aristotle. He wrote seven books on plants and twenty-six on animals, but what he had to say about generation and the development of the embryo was often a step backward. He stated, for instance, that plants were sexless. They grew out of the earth as the animal embryo grew out of the uterus; and the sap they drew from the earth corresponded to the blood which the embryo drew from the womb. In his chapters on animals Albert did, it is true, refute a number of old fables. Hazel grouse are not fertilized by the spittle of the male; the stork does not detect adultery in his mate by his sense of smell. But on the other hand he invented new legends: for example, that weasels are fertilized through the ear and give birth through the mouth.

Albert's readers were probably less interested in his accounts of animal copulation than in his advice on human sex problems. His recommendations were highly imaginative: he prescribed all sorts of talismans, aphrodisiacs, and magic essences to promote fertility and maintain potency. He was also the inventor of a remarkable contraceptive. If a woman does not wish to conceive, she must cut the heel bone of a weasel from the living animal and wear it round her neck.

The theory of generation held by the "Universal Doctor" of the Church, Thomas Aquinas, was entirely Aristotelian; sperm and blood mingle and thereby create new life, the sperm functioning as the active agent, the menstrual blood as the passive substance. Thomas, however, presented a number of possible metaphors:

First: The father with his sperm creates a child out of the uterine blood as the artisan with his tools makes a bedstead out of wood.

Second: By means of the sperm the father cooks the uterine blood into a new human being.

Third: The sperm of the father acts upon the blood as rennet acts upon milk: from the coagulate, a child is formed.

For the next two centuries the merits of these theories of procreation were much discussed, but with small result. The question was treated entirely as a theoretical one. No one undertook practical investigations or experiments. The theorizers were not even sure of how the embryo was placed in the womb, how it was nourished or by what stages it grew.

This was precisely the sort of information that Leonardo da Vinci sought. He did not think much of hypotheses or guesses unconfirmed by experience; he was interested in facts. Thus, he made many dissections of both animal and human cadavers, and embodied his findings in magnificent sketches. To him we owe the first scientific representations of the male and female sexual organs, the sex act, and the child in the womb.

Leonardo's sketch, "The fetus in utero," shows a section of the womb with a huddled fetus inside it. Leonardo noted on the margin: "The heart of the child does not beat not does it breathe because it continually lies in water. If it breathed it would drown nor has it need to breathe because it is vivified and nourished by the life and food of the mother. The food of the mother nourishes the child within the womb exactly as it does the other parts of the mother's body, that is, the hands, feet, and other members. One and the same soul governs these two bodies, and both share the same desires, fears and pains." Some of Leonardo's conclusions were faulty, of course, but his embryological studies opened the way for the revolutionary change of viewpoint which was to take place in the sixteenth century: the new appreciation of the role of the mother in reproduction.

Leonardo by no means neglected the anatomy of the male sex. He reasoned that the sperm is not "cooked" somewhere in the body, but formed in the testicles, because a male whose testicles are removed is rendered sterile. This last fact had long been common knowledge, for the human race had had much experience with eunuchs and gelded animals. But Leonardo did not unreflectingly accept the changes to be seen in Oriental harem guards and Italian male sopranos, in capons, wethers, oxen, and geldings. He wondered what actually happened in castration. And he arrived at the conclusion that "the testicles increase the animosity and ferocity of animals. The principle is clearly illustrated in the case of castrated animals, for one sees the

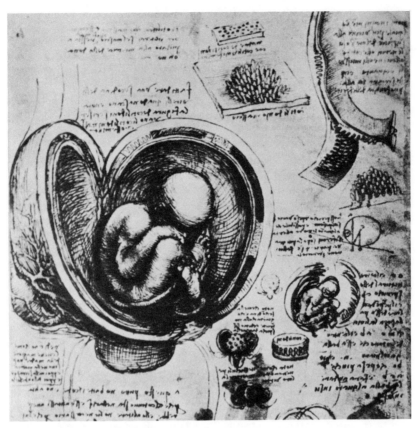

*The human fetus in the womb. Draw-
ing by Leonardo da Vinci.*

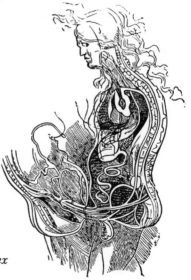

*Anatomical representation of the sex
act. Drawing by Leonardo da Vinci.*

bull, the boar, the ram, and the cock, very fierce animals, which after having been deprived of these testicles remain very cowardly; so one sees a ram drive before it a herd of wethers, and a cock put to flight a number of capons."

Leonardo also ventured into the realm of sexual psychology in his description of the functions of the male penis. The penis, he wrote,

> confers with the human intelligence and sometimes has intelligence of itself, and although the will of the man desires to stimulate it it remains obstinate and takes its own course, and moving sometimes of itself without licence or thought by the man, whether he be sleeping or waking, it does what it desires; and often the man is asleep and it is awake, and many times the man is awake and it is asleep; many times the man wishes it to practise and it does not wish it; many times it wishes it and the man forbids it. It seems therefore that this creature has often a life and intelligence separate from the man, and it would appear that the man is in the wrong in being ashamed to give it a name or to exhibit it, seeking rather constantly to cover and conceal what he ought to adorn and display with ceremony as a ministrant.

Such frank and precise writing was possible in Leonardo's time. Later centuries were a good deal more prudish. Not until the age of Sigmund Freud did the whims of the libido once more come under scrutiny. But Leonardo's studies had little effect on the scientists of his time. He composed no coherent books on science, only notes, aphorisms, fleeting thoughts. In his *Notebooks* precise observations are interspersed with fables, parables, and fantastic inspirations. When he died, on May 2, 1519, in the Castle of Cloux near Amboise, not even his favorite disciple and heir, Francesco Melzi, knew what scientific treasures were contained in the vast body of writings Leonardo da Vinci had left. Centuries were to pass before it became apparent that he had proclaimed the first great vision of a scientific age.

ALL LIFE COMES FROM THE EGG

Throughout the Renaissance, anyone who wished to become a doctor, physicist, or biologist had to go to Italy. The universities of the

Italian city-states were centers of scholarship, as the Dutch universities were to become in the Baroque period. This was why, some eighty years after the death of Leonardo, a young English medical student repaired to Padua. His name was William Harvey; he came from the Kentish town of Folkestone, and he hoped to be instructed by the most famous physician of the time: Hieronymus Fabricius ab Aquapendente.

Fabricius possessed Leonardo's intellectual curiosity, if not his versatile genius. He was greatly interested in comparing the organs of a wide variety of animals; not, as had been the custom since Aristotle, to point up their differences, but to discover their similarities. He showed Harvey the by now familiar stages in the development of birds' embryos within the egg; but he carried this study further by comparing these stages with the different stages of animal embryos. Harvey looked closely and considered deeply.

In 1612 Harvey returned to England with his degree of Doctor of Medicine. He settled in London, built up an extensive practice, and thirteen years later was appointed a professor of anatomy. He won great esteem both as physician and gentleman, enjoyed the friendship of Francis Bacon, and became personal physician to James I and Charles I. His professional and social successes did not keep him from engaging in research, discovery, and speculation in the manner of his old teacher Fabricius. In 1628 he published his book on the circulation of the blood—a discovery which opened a new era in medical science.

He also pursued the embryological studies of his student years. He entertained Charles I with a demonstration of the stages of the chick embryo. The king was entranced. Harvey remarked that he wished he knew whether embryos matured in similar fashion in the bodies of four-footed animals. He could learn a great deal, he thought, if he were permitted to take part in the hunts of the court and to dissect the game. The king graciously invited him to do so. Henceforth, to the annoyance of the courtiers, Harvey would dissect part of their bag immediately after each hunt. He took notes, made drawings, and accumulated a large amount of factual information on embryology. None of it, however, was published until Harvey had reached an advanced age and was no longer practicing.

Before that time came, things took a more somber turn for this darling of fortune. The Civil War broke out, and Harvey, as the king's physician, was needed on the battlefields. He seems to have been badly cast as an army doctor. The story goes that during the Battle of Edge Hill he sat in a tree reading, lost to the world, completely unaware of the course of the fighting. But that did not make him less a Cavalier to the Puritans. When the king was executed, the royal physician's own situation became precarious. His London office was looted; he lost a large part of his scientific notes; and he went into exile for a time. Eventually he returned home to his country estate on Hampstead Heath to live in quiet retirement. A few years before his death he surprised the medical world with the bold and heretical assertion that all animal life comes from the egg.

Omne animal ex ovo—we can scarcely grasp the impact this simple, harmless, and plausible postulate had upon Harvey's colleagues. A more disturbing principle, it seemed, had never before been sounded. Harvey maintained that all female animals, including viviparous animals, produce eggs from which the embryos grow, either inside or outside the body of the mother. Hence new organisms do not arise out of a mixture of sperm and menstrual blood, as Aristotle had taught, nor from a union of male and female seed-elements, as Descartes and others held. All, without exception, come from the maternal egg.

Harvey's book, *De generatione animalium*, seemed to shake a large number of principles theretofore regarded as fundamental. Even more sensational was his view that all organisms including man employed essentially the same method of reproduction. And the most revolutionary aspect of his theory was the assertion that the egg is more important than the sperm; that the mother plays the primary part, the father the secondary, in the creation of new life.

Harvey was the founder of *ovulism*, the egg theory. His principle was later extended to the still more significant slogan: *Omne vivum ex ovo*—all life comes from the egg. According to this school of thought a kind of rough sketch of the future progeny existed within the egg before fertilization; the sperm only gave this slumbering creature the necessary impulse toward development. Thus, for the first time since the days of Aristotle the male principle was seen as secondary to the female.

But was Harvey right? First, two of his premises had to be tested. Was it true that egglike structures were to be found in the bodies of human and animal females which were comparable to the eggs of birds, amphibia, and fish? Then again, supposing that were true, were the germs in those eggs actually, from the first day of development, equipped with all the requisite organs? Were they complete though miniature little creatures?

Today we know that the first premise of the egg theory was correct, but not the second. Both questions could hardly have been answered in Harvey's lifetime by the research methods then available. To the gratification of the ovulists, however, a new device came into use not long after Harvey's death, one better than the keenest eye and the finest magnifying glass: the microscope. And the first microscopists did not merely place tissues, blood, water drops, worms, and insects on their slides, and look for infusorians and other small organisms. They also embarked on a search for the origin of all life: the egg.

In 1672 Regnier de Graaf, a Delft physician, cut open a number of female rabbits and found in them organs similar to the ovaries of birds. When he examined these under the microscope he saw they contained numerous small bladders—obviously, he concluded, the rabbit's "eggs." With an enthusiast's intrepidity Dr. de Graaf promptly made his discovery public. The ovulists were overjoyed with this confirmation of Harvey's theory.

One hundred and fifty years later it turned out that de Graaf had been mistaken. What he had found were not eggs, but the *Graafian follicles*, small sacs of fluid in the wall of the ovary in whose protection the eggs themselves grow. In spite of this error, de Graaf's conclusion was correct: the female mammal also has an ovary and produces eggs.

The ovular theory had no more stalwart exponent than Marcello Malpighi of Bologna, who devoted himself to microscopic study of the development of the germ in the egg. Malpighi was in all respects a successor to Harvey. He investigated embryology, respiration, the circulation of the blood, the structure of the lungs, the spleen and kidneys. He came within an ace of discovering plant and animal cells. knew a good deal about the metamorphosis of insects, and tried—though in vain—to produce artificial fertilization by extracting the eggs from a silkworm and treating them with the spermatic fluid of a male. He also attempted to apply Harvey's ovulistic concept of propagation to plants.

People were ready to believe this eminent biologist when he maintained that the hen's egg, even at the earliest stage of its development, held a complete organism, extremely tiny, to be sure, and barely recognizable as such, but finished and perfect. This germ, he averred, was awakened from its slumber the moment it was fertilized by the cock's sperm, and gradually broke through the egg as the butterfly frees itself from the chrysalis.

Malpighi's "observation" seemed to confirm the second premise of Harvey's theory: the living organism was prefigured in the egg.

His work created a sensation in scientific circles, although Malpighi himself reaped little thanks in his own native land. He too had his laboratory plundered, his instruments smashed and his manuscripts destroyed—not by revolutionaries, as Harvey had, but by envious colleagues and the superstitious mob. Not until the last years of his life did he enjoy peace and quiet—after he had moved to Rome and become personal physician to Pope Innocent XII.

So great was his influence that, in the lavishly illustrated medical books of the time, the drawings of human or animal ovaries invariably showed a miniature figure inside each egg, to indicate that a fully formed infant organism was already present. Certain bold intellects carried Malpighi's ideas further. If this infant organism were female, did it not also have ovaries of its own? If so, in its eggs—miniature but fully formed—the next generation must be waiting, in its eggs the next, and so on.

Thus ovulism passed over into the theory of *Preformation*. The theorists of preformation were only extending previous ideas and researches when they stated that all living organisms that had ever existed on earth and that would ever exist had been present as germs in the first egg since the creation of the world. This idea was given its sharpest and most exaggerated formulation by that same Professor Vallisneri who had been concerned about Adam's tapeworms. The ovaries of Mother Eve, Vallisneri declared, had held the totality of mankind from the beginning to the end of time—one generation tucked into the other.

THE DISCOVERY OF SPERMATOZOA

But the doctrine of ovulism was undermined by a startling discovery. The upheaval took place in the same city of Delft in which only five years earlier Regnier de Graaf had dissected his rabbits, and by claiming he had found the mammelian ovum, won the first battle for Harvey's theory.

In 1677 a student at the University of Leyden came to the acknowledged master of microscopy, Antonij van Leeuwenhoek, and showed him a bottle containing some semen. The semen, he said, came from a sick man who suffered excessive nocturnal emissions, and looked very strange under the microscope.

"In what way?" van Leeuwenhoek asked.

"It's alive," the student replied in a rather frightened whisper. "It's swarming with small, tailed animals. Perhaps these are what have made the man sick."

Van Leeuwenhoek nodded. That might well be. His interest aroused, he took a drop of semen from the bottle, examined it under

one of his stronger microscopes, and saw that the student had described the matter correctly. Innumerable animalcules were swimming about in the fluid. They consisted of a round body and a long,
writhing tail. Probably, he thought, they were infusorians such as
he had been finding for many years in infusions and in the rain water
that collected in roof gutters.

But how had infusorians entered a man's sperm? Was the student
right, that they might be the cause of sickness? Or did every male organism contain such mysterious parasites in his sperm? Van Leeuwenhoek thanked the student heartily, saw him to the door, and resolved to pursue the matter.

Therewith, the young discoverer of spermatozoa vanishes from
history. We do not know even his right name. He haunts the annals
of science as Ludwig Hamm, van Ham or von Hammen. According
to some he was a Dutchman, according to others a German.

Van Leeuwenhoek went on studying this strange phenomenon. For
years the mysterious animalcules in male semen took precedence over
his beloved infusorians. At first, it is true, he felt a certain delicacy
about examining the sperm of his fellow citizens of Delft. But his
correspondents of the Royal Society in London urged him to ignore
such scruples. He went ahead and collected samples of semen from
sick men and men in the prime of health. In all cases he found
swarms of animalcules darting briskly about. Hence the newly discovered creatures could not be agents of sickness. What were they,
then?

The Royal Society suggested that he undertake some animal experiments. Accordingly, Leeuwenhoek gathered the milt of pike and
cod, the sperm of rabbits, dogs, and other mammals. In every case he
saw the same picture under the microscope. Van Leeuwenhoek described his findings to the Royal Society as follows:

> I have seen so excessively great a quantity of living animalcules
> that I am much astonished by it. I can say without exaggeration that
> in a bit of matter no longer than a grain of sand more than fifty thou
> sand animalcules were present, whose shape I can compare with
> naught better than with our river eel. These animalcules move about
> with uncommon vigor and in some places clustered so thickly to
> gether that they formed a single dark mass. After a short time they
> separated. In fine, these animals astonished my eye more than aught
> I had seen before.

Van Leeuwenhoek could not seem to keep the semen-animalcules
alive. They proved very frail outside the body and died quickly. For
what reason? They were found in the semen both of animals and

men. Were they perhaps products of decay, as some scholars in London suggested?

A stout opponent of spontaneous generation, van Leeuwenhoek rejected any such possibility. As a matter of fact, he soon had an inkling of the truth. "Some aver," he wrote to the Society, "that these animalcules arise out of decay, others that they have no life, but are only a kind of fire in the semen; but I maintain that the animalcules consist of a larger number of parts than these people can possibly imagine—of the parts of which our body is composed."

The spermatozoa, as Leeuwenhoek named the little creatures, served the sole purpose of reproduction, he believed. They could be in the semen for no other reason. And if that were so—perhaps the future living organism was located in them rather than in the female egg.

Van Leeuwenhoek was no friend of dry erudition. He had a witty and sparkling mind, and he derived the maximum of fun from his hobby. Thus, he sent the Royal Society a formidable set of calculations to prove that the milt of a single large cod contained ten times more spermatozoa than there were human beings on earth. He had already realized that "the testicles are made solely for the purpose of the animalcules forming in them." At the same time he marveled at the tremendous wastefulness of Nature: "What is intended to be done with all the animalcules that are in human semen?"

Now and then his conscience troubled him. For his intensive occupation with sperm and male organs was not just striking and sensational; to a great many persons it was a breach of morality. Leeuwenhoek was facing the same problem as all pioneers in sexual research. If he made concessions to the sensitivities of the populace, he betrayed science; if he made no concessions, he ruined his reputation. Fortunately, his scientific curiosity was stronger than his sense of propriety. He continued to dissect testicles and to dab drops of sperm upon glass slides; and such respectable gentlemen as Nehemia Grew and Robert Hooke of the Royal Society cheered him on.

Van Leeuwenhoek had more trouble with irate rivals than with prudish critics. When the Royal Society published the results of his researches in its *Transactions,* and when soon afterwards van Leeuwenhoek's letters and communications were also published in Dutch and Latin, a number of physicians protested that they had seen such spermatozoa under the magnifying glass long before van Leeuwenhoek, but that as men of delicacy they had naturally refrained from publicizing this disgusting discovery.

One of these rivals, a fellow countryman of van Leeuwenhoek's named Hartsoeker, was determined not to be forestalled again. He

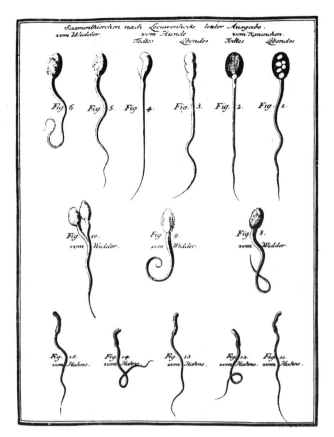

In 1677, a student of van Leeuwenhoek's discovered spermatozoa. Unfortunately his name has vanished from history. But van Leeuwenhoek went on to study and make his own drawings of the spermatozoa of various organisms. When he published his work, which included this drawing, he was attacked by many scientists who claimed that they had made the same discovery earlier, but as men of delicacy had refrained from publicizing their "shocking" findings.

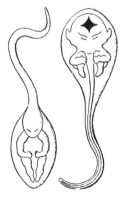

Human spermatozoa with their captive homunculi, as pictured by the 18th-century animalculists who belligerently but mistakenly believed that all vital material for the human life originated in the male.

issued a popular pamphlet proclaiming what van Leeuwenhoek had heretofore only cautiously hinted: that all future generations are contained, preformed, not in the egg but in the spermatozoon. Moreover, he supplied pictures of human semen, and sketched a tiny homunculus in each spermatozoon.

After the publication of van Leeuwenhoek's and Hartsoeker's writings, a strong faction opposed to ovulism swiftly formed. The *animalculists*, as the group was called, argued that all life came not from the maternal ovum, but from the animalculi in the paternal seed. At the beginning of the world God had placed the whole future human race in Adam's loins, not in Eve's womb. The egg functions only as a nutritive medium for the growing organism, and the womb as an incubator. Just as the seed of plants is sowed in the earth, so the sperm is sowed in the womb and there begins to germinate. This—and the animalculists, good Aristotelians that they were, stressed the point—corresponds with the natural dominance of male over female which can be observed everywhere in life.

The contest between the ovulists and the animalculists went on well into the nineteenth century. Both views had prominent spokesmen. Such authoritative personalities as Swammerdam, Spallanzani, Albrecht von Haller, and Charles Bonnet were on the side of ovulism. Among the animalculists, besides Leeuwenhoek and Herman Boerhaave, Holland's greatest naturalist, there were the philosophers Leibniz and Malebranche, who worked out a metaphysical foundation for the idea that the future world was contained, encapsulated, in the present generation.

During the scientific warfare that continued for more than a century, the animalculists began with a slight advantage. Van Leeuwenhoek had already won the first battle for them.

A questionnaire was sent by the Royal Society to seventy scientists. All reported that they had never observed traces of sperm or spermatozoa in the womb. Informed of this, van Leeuwenhoek promptly took action. He killed a number of female rabbits and dogs directly after copulation, dissected them, and observed that their genital passages were swarming with spermatozoa all the way up to the womb and the oviduct.

The ovulists were not slow in launching a counterattack. Their most powerful argument was supplied them by the chief of the opposing faction, van Leeuwenhoek himself. For he had made some interesting discoveries concerning virgin birth in plant lice.

VIRGIN MOTHERS

The Dutch have always been passionate flower lovers, and also keenly interested in the habits of plant pests. They put all the insects they found crawling about their flower beds under the magnifying glass. Thus, as early as the seventeenth century, the plant louse had become one of the favorite subjects of study for Dutch amateur scientists.

When van Leeuwenhoek and Swammerdam cut their roses, they noted that the green aphids were milked by ants and eaten by ladybugs. They further discovered with considerable amazement that from spring to late summer the roses were infested exclusively by female plant lice, and that these, in spite of the absence of sexual partners, busily propagated and produced exclusively females. Males suddenly began to be born in the cool days of autumn. They paired with the females and each fertilized female laid a single winter egg. From this egg the founder of a new population of plant lice hatched the following year.

It turned out that virgin reproduction, or *parthenogenesis*, similar to that of the plant lice in the summertime, took place in other species of insects, and likewise in water fleas and rotifers. Later a number of stick insects, hymenoptera, and myriapods were discovered in which sexuality had entirely vanished. These creatures existed only in the female form, and reproduced endlessly without fertilization.

The ovulists exulted when they learned these facts. In certain cases, evidently, the male could be entirely dispensable. If so, the egg and not the sperm must be the ultimate source of all life. Harvey was right and van Leeuwenhoek wrong. Moreover, ecclesiastics hastened to point out, these observations proved the possibility of virgin birth.

The animalculists found some difficulty in reconciling the facts of parthenogenesis with their theory. They vaguely implied that possibly the atmosphere from spring to fall contained enough plant louse semen to fertilize the female generations. A number of particularly audacious theoreticians even suggested that all water and air might be impregnated with germs or organic molecules, so that in some cases not only insects and shrimps but even higher animals and man might be fertilized by them.

That idea was taken up not only by a few visionaries, but also by serious naturalists and philosophers. Reports were published about virgin mammals and young girls that had become pregnant without benefit of sexual intercourse. Naturally cynics made fun of such fantastic views. A lampoon published in 1750 (quoted by the witty French biologist Jean Rostand in his *La Biologie et l'Avenir humain*) had this to say about fertilization without copulation:

> May couples riven by conflict return to harmony, trust, and mutual respect! May slandered women bid gossiping tongues be silent! A woman living apart from her husband can nevertheless present him with the joys of fatherhood, fruit of a boating trip or a country walk. The woman only wanted to get a breath of fresh air, and the organic molecules needed only a draft, a slight breeze, to establish themselves in her. A widowed lady has children, and gossip names their fathers. But there is no need for any such assumption: she merely breathed the air and the molecules crept into her along with it. A girl becomes a mother before marriage: again only the air she inhaled is to blame. Why should humanity be in a worse plight than ordinary insects? . . .

Today we no longer think parthenogenesis of higher organisms as ridiculous as did the anonymous author of this pamphlet two hundred years ago. On the contrary, the whole question of parthenogenesis has become a highly topical one in the past few decades and is once more being discussed as energetically as in van Leeuwenhoek's time.

ABBÉ SPALLANZANI'S FROGS IN BREECHES

For some time the great discoveries of Antonij van Leeuwenhoek contributed little to solving the mystery of procreation. The minds of scientists and philosophers were steeped in preconceptions on the subject. Almost a hundred years after the discovery of spermatozoa by van Leeuwenhoek's student, confusion in the field of sexual biology was still almost as great as it had been in Harvey's time. Disputes between the partisans of Adam and Eve continued to rage. The animalculists were now promoting the theory of telegony, of continuous influence of the first sire upon all subsequent offspring. If this were true, then the sperm was more than a mere stimulant to the development of the germ. The ovulists countered with another consideration: If the germs of future life were contained in the sperm, then the spermatozoa must have a kind of soul. But that was obvious nonsense. For day after day countless billions of spermatozoa died unused. How then could they be creatures with a soul? What happened to the innumerable souls in wasted semen?

This debate over the souls of the unborn occupied the natural philosophers so intensively that exact experimentation receded into the background. If experiments were undertaken, their aim was to prove the ovulistic or animalculistic theory, not to discover new facts. Polyps, worms, larvae, crabs, and newts were dissected and fragmented. It was found that a good many of these creatures could replace lost parts, and this capacity for regeneration was considered to be proof of the doctrine of preformation. Obviously every organism must have been preformed—either in the egg or in the sperm—since the very beginnings of life, and when this primal form, this archetype, was destroyed, nature corrected the loss at once by means of mysterious powers of renewal.

Abbé Lazzaro Spallanzani, who will be remembered as having dealt a blow to the theory of spontaneous generation, was also a believer in preformation. Within that school he was inclined to agree with the ovulists, and he maintained that the fetus was not a "worm" floating in the semen which passed, during coition, from male to female. Unlike most of his colleagues, Spallanzani attempted to prove his ideas by experiment, and with remarkably sure instinct chose the ideal experimental animals, which to this day—two hundred years later—have remained models for the biology of reproduction: frogs and toads.

First of all he dealt with the dogma which had been postulated by the greatest naturalist of the age, Linnaeus: "In all of nature no impregnation or fertilization of an egg takes place outside the body of the mother." Linnaeus liked to hand down such pronouncements, most of which later proved to be incorrect. The founder of biological classification had failed to observe that countless invertebrate animals as well as most fish and many amphibians reproduce by external fertilization. Nevertheless, his contemporaries were quite used to accepting dogmas; they simply assented to his theses, which he propounded with the inflexibility of an Aristotle.

Spallanzani, however, did not regard the great Linnaeus as a god. He took one hundred and sixty-five female frogs in the act of copulation, cut them open, removed the eggs which had remained in their bodies, and placed the eggs in water. All of them speedily rotted; hence they could hardly have been fertilized inside the frog. But those eggs which had already left the female's body during the act of copulation developed normally into tadpoles. Had fertilization taken place at the moment of expulsion of the eggs, or afterwards? "To determine the question," Spallanzani reported,

I placed some couples, of which the female was beginning to discharge her eggs, in empty vessels. As I knew that in these amphibious animals fecundation always takes place in water, my hopes from this expedient were not very sanguine; but fortune was more propitious than I could have expected. The male is so much attached to the female that, notwithstanding he is taken out of his natural element, he persists in performing his office. I now saw that there spurted a small jet of limpid liquor from the tumid point in the vicinity of the anus, upon the eggs hanging out at the vent of the female. . . . The eggs being afterwards put into water, and bringing forth young, I hesitated not to suppose that the liquor emitted by the male was real semen.

Thus Spallanzani discovered external fecundation—a process which is just as widespread in the animal kingdom as internal fertilization. In order to make certain that the observed fluid was in truth semen, Spallanzani made an ingenious experiment. He dressed some male frogs in "little breeches of oilskin," left others undressed, and placed both the trousered and the untrousered males with females ready for copulation. The result was what he had expected. The eggs from the mating with naked bullfrogs were fertilized and developed; the others remained sterile. "The eggs are never fruitful, for want of having been bedewed with semen, which sometimes may be seen in the breeches in the form of drops."

Spallanzani thought his problems through to the end, and went beyond the limits of this experiment. If fertilization outside the body of the mother was possible, then it should be possible for the scientist to imitate this method and "to attempt the fecundation of animals by art." Once again he took up his knife, opened a pair of toads, removed the cluster of eggs from the female and the seminal vesicle from the male, then dipped a pencil into the seminal fluid, spread it on the eggs and placed them in water. His artificial fertilization succeeded: the eggs developed and normal toad tadpoles resulted. "Thus I called into life," Spallanzani wrote with pardonable enthusiasm,

a number of animals, by imitating the means employed by nature. The reader will conceive the satisfaction I derived from the success of an experiment so precarious and uncertain. He will easily imagine that I was not disposed to stop at my first discovery, but that I determined to repeat and vary my trials, in order to deduce such consequences as might illustrate the subject.

Spallanzani could not, of course, remotely suspect the wide consequences which would result from his pioneering labors. Today artificial fecundation is practiced with trout, carp, chickens, sheep, cattle, and horses, either for simple practical reasons or to improve the genetic stock. Moreover, the fertilizing syringe employed by physicians has for some time been playing a modest but much-discussed part in the reproductive life of man.

Spallanzani's achievements had much in common with those of van Leeuwenhoek. Both men were pathfinders whose discoveries ushered in a new era; both were at the same time children of their times. And the times were reluctant to shake off established patterns of thought. Spallanzani lived until the last year of the eighteenth century, and remained an ovulist to the end of his days. He had recognized the importance of the sperm in the process of fertilization more clearly than any scientist before him, and was in truth only a tiny step away from recognition that both sexual elements—egg and spermatozoon—had an equal share in the generation of new life. But he did not take that step. He continued to regard the sperm as merely a stimulus to the development of the preformed germ within the egg.

The theory of preformation continued to hold sway over the minds of most thinkers. The question could not really be clarified until some conscientious microbiologist succeeded in demonstrating that no embryonic germ existed either in the unfertilized egg or in the spermatozoon. The first man to make that demonstration appeared in the lifetime of Abbé Spallanzani. He reaped neither applause nor agreement, only ingratitude, mockery, and oblivion.

THE DISK IN THE YOLK

A regular part of the instruction of medical students in the eighteenth century was based on the classic experiment with unfertilized and fertilized chicken eggs. This was supposed to illustrate the mysteries of embryonic development. The professors, all of them stanch ovulists, never failed to point out that even in the unfertilized egg a tiny chicken was present, awaiting only the arrival of the male impulse to awaken it to life.

The students took that principle on faith. But one young candidate for the doctor's degree, a medical student at Halle, examined the contents of the egg closely under the microscope and shook his head. He began to occupy himself with embryological studies. In 1759 this young man, Kaspar Friedrich Wolff, son of a Berlin tailor, presented a dissertation entitled *Theoria generationis*. In this work on the "theory of generation" Wolff stated flatly that all previous embryologists had been proceeding from false assumptions. The unfertilized chicken egg, he declared, contained no preformed organism, nor was there anything of the sort in the freshly fertilized egg. All he had actually found was a small round disk, a *cotyledon*, from which the organs and parts of the body gradually developed in the course of a "series of new formations."

The concept of "seed leaf" or cotyledon which Wolff formulated has become an established part of the vocabulary of biology. At the time it was something incredibly new. Was it possible that a new organism could develop out of a leaf-shaped structure, a small disk? The authorities shook their heads. And when Wolff, after winning his doctorate, continued to argue for the existence of his seed leaf and his theory of development, such bigwigs of science as Albrecht von Haller called him to order. No university dared to appoint a man of such a heretical cast of mind, and after a short spell of surgery and lecturing without pay, Wolff emigrated to Russia. He found a post at the St. Petersburg Academy of Sciences, but what he did there has vanished from sight.

Not until the nineteenth century did biologists realize that Kaspar Friedrich Wolff had been an overlooked genius. Ernst Haeckel in his *The Riddle of the Universe* exclaimed:

> Although this great discovery—one of the most important of the eighteenth century—could have been directly proved by a verification of the facts Wolff had observed, and although the "theory of generation" which was founded on it was not a theory at all, but a simple fact, it met with no sympathy whatever for half a century. It was particularly retarded by the high authority of Haller, who fought it strenuously with the dogmatic assertion that "there is no such thing as development: no part of the animal body is formed before another; all were created together." Wolff . . . was long in his grave before the forgotten facts he had observed were discovered afresh by Oken at Jena in 1806.

Oken, whom Haeckel cites as the rediscoverer of *epigenesis*, the theory of development out of the germinal disk, was scarcely a clear thinker. His observations had been similar to those of Wolff: that the germ in the freshly fertilized egg was not a tiny organism, but merely a small, amorphous bubble, technically called a vesicle. Oken also concluded that this vesicle had arisen from the union of egg and sperm. But he envisioned this process in the most grotesque terms. The sperm, he said, worked like a putrefying toxin; it decomposed the germinal vesicle, causing it to fall apart, and from its disintegration the fetus grew, just as new life springs forth from rotting humus.

Twenty years later a somewhat saturnine zoology professor from Estonia was discussing Harvey's "all life comes from the egg" with a colleague in the city of Koenigsberg, East Prussia. The Estonian, a man of thirty-five by the name of Karl Ernst von Baer, pointed out that the serious scientist must first determine whether the ovaries of viviparous animals actually contained eggs. His colleague, Professor of Anatomy Karl Friedrich Burdach, was of the same opinion. For Baer had meanwhile found out that the Graafian follicles, which Regnier de Graaf had once taken for mammalian ova, were not eggs at all.

Burdach owned a bitch who happened to be pregnant at this time. He sacrificed the dog to science. Baer dissected her, opened some of the Graafian follicles, and discovered in each of them a "yellow dot" which he examined under the microscope. Baer himself has described the result: "I started back thunderstruck; for I saw distinctly a very small, sharply delineated sphere of yolk. It took me a moment to recover, for I feared that I had been deceived by a phantom. It seems strange that a sight one has expected and longed to see can excite such alarm when at last it appears." Baer had discovered the mammalian egg! "I had not thought that the content of the ovum of mammals would so much resemble the yolk of a bird's egg."

To a certain extent, then, Harvey had been right. Throughout the animal kingdom, except for unicellular animals and other lower groups, life emerges from the egg. And the eggs of various classes of animals resemble one another amazingly. Now, however, Baer wanted to test whether Wolff and Oken were also right. What happens in the egg after fertilization? Once again he selected those ideal experimental subjects from which Abbé Spallanzani had learned so much: the eggs of frogs. And he saw what no one but Wolff had observed: within the fertilized egg there was in truth at first only a "germinal disk." It divides "first in two halves, each half splits again into two quarters, the quarter into two eighths, and so the division continues regularly. . . ."

Karl Ernst von Baer had thus also discovered the segmentation of the egg cell, although he had never heard of such a term as cell. In years to come Baer and other embryologists were able to prove that the fertilized ova of all animals, including those of mammals and man, divide in similar fashion. Baer also drew the proper conclusions from his observations. By means of division the egg is transformed completely, and in the course of the complex process the fundamental organs of the body gradually arise. Later, in the second half of the nineteenth century, biologists were able to arrive at neat descriptions of the step-by-step growth of skin, tissue, and abdominal cavity, digestive tract and buccal cavity, or—in the higher animals—flesh, blood, vessels, and organs.

The theory of preformation was laid to rest at last. All the ovulistic and animalculistic writings which had loomed so large in reproductive biology ceased to possess anything but historical interest. And when, a few years after von Baer's researches, Schleiden and Schwann discovered the cell, it became clear that the egg and the spermatozoon were *sexual cells*. Robert Remack and Albert Kölliker thereupon demonstrated that the egg is nothing but a simple cell which after fertilization divides into daughter cells by segmentation. Kölliker drew the final conclusion: the spermatozoon is also a cell, which, unlike the ovum, can move by swimming in the manner of certain unicellular flagellates.

Since by now it was known that two unicellular animals can unite and form a new organism, this knowledge was applied to the sexual cells. Biologists in the second half of the nineteenth century seemed gripped by a feverish desire to enlighten the public. The mystery of fecundation seemed at last to have been solved, and they wanted to let laymen know what really took place in the reproductive act. A spate of books intended for the common reader described how sperm cells swam like tadpoles to the waiting ovum; how one of them won the race, penetrated into the egg cell and united with it to become a germ which then matured by a complicated process of development into a new individual.

It all sounded highly plausible. But until 1875 no one had seen with his own eyes whether this process really took place. What happened in the course of this union of the sex cells and exactly how it took place, was not known. Moreover, no one had any idea why a frog's egg invariably produced a frog, and why children were like their parents. The laws of heredity, although they had long since been discovered, still lay filed away in the archives of an Augustinian monastery.

DANCE OF THE CHROMOSOMES

Sea urchins have a number of characteristics which lend themselves beautifully to biological research. In the first place, like many lower animals the sea urchins simply deposit their sex cells in the sea and leave it to the spermatozoa to seek and find the eggs. In the second place, both their eggs and sperm can be kept alive and observed for a considerable time in a vessel of sea water.

In 1875 a pupil of Ernst Haeckel's named Oskar Hertwig, who was then only twenty-six, perceived these advantages and decided to study the sex cells of sea urchins in order to trace the actual events of fertilization. He placed a sea-urchin egg under the microscope, added some seminal fluid, and watched the sperms swarming around the egg. He saw one of the spermatozoa actually penetrate the egg—just as had been postulated. But he saw considerably more. The egg immediately formed a firm shell, a *fertilization membrane*, which prevented the entrance of additional spermatozoa. And in the ensuing minutes strange changes took place within the egg. Hertwig was able to see these processes and describe them accurately, for the microscopes available to him were far superior to those which had existed in the days of Karl Ernst von Baer.

First he saw that only the head of the spermatozoon penetrated into the egg. The taillike appendage broke off and disintegrated. The head then made its way further into the yolk, where it formed "an extraordinarily characteristic starlike figure." It attached itself to the cell nucleus of the egg and fused with it. Hence Hertwig concluded that the head of the sperm is the real nucleus of the sperm cell and that "fertilization is based on the fusion of sexually differentiated cell nuclei."

Hertwig did not yet suspect what the two nuclei did when they fused, and it was many years before he found out. While he was pursuing his studies and pondering the how and why of nuclear union, two scientific parties were debating the question of how parental characteristics were transmitted to offspring. One party believed in the inheritance of aquired characteristics, by which it meant that all cells of the parent organism were capable of influencing the sexual cells. The other group held for a strict division between body cells and germ plasm. The germ plasm, it maintained, was unchangeable; distinct although still unknown forces caused it to pass the specific traits of the parents on to the next generation. The first view seemed logical and reasonable; the second savored of biological mysticism. Neither of the contending groups was aware of the experiments undertaken by an amateur scientist which had already proved that the second party was right.

For many years an Austrian monk named Gregor Mendel had experimented with crossing peas and beans in the garden of the monastery of Altbrünn. He had observed that the parental characteristics reappeared in the next generation in a specific, calculable, numerical

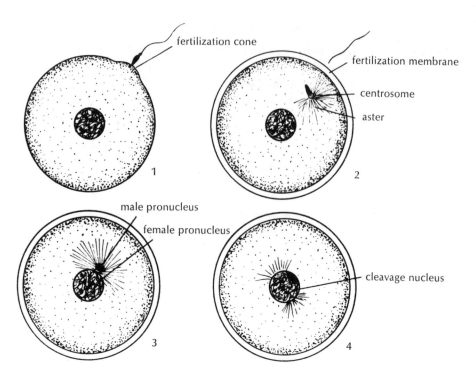

1 — fertilization cone

2 — fertilization membrane, centrosome, aster

3 — male pronucleus, female pronucleus

4 — cleavage nucleus

The process of fertilization was discovered in 1875 by Oskar Hertwig when he was twenty-six years old, as a result of his study of the sea-urchin egg.

Oskar Hertwig

relationship. He had kept records and drawn up tables, and he gradually became aware that a definite law governed the results.

On February 8, 1865, in a lecture delivered to the members of the Natural Science Society in Brünn, Gregor Mendel explained his three laws of heredity. But the good nature lovers of Brünn were simply bored by the formulae he listed on the blackboard. They did not realize that all this data about wrinkled and unwrinkled peas represented laws which would revolutionize a whole branch of science. The following year Mendel had his lecture printed and sent copies to a number of scientists. No one was interested. Disappointed and embittered, Brother Gregor abandoned the matter and devoted himself to his monastic duties. When he died in 1884, no one remembered his researches; the obituary mentioned only that Brother Gregor had raised excellent fruits and vegetables.

In 1900 the Mendelian laws were rediscovered. It is one of the curiosities of scientific research that three biologists, simultaneously and independently, made the same discoveries as the obscure Augustinian monk. They were Erich von Tschermak-Seysenegg of Vienna, Karl Correns of Berlin, and Hugo De Vries of Amsterdam. The science of genetics then progressed by leaps and bounds. Geneticists began experimenting with fruit flies, mice, rabbits, and countless other creatures. They learned that there are hereditary diseases which recur in certain families exactly in accord with Mendelian law. They discovered the *chromosomes*, those coils of giant protein molecules in the nuclei of the sexual cells, and the *genes*, the carriers of hereditary characteristics, which hang like pearls along the strings of chromosomes. Finally they learned that the mechanism of heredity is not so rigid as the Mendelian laws implied. New forms and characteristics can arise by *mutation*, abrupt changes in the hereditary material. And mutations, it is now believed, are the principal means by which evolution operates.

With the discovery of the chromosomes, it was at last possible to decipher the processes which take place during the fertilization of the egg. Oskar Hertwig and many other scientists once more watched the spermatozoa swarming in an intricate dance around the sea urchin's egg. The German biologist Theodor Boveri counted the chromosomes in the immature and mature sexual cells of the equine tapeworm. The American geneticist Thomas Hunt Morgan attempted to localize the genes in the chromosomes of the fruit fly *Drosophila* and to learn the particular spots in the coils at which the genes for particular traits and hereditary diseases were located. After much work of this sort it was clear that in fertilization the chromosomes of male and female parents fuse—and thus the characteristics of father and mother are united. Before the union the egg and sperm cells each expel half their set of chromosomes; thus, when the two cells fuse, the fertilized cell will once more contain the normal number of chromosomes—but half will have come from the mother and the other half from the father.

This process, which we have described in greatly simplified form. contains the deepest mystery of generation. Many intensive studies have rounded out the picture. Sex *hormones* were discovered; these determine the formation of the secondary sexual characteristics. Insight into the interior of the fertilized egg cell has, however, not only solved the greatest puzzle of life, but has also changed man's consciousness, initiating a process of revision and rethinking which is not yet complete. The German zoologist Wolfgang von Buddenbrock has expressed one aspect of this intellectual revolution as follows:

> Only as a result of these discoveries can the relation between man and woman be seen in its true light. For thousands of years woman has been regarded as the inferior. She, it was thought, brought forth the substance, but man contributed all that was of a higher nature. Now we know that in the act of reproduction both sexes perform an equal task. Each parent contributes precisely one half of the inheritance of the child. Each individual chromosome of the mother unites with the corresponding chromosome of the father to form a pair. No mathematician could conceive of a more exact mechanism for assuring complete equality.

But there is also a diabolic factor in this union of the chromosomes. The generative process is a game of chance. Chance alone determines which genes are lost, which are preserved and passed on; which traits lie latent and which are brought forth. Chance alone determines sudden mutational changes of the hereditary material, and which of the mutants will survive. Not only individual destinies depend upon Nature's game of chance, but the development and evolution of all the organisms on our planet.

■

CHAPTER THREE

THE GENEALOGY OF SEX

In their search for the origin of life, men have learned that the animal world presents a wide variety of reproductive methods, some of them quite bizarre. A great many styles in reproduction have flourished before there evolved the one we find in the higher animals and man. Let us start now at the bottom of the evolutionary ladder and work our way up through this extraordinary genealogy of sex.

THE MANY-HEADED HYDRA

One day in November of the year 1740 Abraham Trembley, tutor on a count's estate near The Hague, gazed in amazement at some water plants which he had fished out of a ditch and had been keeping in an aquarium. A number of small, strange objects, green in color and very peculiar in behavior, had appeared on these plants.

At first Trembley thought them to be parasitic plants growing on the other plants as mistletoe grows on trees. But then he saw that the small green things moved. They expanded and contracted, and could actually change their position. This mobility, he later wrote, "aroused in me the thought that they were actually animals." The creatures Trembley had discovered were fresh-water polyps—coelenterates belonging to the same phylum as sea anemones, sponges, and corals. Naturalists of the day assigned such coelenterates to the plant kingdom. Linnaeus had classified these "flower animals" among the spore plants.

73

Abraham Trembley disagreed, at least as far as his fresh-water polyps were concerned. He was inclined to return to the view of the Neapolitan pharmacist Ferrato Imperato, who even before 1600 had modestly suggested that sea anemones were not flowers and that corals were neither mosses nor ferns. For Trembley saw plainly that his polyps not only moved, but also reached out with their tentacles for water fleas and consumed them. To ascertain the true nature of these plantlike animals, he subjected them to all sorts of experiments under the microscope. He beheaded them, cut them to pieces, divided a single polyp into a hundred fragments—and within a short time each piece grew into a whole animal. He produced the strangest monsters by causing two polyps to grow together; he grafted one polyp onto another and actually produced two-headed and many-headed polyps. His most original idea was to turn a polyp inside out over a hog bristle. Even after this frightful operation, the creature lived. "It is nothing to a polyp to be impaled on a spit," Trembley commented.

Today we can no longer conceive the excitement aroused in scientific circles by this news of this organism less than half an inch in length: its tenaciousness of life, its incredible powers of regeneration. its animal nature. It recalled the Hydra, the many-headed monster of legend whom Hercules had fought only to discover that whenever he cut off one head, two grew in its place. The fresh-water polyp and its closer relatives were therefore named *hydroid polyps*.

The regenerative abilities of the hydras proved to be even greater than Trembley had imagined. Fifteen years after the discovery of the green monster, a German naturalist crushed to pulp a number of polyps of a different, somewhat larger type. Within two weeks the pulp had been transformed into lively individual animals—exactly the same number as there had been before.

The man who made this polyp pulp was one of the most ingenious and likable personalities in the early days of biology. He was not a naturalist by profession, but an engraver by the name of August Roesel von Rosenhof. In 1753 Roesel began publishing a monthly magazine of biology gaily entitled *Allmonatliche Insecten-Belustigungen* ("Monthly Insect Diversions"). By "insects" he meant not just the class of animals we would today call Insecta, but the whole range of small creatures from infusorians to earthworms, snails, and spiders. And the animal which evidently most diverted him, and on which he wrote long illustrated treatises, was the fresh-water polyp.

It was hardly likely, Roesel thought, that such polyps reproduced by voluntarily tearing themselves to pieces; they must have other methods of propagation. He described in detail one of these methods—which, however, he mistakenly considered the only one. (It so closely resembled the propagation of plants that some investigators began to wonder whether the polyps might not be, after all, "sensitive plants.") This method was budding. Budlike extrusions sprout from the mother polyp at various parts of the body, and grow into young polyps. Roesel described the process vividly, if somewhat verbosely, in one issue of his magazine:

Before the young polyp has acquired its arms and can employ them for catching prey, it receives its nourishment from the body of the mother, with which it is connected like a branch of a blood vessel to the stem, so that it opens into the hollow channel of the mother. But when it can use and stretch out its arms, it at once attempts to obtain food for itself, even though it may still be attached to the mother. It does so, as I have seen many times, by snatching and swallowing a small insect here or there. Once the young polyp is mature, and its time has come, one can observe even under slight magnification that it is preparing to free itself. For the darker channel of the offspring grows thinner and thinner at the hind end, where it has a visible connection with the mother; and at last this end grows so delicate that no attachment can be perceived even under the strongest magnification, although the young one is still clinging to the mother by means of the lighter, external cortex. This tie does not last long. For when that point has been reached, the young polyp begins to stretch its body as well as its arms so vigorously that at last the movement pulls it free. Once this is done, it attaches itself somewhere by its hind part, just like the mother, and thereafter provides for itself.

Roesel came very close to recognizing that alongside this asexual reproduction the polyp also practices the ordinary method of sexual reproduction. He saw boillike capsules develop in the middle of the bodies of polyps; in some these took the form of breasts, while other

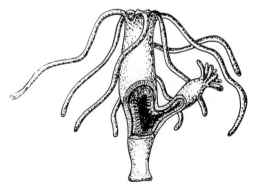

Budding as it looks in the fresh-water polyp.

polyps produced brown, prickly spheres "like a sea urchin or a sea cucumber," which finally broke off and dropped to the bottom. He collected and observed these brown excrescences for a while, but since nothing developed out of them, he decided that both forms were morbid growths.

Today we know that the male sex cells form in the breastlike knobs. and that the prickly spheres are the eggs of the polyp. Several varieties are hermaphrodite: the same creature produces both sperm and egg cells at the same time. In other varieties, separation of the sexes has been developed. Sexual propagation replaces asexual when the weather turns cooler and food is scarcer. Under such conditions the polyps cannot continue budding and extruding parts of themselves. (It has been calculated that a single polyp can in the course of a summer produce twenty-five thousand offspring by budding; they must economize in order to survive the lean months.)

The process is as follows. The sperm are discharged into the water from the "breasts"; they seek the eggs, which are still attached to the bodies of the polyps, and fertilize them. In such a situation a hermaphrodite may fertilize itself. When the germ in the egg has reached a certain stage of maturity, it surrounds itself with a hard winter shell. The eggs then fall off the polyp and survive the time of scarcity in mud. When favorable weather returns, a young polyp grows from each egg and busily reproduces by budding until the next period of drought or cold. That Roesel had had no such results from his "sea urchins" was probably because the temperature was too low.

Polyps are far down on the scale of evolution, as are the whole phylum of the saclike animals called coelenterata. The reproductive devices employed by the coelenterata are fundamentally the same as those of unicellular animals, but considerably refined. One of these methods is the alternation of generations, the classic form of the creature alternating with jellylike medusae. Medusae are motile, free-swimming sexual animals which have freed themselves from the sessile polyps and which reproduce in open water. New polyps arise from the fertilized medusa eggs. These polyps cling to the pond bottom and after reaching a certain stage of development extrude ring-shaped disks which finally separate from the mother animal and swim off as a new generation of medusae.

There are innumerable gradations. Some fresh-water polyps and sea anemones release their sex cells into the water directly, without an intervening medusa generation. On the other hand, there are the sea nettles and "sea gooseberries" (ctenophores) which interpose no asexual generation; their eggs hatch directly into small jellyfish. There are coelenterate colonies which engage in reproduction by sending forth myriads of swimming larvae. Included in these are many types of corals, the animals whose gigantic reefs have changed the face of the earth more than all other multicellular animals put together—aside from man. Other coelenterate colonies float along below the surface of the sea by means of gas-filled bladders. These colonies, such as the "sail jellyfish" *velella* and the Portuguese man-of-war *physalia*, consist of innumerable polyp units which have assumed various functions: swimming, eating, digesting, sensing and catching prey. The colony will also contain special reproductive individuals.

The colonial medusae are, along with the corals, the most beautiful of the coelenterates. They also anticipate the complex organization of higher animals. As a tribute to their beauty, Ernst Haeckel named one of the species after his first wife, Anna Sethe, who died while still a young woman. The medusa has since been known as *Desmonema anna-sethe*. The species continued to be the special darlings of Haeckel in his study of the mystery of organic life.

The medusa.

FROM THE MORULA TO THE GASTRULA

When the evolutionists of Darwin's era began drawing up the first genealogies of living organisms, one of the principal questions they faced was: How did the unicellular animal become multicellular? How did the protozoan develop into a coelenterate—a creature "consisting only of gut and skin," as someone once put it?

In 1866 Ernst Haeckel hit upon a simple and ingenious idea which he reduced to the formula: "Ontogeny is a brief and rapid recapitulation of phylogeny." Or, to put this in less scientific language: We can read the evolutionary history of any living organism from the embryonic development of that organism. The frog is first an egg, then a loose association of cells, then a germ cup (gastrula), then a wormlike larva and a fish-shaped tadpole, until it acquires legs and matures into a four-legged amphibian. Similarly, the frogs in the long course of their evolutionary history were first unicellular organisms, then groups of cells, coelenterates, worms, fish, and newts, before they developed into the amphibian frogs we know.

Haeckel called this idea the "fundamental biogenetic law." Contemporary biologists speak more cautiously of *biogenesis;* for the development of the individual (the ontogeny) does not recapitulate the development of the phylum (the phylogeny) in every detail, but only in general features. All the same, Haeckel's theory was correct. Any human embryo demonstrates this. The wormlike shape, the gill slits, the tail, all to be seen at various stages of embryonic development, clearly reveal the animal ancestors of the lord of the earth.

Since Haeckel was especially interested in the developmental leap from the unicellular to the multicellular organism, he devoted much study and close detective work to the eggs, germs, and larvae of the lowest multicellular animals: the sponges, corals, and jellyfish. In 1872 he wrote a treatise ambitiously entitled *Philosophy of the Calcareous Sponges,* in which he once more advanced a theory. It is known as the gastraea theory.

From the fertilized egg, the theory goes, there first develops by cleavage an undifferentiated mass of cells shaped like a mulberry—called *morula,* from the Latin word for mulberry. This mass collapses inward—invaginates, in technical language—to form a *gastrula* or germ cup, the cavity of which represents the primitive intestine and the opening the primitive mouth. According to Haeckel, all tissues and organs have developed out of these two germ layers of the gas-

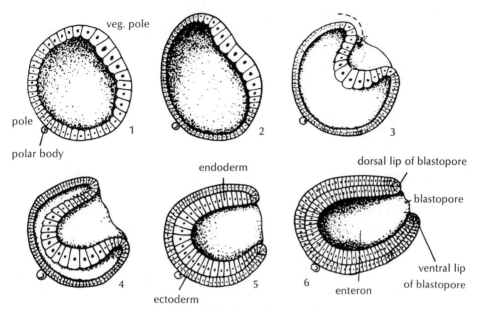

From the blastula to the gastrula.

trula, the skin layer (ectoderm) and the intestinal layer (endoderm). Haeckel's conclusion, applied to the history of the race, was this: First we were unicellular organisms, then morulalike accumulations of cells, then gastrulalike coelenterates. All multicellular animals from polyp to man had descended from a simply constructed coelenterate formed like a gastrula. Haeckel called this hypothetical original form *gastraea.*

The next step was to determine whether any animals existed which looked like morulae and gastrulae. If any could be found, Haeckel's case would be immensely strengthened. And they *were* found. The disciples of Darwin, Huxley, and Haeckel were lucky people. No soooner was the ape-man hypothesis put forward than they discovered early Javanese man; after the gastraea theory was advanced, living organisms of the morula and gastrula form turned up. These organisms had, in fact, long been known. But interest in them was reawakened by the idea of biogenesis.

The volvox (*Volvox globator*) is a mulberry-shaped unicellular animal and belongs to the class of flagellates, which the human spermatozoon so amazingly resembles. But at first glance the volvox does not appear unicellular. What we see is a round green sphere half a millimeter in diameter, composed of some twenty thousand one-celled individuals. Protoplasmic bridges link the animals with one another, and a "vegetative pole" directs the whole.

"These cells," Bölsche writes, "are not united sexually. . . . They have merely placed themselves in close contact with one another, and as it were anchored themselves to one another. . . . In so doing they have taken a great step forward: they have advanced beyond the union of sex to the formation of a social bond."

Volvox, the unicellular inventor of the social bond, made other tremendous advances. It invented the separation between body plasm and germ plasm. The small green spheres contain two groups of volvox cells. One group concerns itself with feeding, movement, and response to stimuli; it corresponds to the somatic cells of multicellular animals. The other, numerically smaller, group is responsible for reproduction; it corresponds to the sex cells. Unlike multicellular organisms, volvox has three rather than two types of sex cells: *agametes*, which propagate by dividing rapidly inside the ball; *macrogametes*, which function like ova; and *microgametes*, which are expelled like sperm cells and fertilize the macrogametes of other volvox spheres.

But in introducing sexuality, volvox also brought in death. These animals are not immortal like other protozoans, which reproduce solely by division. When the daughter spheres are mature, the mother sphere bursts and all its body cells die. The daughters paddle away through the water like tiny galleys, leaving a corpse behind. And that is the law which in one form or another rules the entire organic world.

Animals of the gastrula type, representing the next stage of evolution, inhabit all the seas of the world—there are more than five thousand varieties of them. Some also occur in fresh water. They form colonies which often assume the most bizarre and wonderful shapes. The skeletons of lime, horn, or silica in which these animals live may look like vases, flower baskets, or superb samples of the glassblower's art. These are the organisms Haeckel treated in his monograph: the sponges.

Until late in the nineteenth century even the most prominent naturalists had a hard time deciding whether sponges belonged to the plant or the animal kingdoms. The question was first settled by John Flemming, professor of natural history at King's College in Edinburgh, who fished the sponge beds and examined with great care the artfully shaped structures he brought from the depths. Every individual in such colonies, he found, is a multicellular animal organism of very simple structure, fundamentally a tube which draws water and nourishment into itself by the motion of its flagellae.

If an inventive zoologist had wished to construct a hypothetical primordial animal which would exemplify the gastraea theory, his creature would have looked much like the tube-shaped or cup-shaped individuals of a sponge colony. What is more, the larvae of sponges show the development of the morula into the gastrula type of animal. Little balls resembling volvox, they swim through the water by the aid of flagellae, settle down somewhere, and convert themselves into little cups by turning inward, "invaginating." These cups reproduce asexually by budding, manufacture a supporting skeleton of lime or silicate, and thus grow into colonies and virtual hives of sponges. These colonies send out sperm cells which fertilize the egg cells of other colonies. And the larvae which emerge from the fertilized eggs swim away to spread the species elsewhere.

Sponges are hermaphrodites. Each animal produces both eggs and sperm, but at different times, so that self-fertilization does not occur. This method is found in other, higher hermaphrodites also. Sponges have another strange and quite fantastic talent. If a living sponge is pressed through a firm gauze net, so that it is broken up into individual cells, these cells creep like amoebae toward one another and unite into clusters of cells which resemble the morula. This artificial morula then develops like the germ in the egg. It invaginates, becomes a gastrula, and grows into a new sponge.

This atomizing of the sponge is essentially the same experiment Roesel von Rosenhof had undertaken with his fresh-water polyps. The remarkable regenerative capacities of these animals have led to some strange speculations. Does the sponge or polyp pulp obey some magical power which commands it to return to wholeness? Zoologists of the present day smile at such philosophical flights; the motive force which impels the separated cells to reunite is not at all magical but chemical.

Sponges existed half a billion years ago. The phylum is an ancient one, a sideline of evolution which must have branched off from the tree of life very early. Haeckel's hypothetical gastraea may have resembled the individual of a sponge colony but was probably not a true sponge, rather a cup-shaped polyp. For the evolution of the polyps continued. From them developed flower animals of glowing colors, reef-building corals, bell-like jellyfish, and majestic colonial medusae drifting over the sea.

From them there also developed something entirely new: the symmetrically constructed cup, the first worm. This was an evolutionary step of tremendous importance to the history of the earth. An animal arose which no longer looked like a tube, but like a pipe with two openings. This was the first animal with an alimentary tract, the basic model for all other animals up to man. Henceforth all animals with few exceptions would have an upper and an under side, a right and left half of the body, a front and rear.

And the second opening in the rear of the body, which first appeared in the worms, was henceforth to play a special part in the history of sexuality.

LABYRINTH OF THE WORMS

No group of animals has presented more problems to the classifiers or has given rise to more furious disputes among system builders than the worms. For what are worms? "A huge conglomeration of animals of the most diverse shapes," one writer on biology once stated with hopeless resignation. A hodgepodge, a zoological lumber room into which, since the days of Linnaeus, a vast variety of lower animals have been stuffed—all those that could not be fitted in elsewhere.

Whenever the subject of worms came up at congresses of zoologists toward the end of the nineteenth century a certain corpulent, witty man used to quote a dictum of Wilhelm Busch: "The worm comes in different lengths." That sentence, he declared, was the gist of what his respected colleagues had so far discovered about worms. The corpulent man's name was Karl Vogt; he lived in Geneva and was nicknamed "Monkey Vogt" because he was one of the most ardent followers of Darwin. Karl Vogt was also a specialist on that motley group of animals thrown together under the common denomination of "worms."

Worms not only come in different lengths but fit into many different places on the tree of life. All the higher animals that populate water and land have evolved from wormlike organisms. Worms are ancestors of mussels, snails, and squid; of starfish, sea urchins, and sea lilies; of crabs, spiders, and insects; and even of the vertebrates. Among the multitude of worms, therefore, are types which today are included among articulate animals, others that are placed among the ancestors of the mollusks, still others which lead to the echinodermata or "prickly-skins," and finally some which suggest a distant kinship with the first vertebrates.

Zoologists who have groped their way through the labyrinth of the worms have encountered not only forms that bear promise of the future, but strange outsiders that have drifted into blind alleys of evolution. Many of these have become parasites, living on and bringing death to plants, animals, and man. The whole earth swarms with such parasitic worms, and many remain still to be discovered. The threadworm group—to which the roundworm ascaris, the trichina worm, and a number of plant pests belong—embraces about half a million varieties, modern parasitologists estimate. Probably only two per cent of these are known and have been described.

Man has hated, cursed, and fought these worm parasites since the beginnings of human consciousness. But if we can free ourselves temporarily from a natural and apparently primordial revulsion, we must admit that parasitic worms, disagreeable as they are, are also among the most interesting creatures on the face of the earth. Certainly they provide fascinating chapters in the story of reproduction.

Their strangely complicated lives and sexual behavior can be reduced to a simple formula: Haeckel's biogenetic law, stating that every animal is compelled by its heredity to repeat, in the course of its individual development, the key stages in the history of its phylum (see page 78). Many parasitic worms may be regarded as sterling examples of biogenesis. They pass their larval period as free-swimming creatures in water; their further development takes place in the interior of a cold-blooded lower animal; they reach sexual maturity and reproduce inside a warm-blooded higher animal. That is to say, their distant ancestors were free-swimming gastrula worms which gradually adapted to the life of parasites upon lower aquatic animals. Along with their hosts they were swallowed by fish, and developed into fish parasites. With the fish they passed into the intestines of fish-eating birds and mammals. When man appeared and began to be a fisherman, hunter, and cattle raiser, some varieties adapted to the new conditions. The final site of their evolution was the body of *Homo sapiens*.

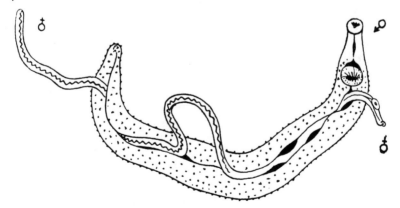

The fluke Schistosoma haematobium *lives in a state of eternal copulation. The female lies in the fissure of the male's body as in a case.*

In 1851, when this many-step development was still unknown, the
German doctor Theodor Bilharz discovered one of the most dangerous of the worm parasites that afflict humanity: the blood fluke *Schistosoma haematobium,* the agent of bilharziasis. The African blood
fluke and two related varieties in Asia and South America are parasitic in the portal vein and in the veins of the intestines, liver, and
bladder of man. They live in couples; the male's body is shaped like
a case in which the thin, threadlike female is held tightly until fertilization. To lay its eggs the female frees itself from the male's embrace and travels to the pelvic organs of the human host, the blood
vessels of which often become blocked by such huge quantities of eggs
that they swell and burst. Bloody urine and acute diarrhea of the victims denote the time at which the eggs reach the outside world by way
of the urine or feces.

The fluke is a terrible enemy of man. Bilharziasis still affects more
than a hundred million persons annually, many of whom die of general debility. Until a few decades ago no one knew how man became
infected with the blood fluke. The inhabitants of tropical countries
were warned against drinking unclean water, but no one had any
conception of the complicated stages of development through which
Schistosoma haematobium must pass in order to mature its deadly
pairs of flukes.

It remained for modern tropical medicine to discover the true history of Dr. Bilharz's blood fluke. The fluke's reproductive cycle provides a classical demonstration of the journey the water worm makes,
first preying upon a cold-blooded animal and then becoming a parasite on man. When the eggs excreted by infected human beings reach
water, a generation of larvae hatch out of them. These *miracidia,* as
they are called, swim about until they find fresh-water snails. They
bore into the skin of the snails, and inside these hosts undergo a metamorphosis into a second larval stage, in which they are known as
cercaria. The cercaria leave the snail hosts and swim through drainage ditches, pools, or flooded rice fields until they encounter human
beings bathing or wading. Entering through the pores of the human
skin, they make their way to the blood vessels and there undergo a
third change. Caselike males and threadlike females appear, couple,
and discharge the next generation of fertilized eggs into the outside
world.

The agent of bilharziasis is related to the liver fluke, one of the most
notorious pests known to sheep and cattle raisers. Its reproduction is
even more complicated. Grown liver flukes prey on the gall bladders
of sheep, goats, cattle, and other ruminants; occasionally they also
infect man. By stopping the bile ducts they produce necrosis of the

liver—a disease which can devastate a herd of livestock. Seventy years ago Rudolf Leuckart, professor of zoology in Leipzig, published statistics on the ravages of the liver fluke. In 1830 alone, some one and one half million sheep died of necrosis of the liver. In 1862 Ireland lost more than one half of her sheep, and eleven years afterward a third of the sheep in Alsace-Lorraine died. In 1876 40 per cent of the cattle in Slavonia were killed by the liver fluke; in southern Argentina more than a million sheep were victims of the disease in 1882. In a single fluke season the farmers in the vicinity of the city of Arles in southern France lost no fewer than three hundred thousand animals.

The man who compiled these statistics is regarded as the true founder of parasitology. Leuckart realized that parasites could be fought effectively only if their reproductive cycle were known. Consequently he spent years making exacting experiments to clarify the sexual habits and metamorphoses of the parasitic worms. His investigation of the liver fluke was crowned with complete success.

When Leuckart began studying the fluke around 1860, he was struck by two curious facts. First, all years of severe liver fluke epidemics had been damp and rainy. Secondly, the livestock seemed to become infected only at specific places. "The experienced farmer," Leuckart wrote, "knows the dangers of such districts; often he even knows the especially suspect places, usually sour meadows or ditches or puddles without proper drainage. He does his best to keep his animals away from such spots." What was it about wet pastures? Why did the cattle fall prey to liver flukes in just those places? Leuckart finally solved the mystery.

The fluke eggs which are excreted with the manure of affected animals die swifty on dry ground. They can only develop if they come into contact with water on flooded meadows. Their first stages of development resemble those of the agent of bilharziasis. Tiny, simply constructed larvae like the miracidia of the blood fluke swim rapidly about in the water, moving by means of their cilia, and penetrate into the bodies of mud snails. Each miracidum there transforms itself into a saclike sporocyst and produces asexually a number of larvae of a more advanced type, for these have mouth, intestinal tract, and anus. In dissecting fresh-water snails in the seventeenth century the Italian naturalist Francesco Redi—the opponent of spontaneous generation —had come across these larvae, but had not suspected what they were. In his honor the fluke larvae of the second generation are now called *rediae*.

The rediae bore into the liver of the snail and there likewise reproduce asexually. Their offspring leave the host animals, infect more snails, and produce more generations of rediae. Finally, the rediae in the snail change to a third larval form: a maternal sporocyst gives rise asexually to a daughter generation, and from these daughters larvae develop which resemble a grown liver fluke except that sexual organs are absent. This is the cercaria stage, similar to that assumed by the larvae of the blood fluke when they go hunting for human victims.

Until the year 1952 the snail was assumed to be the last intermediate host of the liver fluke before it infected the liver of a sheep. The cercariae, it was thought, swam to shore by the aid of a tadpolelike tail, attached themselves by suckers to the grass, there encysted, and in cyst form withstood considerable periods of drought. If a ruminant ate the infected grass, the cysts opened up inside its digestive tract. Young liver flukes emerged, entered the bile duct of the host, and there within two or three months grew into sexually mature flukes.

In 1952, however, two American biologists at Cornell University discovered that the matter was still more complicated. The cercariae do not leave the snail's body of their own accord. Instead, the hosts embed them in balls of mucus and expel them. And these balls of mucus are then devoured by still another intermediate host, which they promptly infect. In 1963 two German parisitologists, Wilhelm Hohorst and Gernot Graefe, after prolonged experimentation, at last confirmed the suspicion of the American biologists that this further intermediate host is the ant.

Ants eat the balls of mucus expelled by the snails. The cercariae then bore through the wall of the insects' crops into the abdominal cavity. There they encapsulate and mature to the infectious stage in which they will subsequently be so dangerous to the ruminants. But how do the liver flukes pass from the ant to the body of the sheep? They make use of a trick that seems utterly uncanny. A single cercaria works its way into the brain of the affected ant, fixes itself in the nerve center, and henceforth guides the behavior of the insect. The ant, guided by the cercaria in its brain, is compelled to clamber to the very tips of grasses and weeds and to cling there. Clustered together, the infected ants hang for hours on the blades of grass; their bodies are stuffed with parasites, and the guiding cercariae in their brains see to it that they—as Hohorst has phrased it—"literally offer themselves to be eaten" by sheep and cattle.

As they graze, the ruminants swallow the ants, thus ingesting the encapsulated cercariae in the bodies of the ants. Now that the young liver flukes have reached their ultimate hosts, they can hatch out and grow to sexual maturity. The Odyssey of the liver fluke, which has at last been completely traced, is one of the most fascinating and complicated examples of parasitic reproduction.

Mature liver flukes are hermaphrodites; they cross-copulate in the bile duct of their final hosts. Their larvae, however, as we have seen, propagate both in the miracidia and rediae stage without fertilization, parthenogenetically. From the biological point of view, this extremely complicated procedure is clear and meaningful. The thousands upon thousands of chances for extermination in the life cycle of this curious parasite are offset by a maximum of offspring; not only the sexual worms but also the various larval forms do their bit to multiply the species.

An even more fantastic life history is that of the fluke *Leucochloridium paradoxum*, whose larva battens on the aquatic amber snail, but which as a mature sexual animal inhabits the intestines of songbirds. The biologists and writers who have dealt with this paradoxical fluke are astounded by its maneuvers. Fritz Kahn writes:

Here is a worm whose rationally inexplicable goal it is to enter the intestines of an immature songbird. Puzzle: How is a worm swimming in the water of a pond to reach the intestines of an immature songbird which dwells in its parents' nest high up in the trees? It crawls into snails and lets these snails carry it to the grass on the shore. But how to get from a snail on the shore of a pond to the nest of a songbird? Obviously, the only way is to be carried there by the mother bird which will be seeking food. The trouble is that songbirds seeking food for their young do not take the time to peck snails from their shells; they only snatch things that are ready to beak, as it were. The worm living inside the snail therefore has to make some extra effort if the bird is to pick it up. It therefore forms a sporocyst inside the snail and sends branches carefully through the snail without killing it until they reach the tips of the feelers. Here they swell so thickly that the snail cannot withdraw into its shell even when a bird approaches. In order to attract the bird's attention, the sporocyst branches are colored green and white like a jockey's jacket, and are plainly visible since the skin of the snail's feelers is so stretched as to be transparent. The bird is deceived; it thinks it has spied a brightly colored caterpillar. It pecks off the garishly colored, twitching feeler and carries it to its nestlings. The worm has accomplished the seemingly impossible: it has transferred itself from snail to the stomach of an immature bird in a well-guarded nest high up in a tree.

The sexual relations of many parasitic worms are as grotesque as their life cycles. The sexual act among threadworms, which include the rye, wheat, potato, and turnip eelworms that devour cultivated plants, is amazingly similar to the copulation of higher animals. The sexes are quite distinct. The larger female has a sexual opening in the center of its body; the smaller male is equipped with a special pouch at the end of its body, in which is a fork-shaped hook which it introduces into the female sexual opening at copulation. But the wildest part of the story is the way the sexual union takes place. In the turnip eelworm, for example, the females at the time of sexual maturity look like tiny lemons. They remain close beneath the rind of the turnip, break through the rind with part of their bodies, and hold their sexual opening out. The males leave their apartments inside the turnip, climb around on the outside of the rind, and choose a suitable "lemon" into which to insert their hooked forks.

The female of the bumblebee eelworm undergoes a particularly strange transformation after fertilization. It becomes a gigantic vagina from which the rest of the body hangs like an insignificant thread. Earlier investigators who found these peculiar cysts inside bumblebees thought that these threadlike appendages must be dwarf male worms which had become attached to the enormously larger female. But search though they might they could find no male sex organs in the supposed male, and so the theory was dropped. It remained for Rudolf Leuckart to solve the riddle of the bumblebee eelworm.

The worms, Leuckart discovered, copulate in the damp ground. Immediately after mating the males die. The females seek out queen bumblebees, which winter in the ground, and penetrate into their bodies. Soon afterwards the vagina of the eelworm undergoes a strange transformation. It grows larger and larger, absorbs womb and ovary, and continues to expand until it is a sac fifteen or twenty thousand times as large as the rest of the body. Finally the body appendage is cast off from the vagina and disintegrates; the huge vagina leads its own life for a short while longer until young worms have hatched out of the eggs. This new generation of worms emigrates from the bumblebee's body in the autumn, crawls into the ground, there grows to sexual maturity, and the cycle is renewed.

Dwarf males do in fact exist among many worms. There is, for example, the starworm *Bonellia viridis* which lives in the Mediterranean and the North Atlantic. The females look like warty, dark-green pickles. The males of *Bonellia* were long hunted in vain, until they were discovered by J. W. Spengel living as parasites in the bodies of the females. Numbers of them lodge in the sexual organs, feeding on the body juices of the female and by their well-controlled collective labors fertilizing all the mature eggs which slide down the oviduct past their stations.

But how do these dwarf males get into this sexual utopia? Among the free-swimming larvae of *Bonellia*, sex is not yet determined. When one such larva succeeds in attaching itself to the proboscis of a mature female, it is transformed under the influence of a hormone secreted by the proboscis into a dwarf male. The male moves down the gullet and from there into the sexual parts of the female. The larvae that do not find females must abandon all hopes of a lazy life of parisitism, and so they themselves develop into females. And those that by one accident or another lose their hold upon the female's proboscis within the first two days are condemned to go on through life as hermaphrodites.

Lilliputian males who lead a parasitic existence on female Gullivers are prevalent not only among worms. Examples are to be found in other classes of animals all the way up to the fish. The arrangement is sensible—it relieves the species of all concern about finding a suitable partner at pairing time.

Some worms have found an even more fantastic way of avoiding the periodic search for a partner—by having the couples live in permanent copulation, like the blood fluke. The nematode *Syngamus trachealis* inhabits the windpipe of various birds; it is a pest dreaded by poultry and duck raisers. The birds ingest the mature worm eggs along with their food. The hatched embryos settle down in the larynx and trachea, where they grow into large sausage-shaped females and small leechlike males. Each male then hastily seeks the sexual opening of the female, attaches itself, and remains thus united with its partner for the rest of its life.

The most amazing of all worms goes a step further. This is the "paradoxical double animal," *Diplozoon paradoxum*. It is a parasite on the gills of carplike fish, and is a hermaphrodite, theoretically capable of mating with itself. But in the course of maturing two of the worms grow together in the middle of their bodies and become Siamese twins which do not again separate until death. The vagina of each half of the hermaphrodite becomes permanently attached to the sperm-duct of the other half. "A love monstrosity," Wilhelm Bölsche calls it, "an erotic Briareus with four sexual organs mating crosswise in a double marriage."

Innumerable other aberrations, curiosities, and monstrosities crop up in the reproductive life of worms. But one type deserves special mention: the familiar parasites whose possible presence in Adam's intestines seemed to pose a religious problem to Professor Vallisneri (see page 19). These are the tapeworms, the favorite subjects of the old myths of spontaneous generation.

SEXUAL SEGMENTATION

The appearance of the tapeworm is an oddity in itself. Attached to a head—the scolex, as the zoologists call it—is a chain of "segments" which in some varieties reaches a length of twenty-five to forty-five feet. Each segment contains a complete, highly complicated reproductive apparatus with male and female organs and seminal glands. To expel a tapeworm the vital thing is to get rid of the head. For the head constantly sprouts new segments, while at the other end of the chain link after link breaks off and is excreted into the outer world with thousands of fertilized eggs.

The question arises: What kind of organism is the tapeworm? Is it an individual or a colony? Until the middle of the nineteenth century zoologists were unable to agree on this point. Some scientists regarded the head and its segments as a colony of worms which could reproduce both by division and sexually. Others held that a kind of alternation of generations took place among tapeworms as among the medusae-forming polyps; the asexual generation would be represented by the head and the sexual generation by the segments.

Gradually it came to be accepted that the tapeworm must be regarded as a single individual. From head to the last segment, a single neural and vascular system runs through the entire tapeworm. Hence the segments can scarcely be considered single individuals capable of sexual generation. They are nothing but sexual organs which the head repeatedly forms out of itself by budding. The tapeworm mutilates itself by constantly breaking off its sexual segments, and it regenerates itself by substituting new segments for those it has cast off. Both acts serve to reproduce the tapeworm on as lavish a scale as possible and to disseminate the species.

All these matters were still unknown in 1851, when a German doctor named Friedrich Küchenmeister addressed a meeting of naturalists in Gotha on the reproduction of tapeworms. The subject was highly interesting to the assembled naturalists, and they listened respectfully. The doctor claimed to have discovered the route by which the fertilized eggs, which entered sewage systems along with the excrement of infected human beings, once more became tapeworms in the human intestines. Up to that time no one had had the slightest idea how infection took place. It was generally assumed to be due to uncleanliness, and careful washing of the hands was recommended as a preventive measure.

But the audience of scientists soon began to smile and shake their heads. For Küchenmeister asserted that certain curious formations in the muscle tissue of various domestic animals, usually called cysticerci, were in reality the encapsulated larvae of tapeworms. Few of the assembled scholars were willing to believe this. For more than a hundred years the leaders of zoological research had regarded these cysticerci as formed by an independent species of animal, the "bladder worm," which could not possibly be connected with tapeworms.

Küchenmeister had undertaken experiments which, he said, disproved that notion. Tapeworm eggs, he declared, reached meadows and gardens when these were fertilized with "night soil," or reached the outside world by other means. There they waited until they were taken in by plant-eating animals, mice, rabbits, pigs, and cattle. In the digestive tract of these intermediate hosts the larvae hatched out, traveled with the blood stream into the muscles, liver, lungs, or brain, and formed the so-called bladder worms. The future tapeworm then matured in these cysts. When the mouse was eaten by a cat, the rabbit by a dog, the pig or cow by a man, a tapeworm head crawled out of the cyst, entered the small intestines, and developed into a tapeworm.

At that time virtually nothing was known about the alternation of hosts in parasitic worms. The assembled scientists therefore listened to Küchenmeister with thinly concealed skepticism, thinking that the good doctor had allowed his imagination to roam too far. Finally Küchenmeister stated that he had several times succeeded in feeding the cysts in the flesh of rabbits to dogs, and had raised first-class tapeworms in the intestines of these dogs. Sensing the disbelief of his audience, he offered to repeat the experiment forthwith, so the scientists could see for themselves.

The zoologist F. Hempelmann has described the ensuing scene:

Rabbit cysts were available—but no dog. Küchenmeister thought that a cat would probably do as well. And so, with a huge, furious tomcat in a sack, the group repaired to the cellar of the theater in which the naturalists were meeting, and tried to feed the cysts to this cat. The tomcat had no suspicion that he was not the proper host; he scratched and bit and repeatedly spat out the cysts which were thrust into his mouth. At last the force feeding succeeded. After two days the victim was sacrificed to science. But—there was no trace inside him either of cysts or of incipient tapeworms.

The skeptics seemed to have right on their side. But in subsequent years Küchenmeister proved by endless experiments that rabbit cysts did in fact develop into tapeworms in the intestines of dogs. In the intestines of cats, on the other hand, the cysts died. He concluded that the cysts must find their way into certain specific intermediate hosts in order to reach their final form as tapeworms. The dog tapeworm must pass from the rabbit to the dog, the cat tapeworm from mouse to cat; the cysts in pigs and cattle must pass into the intestines of *Homo sapiens* in order to become tapeworms.

But how could this last assumption be proved? Dr. Küchenmeister hit on a rather grisly idea. He suggested that the cysts found in swine be fed secretly, in a good fish soup or in raw chopped meat, to criminals sentenced to death. Once the unfortunates had been executed. he suggested, autopsy could determine whether tapeworms were growing in their bodies. The experiment was actually tried. And as Küchenmeister had predicted, tapeworms were in fact found in the intestines of the victims—worm heads that had already formed their first segments. They were the familiar type of tapeworm, *Taenia solium*, which henceforth became known as the pork tapeworm, although it lives as a larva in the pig and can develop into a mature worm only in man.

Küchenmeister essayed the control experiment at once. He fed grown and suckling pigs with mature segments of *Taenia solium*, segments containing fertilized eggs. After two or three months he had the animals slaughtered and saw that their muscle tissue was swarming with "bladder worms." This was clear proof that—in the words of Alfred Edmund Brehm—"man cooperates with the pig in the rearing of this tapeworm."

Küchenmeister's work inspired a veritable fever of experimentation among zoologists as they strove to determine the life cycles, the intermediate and final hosts of other varieties of tapeworm. Some scientists hired vagabonds, beggars, and other poor devils and persuaded them, for money and the honor of serving science, to eat cystic beef and thus acquire the cattle tapeworm *Taenia saginata*. Others nobly experimented on themselves. Still others contrived to fill their students with such enthusiasm for the cause that whole classes became parasitologists who fanatically swallowed cysts and then, with the aid of worming pills, examined the results. By the time Rudolf Leuckart published (1863-1876) his standard work on human parasites, science had unlocked most of the secrets of the tapeworm's reproduction and development.

Every tapeworm, it was discovered, must change its residence several times in the course of its life. In most cases each residence must be a specialized one. Thus, the tapeworm undergoes the same cycle as other parasitic worms. Some varieties pass through their larval and cystic stage inside fleas or lice, maturing into grown tapeworms only when dogs, cats, or other warm-blooded animals swallow the infected insects. Others, as Küchenmeister had recognized, require a specific carnivore as intermediate host. A third group of tapeworms acts as a parasite in three host animals successively. Among these are the fish tapeworm, *Diphyllobothrium latum*, whose tortuous life history was traced in 1883 by a zoology professor in Dorpat and three students.

The professor, Max Braun, had discovered that cysts appeared in the flesh of pike, eelpout, and other fish. These were not like the "bladder worms" of warm-blooded animals, however, for they had a worm-like shape and a proper head. Since Braun suspected that such fish worms might develop into those broad and extremely long tapeworms which are especially common in fishermen's families, he did what other tapeworm researchers of the day were doing: he fed the cystic fish to his dogs, his cats, and the three students. His suspicion was confirmed. Huge wide tapeworms grew in the dogs, cats, and students. Fish, all four concluded, must be the intermediate hosts and fish-eating mammals the final hosts.

But the matter grew more complicated. If pike or eelpout were fed segments of mature tapeworm, the result was negative. In no case did the characteristic wormlike cysts form in the fish. But if segments with mature eggs were left in water for a time, curious round larvae hatched out of them. These larvae possessed long cilia and for a week swam about briskly. Was it essential for these larvae to be swallowed by fish before they could metamorphose into cysts? Braun tried this experiment—and failed. Like detectives on the trail of a criminal, he and his associates searched for the smallest clue to the first stages in the life of the fish tapeworm. At last they found the answer.

The fish tapeworm expels its egg from the intestines of man or of a carnivorous mammal. This egg can develop only if it reaches water. As a larva the worm penetrates into a tiny crab of the genus *Cyclops*. The cyclops is, next to the water flea, the favorite food of fresh-water fishes. But the cyclops must be eaten by a young fish if the worm is to attain its next stage of development. The worm larva grows in the muscles and later in the liver of the fish, and transforms itself into a worm-shaped cyst which resembles the head of the future tapeworm. Finally the fish must be eaten by a warm-blooded animal—an otter, bear, dog, cat, or man—for the cycle to be completed. In the animal's intestines the worm head becomes a segmented worm, produces sex organs, and discharges eggs which begin the cycle over again.

In so far as the tapeworm is dependent upon certain definite intermediate and final hosts, its development is subject to all kinds of accidents. It may often happen that eggs reach the wrong intermediate host, or that by self-infection they take up lodging in the final host without passing through the intermediary stages. This happens to other parasites, of course, but usually the strays die and do no harm. In the case of tapeworms such a faulty performance can have extremely dangerous consequences for the victim.

The reason is that the strayed eggs of some types of tapeworms do not die even though they are in the wrong host. Instead, they pass through all their stages up to that of bladder worm. The bladder worms, however, which frequently settle in the eye, the brain, or other vital organs, begin to bud monstrously. Daughter and grand-daughter bladder worms arise in which thousands and millions of tapeworm heads can grow. These heads miss their life goal—at some point the life goes out of them. But by then it is often too late for the unfortunate creature in whose organs they have formed.

The tapeworm *Echinococcus granulosus* is particularly notorious in this respect. Normally it passes through its larval and cyst stage in ruminants and attains sexual maturity in the dog. It grows to a length of only a few millimeters and has no more than three or four segments. For this reason zoologists long overlooked it and failed to connect it with certain horrible swellings which can affect all parts of the human body.

The eggs of the *Echinococcus* are easily transmitted to human beings. Dogs have the habit of sniffing the excrement of other dogs. with the result that worm eggs may be on their snouts and tongues. If the hands or faces of human beings are licked by such contami- nated dogs, the eggs may find their way into the human mouth and thence into the interior of the body. There the cysts grow into enor- mous bladders. In some cases—especially if they have settled in the liver—they have attained the size of an infant's head. North African herdsmen and Siberian nomads who use sled dogs suffer especially from this disease. In Iceland the *Echinococcus* plague was so wide- spread at the beginning of the twentieth century that for a long time the keeping of dogs had to be entirely banned.

The tapeworm, then, can be a terribly dangerous creature. At the same time its own life is a succession of perils. Only one out of hun- dreds of thousands of fertilized tapeworm eggs has a chance of being ingested by the proper intermediate host. And of thousands of cysts which form the intermediate host, again only one has some prospect of reaching the proper final host. The worm compensates for these perils by enormous fecundity. The egg production of a single tape- worm can reach astronomical figures.

The record is probably held by the fish tapeworm which Max Braun investigated and which passes through no fewer than five stages before it reaches sexual maturity: egg, water worm, parasite of a crab, fish parasite, and parasite of a warm-blooded animal. It is a giant among tapeworms, attaining a length of fifteen to thirty feet; it is said to live to the age of thirty-five years and to produce in the course of its life some four thousand segments. Each hermaphroditic segment contains after copulation an average of fifty thousand fertilized eggs. Theoretically, a single specimen of this tapeworm could engender two hundred million offspring.

Not all tapeworms, incidentally, can be regarded as useless or harmful. There is, for example, the strap worm, which is parasitic on aquatic birds when it is fully grown, but which lives in fish in its larval stage. These larvae can reach a length of one foot. Most people who catch a fish swarming with worms are inclined to throw it away in horror. "In Italy," the zoologist William Marshall relates, "people are more practical. They eat the parasites along with the fish as a form of fried macaroni and thank God for having so conveniently arranged to provide them with the main dish and the side dish together."

TIDES OF BEGETTING

Every year, in October and November, the sea along the coasts of the Samoan and Fiji islands fills with forms. At dawn, precisely on the day before the last quarter of the moon, the first swarms of worms appear. In the course of the morning hordes follow. By the next day the sea is so full of worms that it is discolored to a yellowish green and appears more solid than fluid. Eyewitnesses have reported that sticks and oars thrown into this swarm of worms remain standing upright for a time, and fall over only after some little while.

The organism which appears in such numbers on the coasts of several island groups in the Pacific is the famous and much-described palolo worm. The islanders know precisely when it is about to appear, and hold a gigantic feast. They wade into the water at neap tide, dip the worms out of the waves with baskets and nets, and pile them in huge mounds on the shore. A gargantuan meal begins. The palolo worms are steamed, roasted, or even eaten raw. Many European visitors to the Pacific have testified that they taste very good indeed.

These delicacies of the Samoans and Fijians are not whole worms, but only the detached sexual parts of the annelid worm *Eunice viridis*, which lives inconspicuously in the deep waters at the foot of coral reefs. The palolo worm produces a chain of segments similar to that of the tapeworm and like the tapeworm it mutilates itself when it reproduces. When the swarming period comes, the posterior ends of the worms, swollen with sex cells, break off and rise to the surface of the sea. There they fall apart into innumerable fragments. Since the palolo worm is bisexual, female posterior ends ranging in color from dark green to indigo blue are found, and male parts which are a yellowish white or ocher yellow. Male and female segments discharge their sex cells into the water; egg and sperm unite, and the fertilized eggs sink to the bottom.

The function of this tide of generation is clear. Sessile worms must find ways to conquer new territory if they are not to die of lack of food and overpopulation. The palolo worm sends its sexual parts on a voyage and regenerates the detached posterior end, creating new sexual segments for the next swarming period. The segments swim through the waves very agilely, writhing like snakes. Moreover, they possess groups of visual cells which aid in orientation.

Relatives of the palolo worm in the Pacific, in Malay waters, near the coasts of eastern Asia, and in the Caribbean south of Florida respond to other phases of the moon. One variety swarms in March and April shortly after the full moon, another in June and July three days before the last quarter of the moon, a third in October and November directly after the new and the full moons. The reproductive habits of many animals seem governed to some extent by cosmic events, but the complete attunement of the palolo worm to the moon has remained to this day the most wonderful and mysterious of these phenomena. As Rachel Carson writes in *The Sea Around Us:*

> Concerning each of these, the question recurs but remains unanswered: is it the state of the tides that in some unknown way supplies the impulse from which springs this behavior, or is it, even more mysteriously, some other influence of the moon? It is easier to imagine that it is the press and the rhythmic movement of the water that in some way brings about this response. But why is it only certain tides of the year, and why for some species is it the fullest tides of the month and for others the least movements of the waters that are related to the perpetuation of the race? At present, no one can answer.

A number of other marine bristle worms belong to the same phylum as the palolo worm *Eunice.* Zoologists have given them pretty names out of Greek mythology: *Aphrodite, Hermione, Syllis, Nereis.* It is not, however, lovely Aphrodite who leads the most interesting love life among them. Linnaeus probably named this worm, which looks like a piece of felt, after the foam-born goddess of love only because its bristles sparkle with all colors of the rainbow. But the sexual habits of the syllides and the nereids or clam worms are far more remarkable. They live in tubes in the slime of the ocean bottom, are also dependent on the moon for the time of their reproduction, and have developed a number of interesting tricks for spreading their kind as far as possible.

In one variety of *Syllis,* the posterior end of the body severs off as it does in the palolo worm. But this posterior end then grows a new head, so that the sexual part can set out on its mating expedition as a complete worm. In another type the females of the sexual generation emanate a steady light, while the males sparkle, flash, and blink like fireflies. If a couple mates, their lights instantly go out. In a third type the female will change to a male once it has laid its eggs, and then seek out the next group of females to mate with them. Such females can be artificially converted into males by cutting off half of the posterior ring of their bodies.

The clam worms normally crawl through the ooze of the ocean floor without being able to raise themselves above it. But under pressure of the sexual impulse they change into swimming worms so different in appearance that for a long time they were thought to belong to a separate variety. In 1860, however, Ernst Heinrich Ehlers, a Göttingen naturalist, recognized that these *heteronereids* were sexual forms of the ooze-dwelling nereids. The males perform wild rutting dances—often at the new moon and at high tide—during which they emit their sperm; the females swimming through the water are stimulated to deposit their eggs by hormones released from the clouds of sperm. A zoologist has trenchantly compared the male sperm dance with the flight of skywriters: "In their ballet of sex the males resemble airplanes veering in wild curves to write 'welcome' to the females."

The height of weirdness is reached by a bristle worm named *Platynereis megalops.* The females of this worm are fertilized by eating sexual parts of the males. The male platynereids consist of two parts: an anterior body, and a reproductive apparatus attached to it like a trailer to a truck. This dual system whips and darts in capricious figures in front of the females, tempting them to feed. Sure enough, the females fall upon the males, bite off the posterior parts, and swallow them. The sperm then travels within the abdominal cavity of the females and fertilizes the eggs.

HOMOSEXUALITY AND CHILD CARE

Some modern systematizers no longer classify palolo worms, nereids, and the many other bristle worms which inhabit the oceans as
"worms" in the true sense. They are regarded as jointed animals—
articulares—members of that phylum which includes millipedes, insects, crabs, and spiders. This first and still wormlike group of arthropods comprises the *annelids* or ringworms. Included among them is
the organism which to the ordinary man is the very prototype of
"worm"—the earthworm.

It is difficult for the nonzoologist (and for a good many zoologists)
to see that the earthworm may be an articulate, not a worm. But when
this creature of apparently simple construction is examined with the
anatomist's eye, it turns out that the new systematizers have a good
argument. The earthworm's body does not consist of an amorphous
tube; it is divided into numerous segments. Like all annelids, the
earthworm possesses well-developed muscle, blood-vessel, and nervous systems; connective tissue; a coelum or body cavity consisting of
a number of different chambers; organs for receiving sense stimuli;
and a simple two-lobed brain. That is, in its basic body structure the
annelid worms resemble the higher animals.

They differ from the higher animals, however, in that their bodies
do not form any such tightly centralized whole as do those of insects,
crustaceans, or vertebrates. If a caterpillar, a millipede, a louse, or a
salamander is cut in half, the animal dies. But a halved earthworm
can grow into two complete earthworms, the anterior end forming
a new posterior, the posterior end a new anterior. Not that this always happens. If the cut does not go approximately through the middle of the body, only one half will regenerate; and if too many segments of the body are lost, the earthworm must die.

The great investigator and champion of the earthworm was none
other than Charles Darwin. In a thorough and fascinating study, *The
Formation of Vegetable Mould through the Action of Earthworms*,
Darwin pointed out for the first time the importance of the earthworm to mankind. He described how earthworms in all regions of
the globe turn over the soil, how they convert dead plants into humus,
mix nitrogen and organic matter in the soil, and stir up the layers of
arable land with the care of a gardener preparing the soil for his choic-
est plants. "The plough," Darwin concluded, "is one of the most ancient and most valuable of man's inventions; but long before he existed

the land was in fact regularly ploughed, and still continues to be thus ploughed, by earthworms."

It is now known that without these useful animals our earth would bear only a fraction of the plants which it can now sustain. Moreover, innumerable carnivorous insects, millipedes, amphibia, reptiles, and birds, as well as a great many small mammals, life chiefly or partly on earthworms. The earthworm belongs among the most persecuted of animals. It replaces its losses by heavy reproduction.

If we examine an earthworm closely we will find in about the middle of its body a glandular organ of a whitish or yellowish color which is called the *clitellum*—Latin for "saddle." This ring has a special function in copulation, in egg laying, and in the nurture of the germ cells. Earthworms are hermaphrodites. Each worm possesses testes in a posterior segment of its body and oviducts in an anterior segment. The idea that couples might mutually fertilize one another seems obvious; such pairing is quite common in many hermaphrodites. And the earthworm's copulation seems at first glance to be exactly that: cross-mating. But in reality it is a far more complicated process.

At mating time two worms lie side by side, so that the head of one touches the posterior end of the other. The "saddle" in the middle of the body exudes a mucus which temporarily glues the two worms firmly together. However, the sperm does not flow from the male segment into a female sex opening. Instead, earthworms exchange their sperm; each worm discharges its sperm into pocketlike seminal receptacles in the other worm. Actual fertilization does not take place at this time; the female half of the hermaphrodite is still inactive. Thus, what takes place is a distinctly homosexual union, after which the worms separate and go their ways.

Some time afterwards the eggs mature. Now the "saddle," the glandular clitellum, assumes a new function. It swells into a girdle which surrounds the body like a muff, and which secretes a nutritive liquid. By muscular effort, the earthworm gradually pushes this girdle forward up to the fourteenth segment, where the mature eggs are located. It discharges the eggs into the girdle and pushes it further forward, to the ninth and tenth segments, where the seminal receptacles have been keeping its partner's sperm. The sperm, too, flows into the girdle. But still no fertilization takes place. By further use of the worm's muscles the girdle is abruptly pushed up over its head like a rolled-up shirt. At once it changes into a closed cocoon which gradually hardens in its hiding place in the ground. And there, in that deposited capsule, the sperms at last fertilize the eggs and young earthworms develop, feeding on the proteins in the cocoon and finally crawling forth, miniature editions of their parents.

With that extraordinary cocoon of the earthworm may be said to begin the story of the nest, of protection for the brood. Countless breeds of crustaceans, spiders, insects, mollusks, and vertebrates similarly do not send their progeny unprotected into the outside world. but provide cocoons, hives, balls of mucus, nests of foam, holes in the ground, and similar shelters against the thousand and one perils of existence. Among social insects, among spiders, cuttlefish, fish, and amphibia, and among birds and mammals, true child care has developed from the simple beginnings of the earthworm's cocoon.

Among other annelids, too, there are signs of such concern for the brood. Leeches, several hundred varieties of which live out their predatory lives in fresh water while a few types dwell on land or in the sea, have a clitellum similar to that of the earthworms. They, too, are hermaphrodites, and they too exchange stores of sperm in the course of copulation. Some varieties, including the well-known leech of medicine, *Hirudo medicinalis*, are equipped with a penis which introduces cartridges of sperm into the female sexual opening. Others—such as the proboscis leech—simply use their tube-shaped organ to penetrate the partner's skin at any point, administering an injection of semen. The spermatozoa must then find their own way to the eggs.

With almost all leeches, the fertilized eggs are stowed away in a cocoon similar to that of the earthworms. After mating, leeches gather —often by the hundreds—on the shore of a pond and dig deep passages into the bank, an inch or so above the water level. Each then forms its cocoon, squeezes its eggs into it, and wraps it in a thick layer of whitish mucus. By then it is nearly as large as a hen's egg. The cocoons are placed in the cave and the leeches linger nearby for several days. Some jawed leeches go several steps further along the way to child care. They twine themselves around the cocoon until the young have hatched, or else they carry the nest along with them. attached to their bellies.

The jawed leech *Marsupiobdella* is the kangaroo among leeches. It has a pouch in which the eggs are stored until they hatch, and does not produce a cocoon. This hermaphroditic annelid is not a genuine female, since it will have earlier fulfilled the duties of a father but it is a genuine mother to the extent that it does not abandon its children until they can take care of themselves.

THE PLEASURE OF PAIN

In 1957 Danish scientists aboard the research ship *Galathea* who had spent three years fishing the deep-sea trenches in various oceans, scored a zoological triumph. Dragging the Pacific, several hundred miles from the coast of Central America, at a depth of 12,112 feet, their net had brought to light one of the most primitive and ancient of all mollusks. These were animals which live under a protective shell like a mussel, but are constructed like certain bristle worms—missing links in the chain of evolution.

The discovery of these living fossils must be counted among the most important finds of the twentieth century. To zoologists it is almost more significant than the discovery of *Latimeria*, the lobe-finned primitive fish of the superorder Crossopterygia which created such a sensation in the popular press about a decade ago. In contrast to the fish, the primitive mollusks from the deep did not impress the public; they were too small, insignificant, and strange. But the find proved what evolutionists had hitherto only surmised: that annelid worms are the ancestors not only of the jointed, armored, swift-moving crabs, spiders, millipedes, and insects, but also of mussels, snails, and squid, however different their appearance.

Mollusks are generally peaceful creatures living a passive life between their own two shells. But there are some varieties which cause considerable annoyance to the human race—the pholads or borers which can destroy wooden ships, dams, and harbor installations; and a number of giant clams which can suddenly snap their shells shut, causing severe injury to the feet of waders. Pearl fishermen and skin divers have drowned as a result of having an arm or leg caught in such a shellfish trap.

Most mollusks, however, are a joy to the eye and the palate of *Homo sapiens*. Their pretty shells are valued by collectors, and oysters, cockles and mussels are great delicacies. The prickly, strangely marked shells of the Venus clam have acquired religious significance in Japan. And, of course, there are many varieties of mollusk which furnish pearls or mother-of-pearl.

Despite their decorative shells, however, the sex lives of these creatures are on the whole simple and monotonous. Males and females, locked tight in their shells, can scarcely associate. The male discharges his spermatozoa into the water. The females of many varieties do the same with their eggs. Others retain the mature eggs in their gill flaps, suck in some of the sperm-impregnated water, and thus accomplish fertilization. The larvae then develop in the gills, swarm away after a time, swim about in the water for a while or use fish as vehicles, until they find a place where they can settle.

As always in nature, there are a few exceptions. The European oyster, for example, is a hermaphrodite. But its eggs and sperm mature at different times, in a rhythmic alternation. An individual oyster can be female one day and suck its neighbor's sperm into its gills. A week later it becomes a male and fertilizes its neighbor's eggs.

This procedure makes for a tremendous fecundity. The discoverer of spermatozoa, Antonij van Leeuwenhoek, was deeply impressed by the oyster's ability to reproduce. He estimated the number of offspring of a single oyster at ten million per year. Today scientists are somewhat more cautious; it is now generally assumed that older oysters can produce a million eggs a year, younger ones somewhat fewer. But that is a respectable achievement in itself. If the annual spawn of a single old oyster stayed alive and reached full size, they would fill twelve thousand oyster barrels. Since every oyster bank contains tens of thousands of individuals, one can imagine the astronomical proportions of their potential annual reproduction.

Van Leeuwenhoek was also the first scientist to deal with another singular aspect in the reproductive life of mollusks: the mollusk offspring which become parasites. The larvae of various river and pond mollusks fasten themselves to fish, allow the skin of their hosts to grow over them, and feed on the body juices of the fish. When their development is completed, they burst the boils in which they have been harbored, sink to the bottom, and there lead a normal mollusk's life. The larvae of the river pearl oyster introduce a small variation into this pattern. They join in a lump and wait to be eaten by fish. As soon as they enter the fish's gullet, a race to the gills begins. Some succeed in anchoring themselves there; the rest are swallowed, which is the end of them. The larvae, incidentally, do little damage to the skin or the gills of the affected fish.

Several varieties of fish turn the tables by using mollusks for breeding sites. The bitterling (*Rhodeus amarus*), a type of carp popular among keepers of aquaria, chooses for this purpose the clam called painter's gaper, whose larvae occasionally trouble it. The curious methods employed by this fish were discovered in 1869. At spawning time the female grows a long, reddish ovipositor, while the male glows in all colors of the rainbow. Both seek and find, with sure instinct, a large painter's gaper on the bottom of the pond. The female protrudes her ovipositor into the clam's gills and injects a number of unfertilized eggs. Then it is the male's turn; he sprays a cloud of sperm over the clam.

The developing fish have an ideal situation in the oxygen-rich gills of their host, and do not leave the clam until they are fully formed and able to swim. The clams do not suffer from their presence, any more than do the fish from the parasitism of the mussels. As the discoverer of the bitterling's sex life, F. C. Noll, observed: "Sheltering the fish eggs and their development in the gills apparently does the clam not the slightest harm. The lamellae of the gills become slightly enlarged, but this seems to be the sole inconvenience for the clam, which continues its life undisturbed."

Altogether different from the harmless and amiable methods of reproduction in clams and oysters is the excessive and in human terms perverted sex life of their single-shelled relatives, the snails. We may take for an example one of the most familiar of them, the edible Roman snail. Everything about it is perverse, strange, topsy-turvy. The sex glands are not in the lower regions of the body, but high up in the shell, on the last steps of the winding staircase. A complicated system of channels leads from them to the sexual orifice and to various subsidiary glands. The spermatozoa travel down these channels when the partner is to be fertilized, and in an upward direction when the snail itself is to be fertilized for, like most snails, edible snails are hermaphroditic. The channels also conduct all sorts of glandular secretions to the eggs, and the fertilized eggs are finally conducted to the outside by way of such channels.

It would be hard to tell from observation that the Roman snail is bisexual—at least not if the observer confined his attention to one of the two partners. On the contrary, the snail behaves like a superman, like the incarnation of maleness. Its penis is a gigantic, erectile generative tube, and its wooing is more passionate and tempestuous than any human Casanova's. Moreover, the creature is apparently inclined to sadism. For after a wild love dance in which the partners rear up sole to sole, rock back and forth and even exchange regular smacking kisses, the excited snail suddenly releases a dagger of chalky material from a kind of quiver and drives it into the body of its mate. Other varieties shoot arrows of chalk at their victim-mates, and these are not aimed at the genital orifice, but are merely intended to wound some part of the mate's body. The wounded snail visibly twitches with pain, and indeed the act seems like the prelude to a veritable sex murder. In fact the love daggers of the Roman and garden snails occasionally penetrate the lung or the abdominal wall of their partners, inflicting deadly wounds.

But so far we have described only one of the mates. The other behaves in exactly the same way during the sex act. It, too, is extremely excited, and its excitement mounts when it is struck by the love arrow. Whereupon the masochist likewise becomes a sadist; it too fires a dart or stabs with a dagger at the body of its partner. It too protrudes a huge penis. And after fierce efforts and writhings, each of the two inserts its member into the genital orifice of the other.

For several minutes the snails remain united in this mutual copulation. The male organ must penetrate as deeply as possible into the female genital canal in order to deposit the semen at the right place, in a bladder-shaped receptacle where it will fertilize the eggs some time later. Each partner in this act is both male and female. And both seem to discharge sperm at the same time. Then they separate and both snails drop exhausted to the ground, where they remain lying almost motionless for some time. At last they crawl away, each in a different direction.

Here, then, is a procedure whose beginning seems strange to us, but whose conclusion is familiar. That pain and pleasure can be mingled in the sex act is indicated by the frequently harsh copulatory acts of many reptiles, birds, and mammals. This animal heritage is still preserved in man. The sexual biting of the mammals has passed into human sex play; according to the sex surveys of Dr. Alfred C. Kinsey some fifty per cent of all the men and women interviewed react positively to such painful stimuli. Among some primitive peoples, such as the Sirione Indians and the Melanesians of the Trobriand islands, the percentage is far higher.

The sexual armament of land snails, however, surpasses anything in the rest of the animal kingdom. There are even some African naked snails which carry a dozen darts an inch to an inch and a half in length. Since zoologists find it hard to imagine that a lower animal can feel much pain, and even less that it can savor the pleasures of pain, they have wondered whether the snails do not use their arrows to inject an aphrodisiac which stimulates mating readiness. There are examples of such behavior in other animals, but there do not seem to be indications of anything of the sort among snails.

It seems, moreover, that snails experience that strange phenomenon which plays so central a part in the sex life of the higher animals and of man—the orgasm, the explosive discharge of muscular and nervous tensions at the climax of sexual excitement. Little factual information is available about orgasm in animals, since animals cannot talk and are therefore in no position to satisfy the curiosity of sexologists. But the curve of excitement in the sex of snails can scarcely be interpreted in any other way.

Roman snails in sex play. After elaborate preliminary courting in which both snails rear up, rock back and forth and even exchange smacking kisses, actual copulation may last for several minutes.

Incidentally, the sex act among the hermaphroditic snails is not limited to two partners. Some gilled and pulmonary snails, the European mud snail and the marine snail *Acera bullata*, for example, can form copulatory chains of five or six mates. In such cases the first snail functions solely as a female, the others serve as males for the one in front and as females for the one behind, and the last in the chain functions only as a male.

The American slipper snail *Crepidula fornicata*, which has recently secured a foothold on the coasts of Europe, has made this chain of copulation a way of life. Grown slipper snails are sessile, like most mollusks but in their youth the animals are motile and are all males. Once a slipper snail attaches itself to some base for life, it transforms itself into a female. Soon it is mounted by a male and fertilized. The male settles on the female's shell; a third snail mounts it, and so on until at last a tower of ten to fourteen individuals is established. The lowest and largest specimens in this tower are female; the middle ones will be gradually changing from males to females; and only the topmost indicates by its penis that it has remained a male.

The vigorous neural and sensual reactions, the elaborate sex play, the intense sexuality, of snails, reach almost supernatural proportions in the higher mollusks. These creatures, the most intelligent of invertebrates, flourished in the Paleozoic and Mesozoic ages. But even to this day, more than a thousand varieties of them inhabit the seas from the surface to the dark abysmal depths. They are the cephalopods: the squid and the cuttlefish. There are extremely tiny specimens among them, such as the two-inch "postilion's horn," *Spirula spirula*, as well as monsters like the giant squid with its twenty-foot body and thirty- to forty-foot-long arms, weighing up to two tons—certainly the most enormous of the invertebrates. The sex life of these supermollusks is equally monstrous and highly developed.

THE NAUTILUS

The layman would hardly place the cephalopods as members of the same family as mussels and snails, for they seem too complete, too elaborately constructed. Their large, intelligent, highly complex eyes, their long muscular arms equipped with powerful suckers, the distinct separation of their heads from their bodies, their delicate nervous systems which induce fantastic changes of color in some varieties, and above all their cunning methods of battle and of capturing their prey. would lead the nonspecialist to the conclusion that they were much higher on the scale of animal existence than the fish or the amphibian.

Of course every animal is perfect after its own fashion. We are especially impressed by the squid and cuttlefish because they react in so many ways like vertebrates. When the common octopus, which inhabits all the warmer seas, seizes stones with its tentacles and uses them to crack open mussels, we see that as evidence of a use of tools. When a squid imprisoned in an aquarium becomes melancholy, falls into a form of madness and kills itself by eating its own arms, we are reminded of correspondingly horrible scenes in human insane asylums and concentration camps. And when two squid embrace in their love dance, their abstracted rocking back and forth forcefully reminds us of certain fashionable dances of the present day.

These dances and copulatory postures of the squid were known to the ancient Greeks. In fact, cephalopods play a great part in the literature, art, and mythology of the Greeks. They are pictured on innumerable vases; they were models for the Lernean hydra, the Gorgon, and also for the shell in which foam-born Aphrodite rose from the sea. Aristotle, who devoted much space to the cephalopods in his *Historia Animalium*, describes the typical mating of two species very common in the Mediterranean—the common cuttlefish *(Sepia officinalis)* and the common squid *(Loligo vulgaris)*—as follows: "Now cuttlefish and calamaries swim about closely intertwined, with mouths and tentacles facing one another and fitting closely together, and swim thus in opposite directions." What happens in such an embrace, Aristotle describes thus:

> When, then, the octopus rests its so-called head against the ground and spreads abroad its tentacles, the other sex fits into the outspreading of these tentacles, and the two sexes then bring their suckers into mutual connection. Some assert that the male has a kind of penis in one of his tentacles, the one in which are the largest suckers; and they further assert that the organ is tendinous in character, growing attached right up to the middle of the tentacle, and that the latter enables it to enter the nostril or funnel of the female.

Aristotle had observed the curious procedure of copulation with a fair degree of accuracy. Later observers were not so careful; as a rule they overlooked the male's copulatory tentacle which Aristotle said was inserted into the breathing funnel of the female. But Aristotle, too, was not entirely clear about what happened to a deviant type of squid much favored by the Greeks. The mantle cavity of *Argonauta argo*, the paper nautilus, was often found to be alive with certain worm-shaped, highly active creatures. Aristotle did not connect them with procreation, but assumed that they were parasitic worms.

In the next two thousand years all naturalists from Pliny to Georges Cuvier, accepted this opinion. Cuvier even assigned a scientific name to the supposed parasitic worm: *Hectocotylus*. Around the middle of the nineteenth century, however, zoologists found they could no longer ignore the strange fact that the hectocotylus bore a disturbing resemblance to a cuttlefish tentacle. And since hitherto only female paper nautiluses had been found, some scientists suggested that the wormlike thing was the complete male argonaut, that is, that it was a dwarf male living parasitically on or in the body of the female like the dwarf males of a good many worms, crustaceans, and fishes.

The puzzle was finally solved by Johannes Müller in 1853. Müller had set out on a three-month expedition to Sicily. He and three colleagues were planning to conduct researches in marine biology principally by fishing in the harbor of Messina. "We are fishing only in the harbor," Müller explained, "because the tremendous current of the Straits pours into it regularly every day; consequently a great quantity of the rarest sea animals may be caught there at any time. The boys of the city besiege our door with creatures they have caught and brought to us in glasses of water."

One of the rare creatures Müller snared was the real argonaut

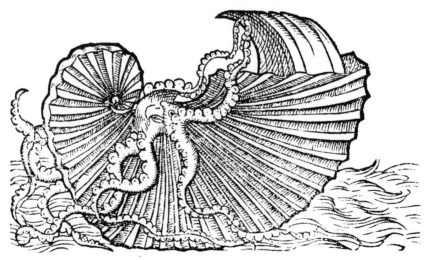

Nautili à Bellonio exhibita icon.

Cuttlefish in shell. The argonauta, *symbol of the womb to the Greeks.*

male—a dwarf male in fact, only a tenth the size of the female, but not at all worm-shaped. Instead, it proved to look like an eight-armed miniature octopus. One of these eight arms, the third from the left, lay in a pear-shaped bladder. In other males this bladder had burst and there unrolled from it the long, whiplike thing which had so often been found in the female's mantle pouch and wrongly interpreted. The hectocotylus, Johannes Müller concluded, must be the copulating tentacle of the argonaut male. But why should such arms be found, severed and nevertheless very much alive and mobile, inside the bodies of the females?

In order to unravel this mystery the zoologists first had to study the copulation of other cuttlefish. The males of all types, the Danish zoologist Johannes Japetus Steenstrup discovered, possess such "hecto-cotylized" structures—tentacles which serve as instruments of pro-creation. In most cuttlefish only one arm is hectocotylized, in some two arms, and in the pearly nautilus, *Nautilus pompilius*, which is still close to the ammonites of the Mesozoic, several arms merge into a penislike organ.

The hectocotylized arms, however, do not contain a sperm duct through which the sperm flows from male to female. In the octopods the male first stimulates the female for a while by letting his hectoco-tylus play over her body. While this is going on, both display lively changes of color, in many cases the erotic color red predominating. After prolonged patient stroking and excitation the male apparently feels that the time has come. He reaches his hectostylus into his own breathing funnel, fetches several cartridges of semen from his mantle cavity, and thrusts them into the female's mantle cavity.

While this is going on the female apparently suffers from asphyxia, since the male arm blocks her breathing funnel. But there is no other entrance into a squid's mantle cavity, and since even a squid is not pleased when it is embraced so hard that it cannot breathe, many of the females violently resist the penetration of the hectocotylus. Furi-ous battles may be fought between male and female, especially if the female is not yet in heat or has already been fertilized, or if the male proves too clumsy and cuts off too much of her supply of oxygen.

The cartridges of semen swell in the female's body and eventually burst, so that the sperm is poured out over the eggs. In some squid, the female saves the male's semen in a special pouch. When her eggs mature, she reaches into her own body with an arm, picks up the eggs one at a time, presses them against the semen pouches and thus fer-tilizes them with her own hands, so to speak. The Canadian marine biologist Norman John Berrill has described the process of reproduc-tion in squid in his book, *The Living Tide:*

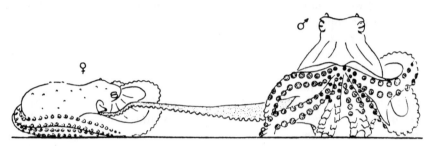

Copulation in the squid. The male introduces his copulatory arm into the female's breathing funnel.

It is a rather complicated business, not so much because the sexes are separate and are not combined in the same individual as in many snails, and only partly because the eggs must be fertilized before they get all wrapped up in jelly. These are factors of course, but it is the combination of these with the free-swimming life of the animals in the open ocean that makes things rather difficult. The interior of the whole pointed end of a female squid is set aside for the production and ripening of eggs. The jelly is added to them as they are passed out of the oviduct into the gill chamber, just before they are deposited. And to develop they must be fertilized on the way. That means sperm must be there in the right place at the right moment. . . . What happens is this. The microscopic sperm cells are made up into small pencil-shaped packages called spermatophores, each about a half-inch long, in a special gland possessed by the male. As these packages accumulate, the male inserts one of his two long arms down into his own gill chamber, grabs a handful of sperm packets, swims alongside a female and shoves the collection deep into her gill chamber. Then later, perhaps very much later, when the eggs are ready to be laid, each packet explodes inside the female, to liberate a cloud of sperm cells which fertilize the emerging eggs. By this time of course, the independent male may be several hundreds miles away chasing a fish or a crab.

In some species the male copulatory arm breaks off as soon as it has penetrated into the female's mantle cavity, and for a while leads an independent life there. When the eggs are ready for fertilization, the detached hectocotylus fires its cartridges of sperm at them. After having fulfilled this task, it is absorbed by the female's body. The mutilated male, meanwhile, swims off to some other part of the sea and grows a new hectocotylus.

In the light of these habits it would seem logical to assume that the hectocotylus arms found in the bodies of the female argonauts are likewise instruments of procreation which have broken off after copulation. But, strangely enough, such arms have frequently been found swimming freely in the sea. These copulatory arms turned "sea serpents" have caused zoologists a great deal of perplexity. Does the nautilus male send his arm out to seek a bride? Does he detach it and let it swim to the female on its own? That would certainly be a remarkable kind of procreation-at-a-distance. This form of reproduction in the nautilus has not been fully proved. The hectocotylus arms which have been encountered freely swimming in the ocean may have accidentally slipped out of the female's body after mating. No one has as yet seen such an arm swim straight to a nautilus female and crawl into her mantle cavity.

As a rule young cephalopods crawl from the eggs quite complete, tiny replicas of their parents. Only a few cuttlefish pass through a larval stage, and a relative of the nautilus, *Ocythoë tuberculata*, whose tiny males live in the cases of sea squirts and similar ascidians, is even viviparous (i.e., it develops its young inside its body and brings them forth alive). The female of the ordinary octopus lays its eggs in a cave in a rock, shields them with its body, and keeps busily pumping oxygen-rich water into the nest. Smaller octopods raise their offspring in mussel shells. But the pleasantest and most appealing infant care is practiced by the argonauts.

One species, *Tremoctopus violaceus*, has four upper arms linked together by a web. It makes a shelter for the eggs by rolling this membrane up in a spiral and hatching the eggs in the resultant fold. Even more interesting is the brooding female of the nautilus proper, *Argonauta argo*. In its two uppermost arms, which widen out into lobes, it carries a silvery, paper-thin shell of extremely graceful shape. Since this shell is not firmly attached to the body at any point, it used to be thought that the nautilus female inhabited a snail shell like the hermit crab. In old pictures the animal is represented as sailing along like the Argonauts' ship of Greek myth, its two lobelike arms held up to the wind as sails and its other arms rowing the "paper boat" to which its popular name refers. Greek mythology even averred that the papery vessel of the nautilus had been the cradle of the foam-born goddess of love.

Today we know that the graceful shell is formed by substances secreted in the two lobar arms. The paper boat is used neither as a boat nor as a dwelling, nor can the lobar arms be employed as sails. Rather, the shell is a sort of perambulator which is clutched in the two broad arms and pushed along through the sea. Within this silvery cradle

The argonaut sails the seas. A 17th-century representation of the squid Argonauta argo, *whose paper-thin shell was thought, in Greek mythology, to have been the cradle of Aphrodite.*

the young of the nautilus are raised. Sometimes the female leaves its paper boat behind for a while and swims about by itself, or takes time out for a meal; then it returns to its task of pushing the perambulator.

STARFISH DIVORCE

Before we ascend the tree of life to the two branches which call for separate treatment—the articulates proper and the vertebrates—we must speak of a number of orders and families of animals that have also emerged from the labyrinth of the worms and gone their own special ways.

Most of them offer little that is new in regard to reproduction; they merely vary the methods we have already seen employed by lower animals. The moss animals, for example, which cover driftwood, seaweed, and the planks of ships like a whitish or brownish slime, stand high above the coelenterates in terms of descent; but they live in colonies like those of the corals of hydroid polyps, multiplying asexually by budding and sexually, quite often, by self-fertilization. Sometimes, however, they care for their young. Two individuals join to form a common brood pouch in which the embryo grows. Some moss animals are even viviparous. The germ cell develops in their intestine, undergoes several fissions there, and sends forth numerous larvae.

Akin to the moss animals are the mollusklike brachiopods, which have left fossil records in the Silurian Period four hundred million years ago. Virtually all brachiopods bear living young—swimming larvae provided with cilia which mature either in the female genital passages or in special brooding chambers. When the larvae leave the mother's body, they swim about freely for a number of days and then attach themselves to the sea floor. There they form shells, from which they stretch ciliated arms like rare flowers into the water. Earlier zoologists considered them mollusks, others crustaceans, until in 1873-74 the studies of Morse and Kovalevski demonstrated that together with the moss animals they occupied a special position of their own in the animal kingdom. They are an arrested twig of that promising branch of the worm group from which the ancestors of the vertebrates eventually developed.

Just as the annelid worms lead to the crabs, spiders and insects, and the primitive slugs to mussels, snails and squid, so several groups of strange looking marine worms lead to the crown of creation—the "new mouths" or Neostomata, as they are now called. In all animals we have so far described, the primitive mouth of the gastrula became the regular mouth of the creature while the intestinal opening was a new formation. In the Neostomata the process was reversed; the primitive mouth became the anus and the mouth opening was formed anew. This is so decisive a feature in the history of animal development that zoologists have seen fit to divide the entire animal kingdom from the worm upward into two great groups—the Archaeostomata (primitive mouths), to which the majority of the worms, mollusks, and articulates belong, and the Neostomata which we are going to discuss.

The "new mouths" are a highly mixed group of animals, some primitive and some remarkably specialized and highly developed. Four classes of wormlike creatures are counted among them; also the echinoderms ("prickly skins"), which include the starfish, sea urchins, and sea cucumbers; and finally the ancestors of the vertebrates and the vertebrates themselves—fish, amphibia, reptiles, birds, mammals, man. The earliest wormlike Neostomata are particularly interesting for us since they are akin to the ancestors of our own race. Little, however, is known about their sex habits.

The four groups of "worms" assigned by zoologists to the Neostomata are: Pterobranchia ("wing-gills"), Balanoglossus ("barnacle-tongue"), the beard worms, and the arrow worms. Their reproductive methods appear rather monotonous by comparison with the fantastic habits of the parasitic worms and the mollusks. There are species which live in colonies like corals, propagate by budding like the freshwater polyp, and also produce free-swimming larvae sexually. There are hermaphrodites and bisexual forms; there are females whose non-reproductive organs have atrophied or vanished completely and whose sole task is to produce eggs. Several arrow worms seem to reproduce exclusively by self-fertilization.

The sexual habits of the echinoderms are not especially original either. Starfish and sea urchins have won a great place for themselves in the history of biology because scientists first used them for close observation of natural fertilization and for experiments in artificial fertilization. But these decorative radial animals served as ideal objects for study only because their reproduction seems so simple. They expel their sexual products into the water as the sessile mollusks do, and leave it to the sperm to find the eggs. Many starfish and some sea urchins, however, practice care of the young. They shelter the eggs or the offspring between their arms or prickles until the young are self-sufficient. Among the wonderfully shaped and colored sea lilies, which likewise belong among the echinoderms, there are viviparous species. The females discharge their eggs into a brood pouch. There swimming larvae hatch out. Later these grow a stalk and attach themselves to the sea bottom.

So much for the dry accounts of the zoologists. To the eyes of a poetic observer of nature, however, even these simple forms of reproduction and care of offspring have their charms. Wilhelm Bölsche, that Victorian enthusiast of zoology, has described the early stages of two echinoderms in lovingly painted genre pictures:

> From the union of the sperm and the egg a tiny, transparent individual arises, apparently absolutely complete in its structure, but resembling anything under the sun rather than an echinoderm of the class sea urchin. The little soft jelly-like body possesses a mouth, gut, and anus, and swims about blithely in the open sea by means of lively motile cilia. From its structure we should regard it as a young developing worm, and if it were to grow sexually mature and produce young, it would simply be classed with certain worms. But it never becomes sexually mature.

Instead, it reshapes itself into a strange creature which Bölsche compares to a "spiked helmet turned inside out." And in the interior of this spiked helmet, in the hollow space between the body wall and the stomach, there grows a new animal totally different in structure: the sea urchin. "The snuffboxlike sea urchin," Bölsche continues,

> grows in the interior of the living spiked helmet in such a way that it includes its stomach. It simply takes it over to itself and makes it its own organ. The spiked helmet, separated from its nutritive organ by the ingrowing guest, naturally decays, dies, and finally drops away from the young urchin, dried up like a withered blossom. . . . The sea urchin, having accomplished the internal halving of its "mother," and in happy possession of the mother's stomach which continues to function uninterruptedly, little cares about the vanishing ghost. It eats, grows, completes itself, and finally becomes sexually mature, like its grandparents.

As for the starfish, Bölsche is inclined to attribute to that creature the beginning of motherliness.

> The adult female starfish, itself a product of the reckless destruction of her antecedent nurse form, unmistakably shows certain motherly feelings toward her offspring. Hidden among stones, you see her sitting like a hen with her arms curved over her fertilized eggs and hatched young. A strange picture, yet constituting one of the first rungs in that huge ladder which culminates high above in the human spiritualized relation of the Child at the breast of the Madonna.

> Some starfishes and other echinoderms have a special pouch in which
> the parent animal carries about her brood as a kangaroo her litter. . . .

Bölsche also finds in the starfish evidence of what he calls the first
divorce, "a divorce with a special refinement that no modern novel of
manners has as yet conceived: for the starfish divorces itself from itself." In spite of their complicated structure, starfish often succeed in
dividing into two halves like unicellular animals. All their organs
split in two. "The terrible cleft then becomes glued together and heals
by simply regrowing the parts lacking in each of the two halves."
And with a stab at *Homo sapiens*, Bölsche adds: "At times it appears
to me that such a divorce within one's own self would be an excellent
thing for a good many excessively consistent individualists of the
human race."

In Bölsche's day the contemplation of such natural phenomena
quickly gave rise to metaphysical speculations. "What are we to suppose the animal 'thinks' while it is undergoing the process?" Bölsche
asks. "How long does it think as 'it,' as 'one,' and at what point do two
souls constitute its thinking ego? Is the division a death in which the
individual dies, or is it a step to a larger life, a regeneration of the one
individual into a higher form?"

Nowadays serious scientists would not allow such misty ideas to
enter their heads. No one would think of comparing a sea urchin nur-
turing its brood to a Madonna, or of ascribing a split personality to
the dividing starfish. Today the talk is all of instincts, reflexes, mechanisms directed by physicochemical stimuli. After a period of excessive anthropomorphism, animals have once more been put in their
"place." In doing so, present-day naturalists may err as much on the
one side as those of Haeckel's and Bölsche's era erred on the other.
Imaginative spirits have not only projected themselves into the
psyches of animals; they have also made valuable zoological discoveries. One such discovery leads us to the trail of the first vertebrate,
the forerunner of that branch of the animal kingdom from which we
ourselves have stemmed. The discoverer was one of the poets of the
German Romantic movement, Adelbert von Chamisso.

THE SEARCH FOR THE FIRST VERTEBRATE

With the first expedition of James Cook in 1769, voyages of discovery had become enterprises less of the conquistador than of the
scientist. The ships which then began to circumnavigate the globe

were apt to have distinguished naturalists for passengers—such men
as Sir Joseph Banks, Johann and Georg Forster, and Peter Pallas.
During the fifty years which culminated in Darwin's voyage on the
Beagle, more secrets of nature were learned than on all previous voyages of discovery put together.

One such research expedition set out in 1815 and sailed the oceans
of the world for three years, plying the Pacific in all directions. One
of its members was a thirty-six-year-old scientist, an emigrant from
France who later became assistant at the Botanical Gardens in Berlin.
Adelbert von Chamisso had already made a name for himself as a
poet. His friends, however, knew him by a special nickname, "the
poor Schlemihl," after his finest work, *The Strange Tale of Peter
Schlemihl.* But as a naturalist he had so far accomplished nothing of
note.

The expedition was under Russian auspices; the ship's name was
Rurik and the expedition leader, Otto von Kotzebue—son of the well-
known German dramatist—played the tough captain. Chamisso did
not get on especially well with his superior, but he had no quarrel
with the lovely Polynesian women, whose free-and-easy attitude toward love he praised as "pure, uncorrupted morals." In addition he
observed and investigated virtually everything there was to be seen
at sea and on land, from algae to mammoth bones and from geologic
formations to the taboos of the Pacific islanders. His curiosity had
twofold results. Chamisso wrote what is probably the finest travel
diary in the German language. He also made a discovery in biology
which secured him a lasting place in the hall of fame of great naturalists. He discovered the alternation of generations.

At that time it was not yet known that polyps, worms, and many
other animals can exist in two utterly different forms: an asexual
generation which propagates by budding, and a sexual generation
which begets offspring only after fertilization. In those days no one
would have ventured to assert that jellyfish were the sexual forms of
polyps, that miracidia and redia were the asexual generation of the
liver fluke, and so on. That two so dissimilar forms of life as the swimming medusa and the sessile polyp could belong to one and the same
species seemed paradoxical, incredible, and utterly ridiculous. Consequently Chamisso was laughed at when, in 1819, he published a treatise on alternation of generations. His essay was ignored until 1842,
when the Danish zoologist Johann Japetus Steenstrup took up the
thesis and proved that Chamisso had been right. By then, however,
"the poor Schlemihl" had lain in his grave for four years.

The animals that led Chamisso to his discovery were not polyps and
jellyfish, but a curious, odd-looking group of marine creatures which

had been a considerable puzzle to zoologists. They are called salps and are transparent, roller-shaped animals found in all seas, frequently in vast schools. They move by the principle of reaction, that is, they pump water into their bodies, squirt it out vigorously through the vent, and in this manner dart ahead like jet planes. In Chamisso's day they were regarded as relatives of the mollusks, or possibly as transitional forms from jellyfish to mollusks. What they really were was not discovered until much later.

Even before Chamisso some naturalists had been struck by the fact that salps do not exist merely as individual jets shooting through the seas but occasionally remain connected for a long time, just as they were in the ovary, and then swim in long rows. That is, salps will sometimes appear as colonial animals forming chains. A salp chain consists of a double row of individuals clinging together. All links in the chain are completely harmonious; each is a hermaphrodite and produces a single egg which is fertilized in the body of the female part.

Chamisso observed that the larvae produced by such colonial salps do not form chains in their turn, but grow into individual salps. And these individuals propagate by budding. Their posterior end sprouts chains of salps, often several in succession, which gradually mature, break off, and swim away. Thus, Chamisso concluded, two forms of salp constitute a single species—one whose individuals are united in large numbers as chain colonies, and one whose individuals live singly. The colonial salps each produce a single offspring sexually; the single offspring then produces more chains asexually. "The daughters never resemble the mother, but the grandmother," was the way Chamisso put it.

Today we know that in some species of salp the procedure is far more complicated. The single animal becomes a "nurse" which produces a number of buds. These buds are seized by certain body cells which are as motile as amoebas, are carried to the posterior end of the nurse and there arranged in ordered rows. The outer buds develop into feeding animals. That is, they become living stomachs which digest the food for the entire colony. The middle buds assume the task of fostering; they carry and care for a third group of buds which finally develop into salp chains. These chains, having reached the age of independence, break off from the nurse colony and beget by fertilization a new generation of nurses.

Animals which unite into colonies for purposes of reproduction are by no means rare phenomena. Nor is there anything unusual about groups of such individuals specializing in specific tasks and thus assuming different forms. Similar specialization exists among the colonial medusae as well as in highly evolved social animals, such as bees, ants, and termites. The real singularity of the salps was only discovered in 1866-68 by the Russian zoologist Aleksander Kovalevski.

There were two brothers Kovalevski who distinguished themselves in the annals of natural science. The younger, Vladimir, was a genius, one of the foremost paleontologists of the nineteenth century. But he was a restless genius with a tendency toward depression. He wrote his now classical monographs on fossil ungulates in three foreign languages simultaneously—French, German, and English. His work was ill-received in his native land because he was a follower of Darwin and Haeckel. Seeking funds for further research, he speculated in petroleum and was financially ruined. When the oil company into which he had put his money went bankrupt, he suffered a nervous breakdown and committed suicide.

His older brother, Aleksander, believed as firmly in the theory of evolution as Vladimir. But while Vladimir spent his life in bitter struggle against mistrust, hostility, and economic stress, Aleksander Kovalevski worked away quietly and undisturbed in his laboratory, seeking to unravel the ancestry of vertebrate animals. In the course of his research he came upon three strange types of animals: the salps, ascidians, and appendicularia. These organisms resemble one another only in one respect: they are covered by a sheath called a tunic or test which is thick and leathery in some, thin and transparent in others. The whole class to which these three types belong has been given the name of tunicates.

We have already discussed the salps. The sea squirts or ascidians present a totally different appearance. The zoologist Viktor Franz describes them as "brownish and irregular knobs full of wrinkles and bumps, dirty, covered with all sorts of squatters. It is utterly impossible to determine from the look of these bodies whether they are vegetable or animal; they feel like hard, dried leather and do not move." These "rotten potatoes," as another writer called them, settle on stones or wood at the bottom of the sea, extend chimney-shaped pipes from their wrinkled tunics, and brush food particles into themselves with motile cilia arranged like the calyx of a flower. If they are disturbed, they spray a jet of water at the supposed enemy. One genus of sea squirts, *Pyrosoma*, forms colonies which swim freely about in the sea and live in symbiosis (permanent union) with luminescent bacteria. The light radiated by *Pyrosoma* is often so intense that, in the words of François Péron, the animal's discoverer, the ocean seems "dipped in fire."

The third type of tunicates, the appendicularia, are tiny marine animals, usually only a few millimeters in length, which move by means of a tadpolelike tail. Their tunics have become traps: they are equipped with a filtering apparatus which captures plankton. When an enemy approaches, or when the filter becomes clogged, the appendicularian slips out of its test and within a few hours the large cells of its skin manufacture a new house. Another curious aspect of the appendicularia is that they resemble the larvae of salps and sea squirts. Scientists therefore assume that they have evolved from ancestral forms which were sexually mature in the larval stage. Such sexually mature larvae which never grow up are also found in other animals. The best known examples are two salamandrine amphibians, the Mexican axolotl and the American mud puppy.

Aleksander Kovalevski realized, however, that the appendicularians differed from all other invertebrate animals in possessing a notochord and spinal marrow. And when he examined the larvae of salps and sea squirts, he found the same notochord, the *chorda dorsalis*. In mature sea squirts and salps, however, this ancestor of the backbone is lost.

This discovery by the Russian zoologist was a momentous one for evolutionary biology. Kovalevski had found the ancestors of the vertebrates! Out of modest, inconspicuous marine animals there had evolved the first representatives of that phylum of the animal kingdom whose ultimate representative, perhaps half a billion years later, was to be man. And from the *chorda dorsalis*, the flexible spinal rod, there had emerged the backbone, the chief support of the vertebrate body without which it would have been impossible for man to walk erect, to keep his head up and to perfect his brain.

No one seeing the knobby sea squirts and the chain-forming salps would suspect the part they had played in evolution. Although these tunicates had set out on a promising road, they had soon forsaken it. Their reproductive methods, moreover, bear no resemblance to those of the vertebrates. In that regard the sea squirts remain almost on the level of the coelenterates, the "hollow guts," if we except the fact that their larvae sometimes hatch out in special brood pouches, for many sea squirts also propagate by budding, as polyps do. It is all the more astonishing that it should be the larvae of sea squirts—not the mature animals—which so strikingly resemble the vertebrate embryo. In addition to the spinal cord, they possess a two-lobed brain and a proper eye with lens and retina. In a short time, however, this extraordinarily promising creature turns into the "rotten potato" which clings, wrinkled and leathery, to wharves and piers.

In order to close the gap between the tunicate larvae and the first vertebrates, we must construct a hypothetical prototype equipped with that fateful spinal cord, an animal that looks like a willow leaf, drawn to a fishlike point in front and behind, possessing gill slits, simple sensory cells, and a fringe of fins. Such an animal actually exists. Some thirty species live on the shores of seas and in the depths, buried in sand at the bottom, hidden and inconspicuous. They are the lancelets.

Amphioxus, the lancelet, was first discovered in 1774 in the shoals off Cornwall and sent for identification to the great naturalist Peter Simon Pallas, who decided that it was a kind of snail. Sixty years later the French zoologist Jean Victor Coste classed it among the fish. But shortly afterwards the mysterious *Amphioxus* was thoroughly scrutinized by two German physiologists, Johannes Müller and his pupil Theodor Schwann, the codiscoverer of the cell. Both determined that the lancelet had no skull and Müller doubted that it could be a fish at all. But then what kind of animal was it? Schwann was already beginning to suspect that *Amphioxus* could only be the most primitive living vertebrate, the "absolutely simplest type of the phylum."

Generations of zoologists worried the modest lancelet, dissected it, peered at its body through the microscope. The European variety—it is nowadays called *Branchiostoma lanceolatum*—became one of the most-studied living organisms on earth. Finally, in 1867, Aleksander Kovalevski declared that the lancelet was the true ancestral model both of the tunicates and the vertebrates—not exactly the venerable ancestor in person, but probably its surviving likeness.

Nowadays a good many zoologists doubt whether this is quite so. Perhaps the lancelets, like the appendicularians, developed out of unknown prevertebrates which were sexually mature in the larval stage. We will probably never learn what these unknown ancestors looked like. "The prospects of our ever finding really illuminating fossil remnants of them are distinctly poor," the Swiss paleontologist Bernhard Peyer has observed. For the creatures must have been so frail that they would not have been preserved as fossils anywhere.

Biology must therefore content itself with the living lancelets. They are, in any case, informative enough—especially in their embryonic history. Their reproduction, on the other hand, is as inconspicuous as the lancelet itself, aside from the fact that their genital organs are located near the gills, rather than in the rear. Males and females discharge sperm and eggs through their gill slits into the water, where fertilization takes place. That, of course, is the procedure with the majority of fish. But the spawning-time sex play, the care of the brood and methods of rearing, which in many species of fish have been refined to remarkable perfection, are entirely lacking in the lancelets.

Nevertheless, the development of young lancelets remains a favor-

ite subject for study among zoologists because it demonstrates with
exceptional clarity the process of biogenesis—Ernst Haeckel's discovery that the embryonic development of an organism is a re-enactment
of that organism's evolutionary history (see page 78). Under the
microscope, we can watch the morula growing out of the fertilized
lancelet egg, can watch it hollowing into a gastrula, and can see the
gradual development of the intestinal cavity, neural canal, and notochord, as the primitive backbone is called. At this point the larva
hatches from the egg. The observer can see it stretch and swim about
freely. The second opening of the body appears. The growing lancelet acquires gill slits. The digestive, sensory, and circulatory organs
develop. Sexual organs appear. This is the very same path that the
most ancient ancestors of the vertebrates traversed—from unicellular
organism to volvox sphere to gastrular polyp and neostomatic worm
to chordate. And they are the same stages the human embryo passes
through in the first few days of its development. It is almost as if nature created the lancelet as vivid demonstration material for inquiring
evolutionists.

When Ernst Haeckel celebrated his sixtieth birthday in Jena in
1894, he offered his guests a significant delicacy: open-faced sand-
wiches covered with lancelets prepared "like sardines." In his autobi-
ography Haeckel attests that this was a dish he would never forget.
For the very taste of *Amphioxus*, he said, would tell a gastronomically
experienced zoologist that it represented the first rung on the ladder
leading from fish to man.

■

CHAPTER FOUR

THE WONDERFUL TRANSFORMATION

SOUVENIRS IN THE BUTTERFLY NET

Caterpillars are, by the average man's esthetic standards, rather ugly, earthbound "worms." Butterflies, on the other hand, are considered the embodiment of ethereal grace and beauty. If we knew nothing about the metamorphosis of insects, we would scarcely connect these two creatures so different in appearance. Of course, many species in the animal kingdom undergo a metamorphosis; their larval forms look entirely different from the sexually mature individuals. But the metamorphosis of insects has long been considered the greatest of these miracles of transformation. The lovely butterfly born from the pupated "worm" is one of the favorite symbols of poetry and literature.

Incidentally, the popular idea that caterpillars, maggots, and other forms of insect larvae are "worms" does not entirely miss the mark. For the ancestors of the insects evolved out of annelid worms, and this fact is perpetuated by every worm-shaped insect larva. There is even a class of articulates—the Peripatidae—which in appearance comes somewhere in between the annelid worm and the caterpillar.

Ever since nature study began, it has been known that the caterpillar is transformed into a butterfly. The first naturalist of antiquity had observed it. The encyclopedists of the Middle Ages had, if they had not witnessed it, at least zealously copied the fact from Greek and Roman writers. During the Renaissance, Leonardo da Vinci summed up existing knowledge about this process: "The caterpillar which through the care exercised in weaving itself its new habitation with admirable design and ingenious workmanship, afterwards emerges from it with beautiful painted wings, rising on these towards heaven." Moralists could seize upon this as an example of the wages of diligence.

The majority of common people, however, had never been quite willing to believe in this magical transformation. To the hard-headed populace, it seemed likely that maggots, caterpillars, and other vermin had arisen out of filth and decay, not out of the eggs of pretty butterflies. In order to refute such vulgar views, an apothecary's son in Amsterdam began, during the second half of the seventeenth century, systematically to investigate and dissect bees, ants, butterflies, beetles, maggots, and pupae. His chief aim was to prove that a nymph or pupal stage was "the sole reason for all the changes of so-called bloodless animals," and secondly to determine "how worms and caterpillars are transformed in the chrysalis."

We have already encountered this man, Jan Swammerdam, as one of the founders of microbiology. He was also one of the founders of entomology, the study of insects. In his time, however, crabs, millipedes, and spiders were counted among the insects, as well as snails, which belong to an entirely different phylum of the animal kingdom. Swammerdam attempted to show that all "bloodless animals"—whether snails, water fleas, spiders, bees, or butterflies—underwent a more or less complete metamorphosis which "by far surpasses the development of all other creatures."

It is interesting to follow Swammerdam's line of thought as he himself developed it, and see with what pertinacity this quiet scholar examined and illuminated every aspect of metamorphosis and how resolutely he fought against all the "contrary opinions of scientists." If we wish to understand the true nature of metamorphosis, Swammerdam held, we must first contemplate the process "like a beautiful painting which the notions of scholars and others have in the course of time stained and tainted, soiled and crusted, confused and made unrecognizable." In order to arrive at the true appearance of this "excellent and pretty painting," it is necessary "to cleanse metamorphosis of the filth of our preconceptions and by removing the adherent impurities to restore its initial brilliance." Plainly, Jan Swammerdam was a strong-minded person who loved his subject and had but a poor opinion of scientific authorities.

At the time the theory was that a living organism could transform itself into another—a worm into a winged insect—by a magical act of nature. To the naturalists of those days this was not nearly so strange an idea as it now sounds. Such magical changes were ascribed to other types of animal as well. Many serious-minded persons, for example, held that a sessile crustacean, the barnacle, could give rise to the barnacle goose. Why should not a worm become a butterfly?

But Swammerdam violently opposed such ideas. Metamorphosis, he declared, was not the transformation of one species into an entirely different species, but

> a sprouting, growing, or extending of the caterpillar. . . . The caterpillar, then, does not change into a pupa; it assumes the form of a pupa by casting its skin. Similarly, the pupa does not subsequently change into a winged creature, but the caterpillar which has donned the form of a pupa develops into a winged animal by the growth of its limbs. This transformation, incidentally, is not different from the transformation of a chick into a hen or of a young frog into an old one. Neither of the two changes from the one to the other; rather, by the gradual extension of its limbs the one becomes a grown chicken and the other a complete frog.

Swammerdam's writings clarified the strange process of metamorphosis. Unfortunately they were not published during his lifetime. For the sober and practical father of entomological research suddenly fell under the influence of a mysterious zealot named Antoinette Bourignon who was going about Europe preaching the dawn of a millennial kingdom. He joined her disciples, led a wandering life for some time, and in 1680 died insane in his native city of Amsterdam. Sixty years passed before the papers of Jan Swammerdam were published, by the great Dutch physician and naturalist Herman Boerhaave. He called the book *Bijbel der Natuure,* and for entomologists it indeed became a "bible of nature"; they continued to draw upon its wisdom until well into the nineteenth century.

Maria Sibylla Merian (daughter of the Swiss engraver and topographer Matthäus Merian, who won world fame with his two thousand engravings of cities) was unacquainted with this bible of nature when she set out to establish an insectarium and to draw caterpillars engaged in their natural activities. At the time, Swammerdam's writings were completely unknown. She, however, independently discovered the same facts as Swammerdam. The caterpillars she tended pupated, and from the pupae came butterflies. Being both an accurate observer and a gifted artist she set down the details of caterpillar metamorphosis in innumerable pictures—drawings which represented the food plant, the eggs, the caterpillar, the pupa, and the complete butterfly of the variety in question. Her approach has since become standard for every book on butterflies.

In 1683 Maria Sibylla Merian separated from her alcoholic husband, Johann Andreas Graff, and having moved to Holland, finished her book, *The Wonderful Transformation and Strange Floral Nourishment of Caterpillars*. The work aroused great excitement, not only among artists and naturalists, but also among the cool-headed merchants of the Dutch West Indies Company. On a commission for the company, she went to Surinam for three years to record in pictures the fauna and flora of the New World. Upon her return she published a magnificent volume entitled *Metamorphosis insectorum surinamensium*, whose beautiful plates record the transformations of South American butterflies and giant cicadas. She also described the metamorphosis of a very curious creature, the Surinam toad, which we shall have occasion to mention later.

Maria Sibylla Merian observed many butterflies, bees, and anthophilous ("flower-loving") flies in the act of visiting blossoms, but apparently she never suspected that these calls had anything to do with reproduction—not of the insects, but of the plants. For in her day it was not generally known that plants have sex and that in many cases insects assist their fertilization. Only one of her contemporaries ventured to speak of sexuality in plants. This bold iconoclast was Rudolf Jakob Camerarius, who in 1695 asserted that the stamens of flowers corresponded to the male genital organs of animals, and that the pistil represented the female organ.

This was a shocking thesis to lovers of chaste, beautiful flowers. But forty years later Linnaeus presented a treatise on the *Nuptials of Flowers* in which he noted that "in the springtime when the bright sun rises to the zenith, the plants also are gripped by love." He painted a highly poetic and unrealistic picture of the plant wedding:

> The petals of the flowers themselves contribute nothing to procreation, but serve solely as the bridal bed, for the great Creator has thus splendidly arranged it, a bed equipped with such noble curtains and perfumed with so many lovely scents in order that the bridegroom may consummate his marriage there with all the greater festivity. When, then, the bed is prepared, it is time for the bridegroom to embrace his dear bride and to offer her his gifts; I mean, we see how the *testiculi* open and pour out *pulverem genitalem* which falls upon the *tubam* and fructifies the *ovarium*.

Pretty as this sounds and correct as it is to employ animal terms for the reproductive organs of plants, in reality Linnaeus had not the slightest idea how the nuptials of the plants actually took place. Another thirty years passed before the botanist Joseph Gottlieb Koelreuter recognized that the nubile blossoms needed the help of the wind or of insects. But this insight, too, did not enter the public do-

Engraving of butterflies and caterpillar from the 17th-century book
Metamorphosis Insectorum Surinamensium. *Its author and illustrator,*
Maria Sibylla Merian, was an acute biological observer and a gifted artist
whose approach to the study of butterflies has become standard.

main. At last on the eve of the French Revolution the brilliant and self-willed school principal Christian Konrad Sprengel happened to examine a number of sword lilies while he was taking a stroll one day. He discerned that each of the blossoms had a specially colored spot which, he concluded, "as it were leads the insects to the nectar." As he himself described it,

> But I found still more—namely, that these blossoms simply could not be fertilized in any other way except by insects, and in fact by insects of a rather considerable size. . . . I then studied other flowers to see whether they too might be so constructed that their fertilization would depend on insects. My studies convinced me more and more that many, indeed possibly all, flowers which have nectar are fertilized by the insects which feed on this nectar and that consequently this feeding of the insects, while from their point of view it is an end in itself, from the point of view of the flowers is only a means, moreover the only means, to a particular end, to wit, their fertilization.

Sprengel, as we have seen (page 11), reaped only grief for his discovery; he lost his post and endeavored in vain to inform his fellow citizens of the usefulness of bees to man as pollenizers of fruit blossoms. But Darwin in 1859, reading Sprengel's book, made a note: "How wonderful all this is!"

Insects became a sort of rage in Darwin's day; the intellectual achievements of bees, ants, and termites sent many nineteenth century materialists into ecstasies of enthusiasm. Equally fascinated but far more serious and scientific was the great French entomologist, Jean Henri Fabre who spent his whole life in his garden in Provence observing his beloved insects and trying to understand their behavior. The son of a small farmer, he had become a teacher of natural science at various lycées. Then came the great turning point in his life. Fabre himself reported it as follows:

> One winter evening, when the rest of the household was asleep, as I sat reading beside a stove whose ashes were still warm, my book made me forget for a while the cares of the morrow; those heavy cares of a poor professor of physics who, after piling up diplomas and for a quarter of a century performing services of uncontested merit, was receiving for himself and his family a stipend of sixteen hundred francs, or less than the wages of a groom in a decent establishment.

The book he was reading "was a work by the sage of entomology, the venerable scholar Léon Dufour. It dealt with the habits of the buprestid beetle."

Dufour had often found a number of very curious metallic beetles

The great French entomologist Jean-Henri Fabre.

(buprestids) in the brood chambers of Scoliid wasps; the beetles served as food for the hatching wasp larvae. Dufour was struck by the fact that the beetles, although to all appearances dead, looked quite fresh, showing not the slightest signs of decay. He thought that probably, when the female wasp stung the beetle to death, she simultaneously injected an antiseptic which acted as a preservative.

Fabre reflected on this for a long time. He could not believe that these wasps could keep their prey in the brood holes as dead, preserved meat. He therefore pursued the matter, and discovered that the great Dufour had been wrong. The wasps merely paralyzed their beetle victims by a single sting. Fabre then studied the prey—crickets this time—of other wasps, called digger wasps, and saw that the paralysis had been accomplished by a triple sting of incredible accuracy. "We discover something that the digger wasp knew long before the anatomist: the cricket has three neural centers which are widely separated. Thus the sublime logic of the thrice-repeated sting."

From that moment on Fabre fell completely under the spell of his insects. He moved to the village of Sérignan and devoted himself entirely to his entomological studies. In the course of time he published ten volumes of a work entitled *Souvenirs entomologiques,* which to this day has remained an almost inexhaustible source of insights into the lives of insects. No one has surpassed the studies of the sex life of insects, spiders, and scorpions written by the "hermit of Sérignan," as Fabre was called.

His accomplishments have come to be fully appreciated only recently, in our age of sober behavioral research. Zoologists the world over have proceeded along the lines laid down by Jean Henri Fabre, who coolly and objectively traced the oddities of reproductive biology among the articulates: the courtship of fiddler crabs, the cannibalism of copulating praying mantis, spider, and scorpion females, the hypermetamorphosis of the oil beetle, the surgical operations practiced by wasps hunting their prey, the wedding rites of bees, ants, and termites.

Since there are more kinds of articulates than there are species of all the rest of the animal kingdom, any description of their sexual and brooding habits is bound to remain incomplete. Fabre required ten volumes to report on merely some one hundred species of the insects of southern France. According to recent estimates our planet has about one and a half million species of articulates, of which half remain as yet undiscovered. No one has begun to provide a full account of them.

Nor has anyone succeeded in explaining the mysteries of animal instincts. We must accept the somewhat resigned comment of the

French zoologist Blanchard which Fabre used as an epigraph for his *Souvenirs:* "To all persons with attentive eyes it is a disturbing and at the same time strangely grand spectacle to see how the industrious insects display the most subtle art in all their works. Their instinct, which has reached the highest degree possible in nature, confounds human reason. Patient and detailed observation only adds to our bafflement."

VARIETIES OF COME-HITHER

One May day a female peacock emperor moth broke from its chrysalis in Jean Henri Fabre's laboratory. That evening, Fabre recorded, there was a great stir in the room next to his. "Little Paul, half undressed, is rushing about, jumping and stamping, knocking the chairs over like a mad thing. I hear him call me: 'Come quick!' he cries. 'Come and see these moths, big as birds! The room is full of them.' "

The invasion of moths had extended beyond Paul's room to the rest of the Fabre house. Innumerable male emperor moths were fluttering on the ceiling, rushing at the light, grazing the faces of the family and trying to reach the laboratory.

> One of the windows in the laboratory had been left open. We enter the room, candle in hand. What we see is unforgettable. With a soft flick-flack the great moths fly around the bell jar, alight, set off again, come back, fly up to the ceiling and down. . . . The scene suggests a wizard's cave with its whirl of bats. Little Paul holds my hand tighter than usual, to keep up his courage.

For a full week Fabre observed the moths. They must have come many miles.

> Each time it is pitch dark, between eight and ten o'clock, when the moths arrive, one by one. It is stormy weather, the sky is very much overcast, and the darkness is so profound that even in the open air, in the garden, far from the shadow of the trees, it is hardly possible to see one's hand before one's face.
>
> In addition to this darkness there is the difficulty of access. The house is hidden by tall plane trees; it is approached by a walk thickly bordered with lilac and rose trees, forming a sort of outer vestibule; it is protected against the mistral by clumps of pines and screens of cypresses. Clusters of bushy shrubs make a rampart a few steps away from the door. It is through this tangle of branches, in complete dark-

ness, that the Great Peacock has to tack about to reach the object of his pilgrimage.

What signals, Fabre asked himself, did the female send in order to attract the males from such a distance and enable them to come straight to her? Light was out of the question. Fabre thought at first of sounds beyond the range of human hearing, then of electrical or magnetic vibrations or of mysterious radiances. Finally he concluded that it must be a scent which the female emitted. But how could a scent have so magical an effect upon the olfactory organs of males over a distance of many miles? Fabre undertook a great variety of experiments with peacock emperors, oak beauties, and other moths. He discovered that the large, conspicuous feelers of the males, which look like "doubly combed plumes" in the peacock emperor, were of vital importance in the hunt for the female. Males whose antennae he amputated could not find their way back to the caged female.

But he found it hard to believe that male moths were able to scent the females over such distances. In his laboratory he released essential oils, sulfur dioxide, and other smells of such strength that "every fine scent should have been smothered by them." But these artifices came to nothing. Even through the intense smells of other substances, the males found the caged females. Finally he reasoned—though his dissatisfaction with the explanation can be sensed between the lines— that the moth females must produce something like "olfactory X-rays, smell-vibrations which can spread to incalculable distances by actual diffusion of matter."

But Fabre was mistaken in his theory that "smell like light has its X-rays." A short time afterwards the Swiss psychiatrist, sexologist, and entomologist August Forel undertook similar experiments. He, too, saw that female moths could attract the males over a distance of miles. In order to discover whether actual scents or inexplicable vibrations were the lure, he placed a female on a piece of paper for a while, then hung this paper outside the window. The males promptly flew at the paper and tried to mate with it. Since the paper could scarcely emanate vibrations, the scent theory must be correct, Forel concluded. The tiny amount of smell transmitted from the scent glands of the female on contact with the paper had sufficed to stimulate the antennae of the males. Another experiment demonstrated that a male managed to fly a mile in six minutes down the scented highway that led straight to the female.

The search for the olfactory secrets of moths helped to answer one of the greatest questions in reproductive biology: How do the partners find one another at mating time? For the moth fluttering alone through shrubbery, the beetle creeping along the bark of a tree, the mosquito buzzing by itself, would all miss their life's purpose if they did not, during the few weeks of their sexual maturity, at some point meet a member of their species of the opposite sex.

Scents are used as aphrodisiacs by a large number of animals. Both males and females perfume themselves to attract the other sex and to increase sexual excitement. Among the favorite aphrodisiac scents is musk. It is produced at mating time by alligators, musk drakes, musk-rats, musk oxen, musk deer, and even by several turtles, beetles, snails, and squid. Before techniques of making synthetic perfumes were learned, *Homo sapiens*, who responds to musk in the same way as these animals, used to massacre droves of musk-producing creatures in order to obtain the sexual scent for his own purposes.

While the female moths lure the males by emitting scent, the males make the females ready for the sex act by exuding a sexual odor. Many butterflies and moths possess scent-scales and scent-spots, or scent-plumes which are extruded from special pockets as soon as a female approaches. Most of these scents are not discernible by the human nose. The death's-head moth, however, one of the most impressive of the European sphinxes, gives off a penetrating smell of musk. Other moths at mating time have the sweetish smell of raspberries, vanilla, or caramel.

Beetles, mosquitoes, and other insects also emit attracting scents. The firefly, or "lightning bug," has two methods of mate-finding: scent and the glow which we human beings regard as even more poetic. The brilliant, sometimes extravagant-minded Austrian biologist Paul Kammerer shut up female fireflies in a cardboard box which no light signal could penetrate. He also killed female fireflies and crushed their bodies to a pulp, so that again there was no glow. In both cases males swarmed around the box or around the remains. If the experiment is reversed and females are shut up in glass test tubes so that their light but not their scent can reach the outside, the males will also appear. Both sense impressions—sight and smell—are effective with these insects.

Luminous organs of the most varied shape, arrangement, and intensity, sometimes sending out a number of colors, are to be found among dwellers in the sea. Monocellules, worms, tunicates, crustaceans, squid, and fish that emit light or luminescent substances have for centuries been among the marvels of the ocean. Biologists still know very little about the life and habits of the deep-sea dwellers; oceanographers assume that the glow of the deep-sea shrimp, squid, and fish has the same function as that of the fireflies of our May and June nights: they are seeking sexual partners.

The females of some species of fireflies are wingless. Their luminescent bands or spots are often found on the ventral side. By day these "glowworms" rest in the grass, and their light is hidden. But at evening when the winged males dart about the air, a horde of glowing dots, the females turn over on their backs, raise their abdomens and present their cold, greenish light to show the males the goal of their desire. Some South American species are able to flash their light at definite intervals and thus to give one another beacon signals. Their precision is extraordinary. The American entomologist Alexander B. Klots writes:

> In one luminous species it was shown that the time interval of 2.1 seconds between the flash from the male and an answering female was the important factor in attracting the male to the female. A dilatory or too eager female would attract no male, and a male answering a flash after such an interval would be liable to be mistaken for a female.

Other insects, too, are able to produce cold light with the aid of their glands. The luminous efficiency of some species surpasses anything that human engineers have been able to achieve: no less than 98 per cent of the energy expended goes to produce light; only 2 per cent is lost as heat! Among the luminous insects are several springtails and mushroom gnats. The supreme master of illumination in the insect world is a large click beetle which lives in the islands of the Caribbean, where it is called cucuyo. It shines its lamp of love so brightly that the inhabitants imprison it in a gauze bag and wear it in their hair as a luminous jewel or as a living hurricane lamp for nocturnal strolls.

Just as the females lure males by scent and light, males attract willing females by dance and music. The swarms and clouds of male midges and dayflies which dance up and down over stagnant water, often looking from a distance like columns of smoke, gather in such formations with the sole function of drawing the attention of females. The females, which have hidden in shrubbery or grass, are apparently fascinated by the dancing swarm of males. If a female happens into it, the cloud masses into a tight sphere in her immediate vicinity. The males who have caught sight of the female stop their dance, and the one which reacts fastest performs the mating.

It is evident that female gnats and ephemera are receptive to optical stimuli entirely different from those that affect the males. They are lured by the general image of the dancing swarm, while the males must respond to the swift darting of a single individual female. Corresponding to this, the eyes of most male dayflies are built quite differently from those of the females; they are enormously enlarged and in a good many cases bipartite, so that the insect has four instead of two compound eyes. Since these male eyes stand out from the head like turbans, entomologists call them "turban eyes." These optic organs do not give the dancing male particularly keen sight, but they do enable him to detect swift movements in the dusk of evening. That is, the male sees his surroundings and the swarm of his fellow males rather hazily, but even in dim light his turban eyes instantly focus on the flight of a female.

Since these turban eyes register only movement without giving any clear image of its source, the males quite often fall victim to grotesque errors. All insects of appropriate size that happen to fly above the dancing swarm are taken for females. Thus there are frequently sudden crowdings around an insect of an altogether different species, and pursuits and attempts at mating are undertaken before the males discover that their eyes have betrayed them.

The dayflies—the ephemera, as they are so prettily called by zoologists—have been regarded since the days of classical antiquity as symbols of the transitoriness of life. Most species of *Ephemeridae* have only brief lives as winged, sexually mature insects; some live for only a few hours. But previously, in the larval state, they have spent six months, a year, or several years—depending on the species—living in water and feeding on all sorts of plant materials. The complete insect, however, does not eat, and most of its organs are without function. It dances away its few hours of life only in order to mate and lay its eggs. The short-lived character of such a dance of life and love was described by "Dr. Cornelius" (a pseudonym adopted by the prolific British author William Howitt), back in 1848. He witnessed the drama as played out by the largest Central European species, *Palingenia longicauda*.

One June day, about seven o'clock in the evening, Cornelius went for a walk along the bank of the Lippe in Westphalia, where these dayflies emerge from their chrysalis. Some fishermen who caught them to use as bait, showed him where they were to be found. When he reached the spot, barely half a dozen of the flies had come out. Within a few minutes the scene changed so rapidly that counting became out of the question.

The mass of insects rising out of the water grew thicker and thicker; at last the surface of the river was almost entirely covered with them, and the movements of the dayflies in their efforts to free themselves from the shell and rise from the water made a sound as if the water itself were boiling. . . .

Half an hour later the air was filled with a tremendous swarm of dancing males. The swarm rose

> higher and higher and sailed in crisscrossing orbits through the air to a height of eighty or a hundred feet with undiminished density, keeping always above the river. Many males seemed to enjoy the flight for its own sake; others could be seen pursuing a female; sometimes numerous males quarreled over a single mate and in the heat of their conflict formed a huge lump which threatened to fall into the water. . . . After about eight hours the spectacle reached its culmination.

An hour later, Cornelius reported, no more insects were rising from the water. The swarm thinned, and soon afterwards it had disintegrated. Millions of dead dayflies could be seen covering the fields, meadows, and water like a heavy fall of snow. The two-and-a-half-hour sexual dance had brought fulfillment to at most one per cent of the dancers.

Insects also use music as a means of stimulating sexual desire. The music, like the dance, is practiced chiefly by the male sex to arouse the females. It is quite the reverse of the Greek image of seductive sirens luring men by their song; among insects, the male locusts. crickets, and cicadas fiddle, chirp, and sing to declare their sexual charms.

The fact was known to the ancient Greeks, or at least to the poet Xenarchus. His exclamation, "Fortunate are the cicadas, for they have dumb wives!" has echoed down the centuries. As a matter of fact it is not accurate. In some few species of singing cicadas the females make just as much noise as the males. The apparatus which produces this song is among the most interesting and complicated devices for the production of sounds to be found anywhere in the animal kingdom. In his *Living Insects of the World* Alexander Klots describes it in technical detail:

> Typically the apparatus is formed around four small cavities located on the lower surface of the body. These are covered by a pair of earlike flaps, which are projections of the rear margin of the thorax, each one covering two cavities. The contraction and expansion of a large muscle in the second abdominal segment vibrates a membrane, the timbril, in the inner wall of each lateral cavity. These vibrations are transmitted by a large air chamber within the body of the folded membrane that lies on the anterior wall of each ventral chamber and to the iridescent mirror membrane that is located in the posterior wall of the same chamber. Acting as resonators these greatly

increase the sound, and the opening and closing of the ear flaps give a rhythmic increase and decrease of the loudness.

The non-specialist may find it easier to appreciate Fabre's comparison of the sounding apparatus of the cicada to a toy that it still sometimes seen and, alas, heard. Fabre, whose own garden resounded with the cicada's song all summer long, wrote:

> Twenty years ago, all Paris went mad over a silly toy called the Cricket, or Cri-cri, if I remember rightly. It consisted of a short blade of steel fastened at one end to a metallic base; alternately pressed out of shape with the thumb and then released, the said blade, though possessing no other merit, gave out a very irritating click; and nothing more was needed to make it popular.

Like the Cri-cri, the resonating cavities of the cicada alter their shape, then return to their former state. They thereby produce two sets of vibrations which are the rising and falling sounds the insect sends forth. There is no obvious sign that the cicada's endless, repetitive song is intended to lure the opposite sex. Fabre had his doubts: "Are we to take the endless cantilena for a passionate call? I am not sure. In the assembly the two sexes are side by side and you do not spend months on end in calling to someone who is at your elbow."

Fabre was, in fact, inclined to think that cicadas produced their sound out of pure pleasure in being, much in the way we may rub our hands together in a moment of satisfaction. Nevertheless, he admits the possibility that these insect concerts may also be wedding cantatas. And if we may draw analogies from grasshoppers and crickets to the cicadas, there can be little further doubt.

Behavorial scientists have undertaken careful experiments with crickets and grasshoppers in order to determine whether the music of the males is practiced merely for self-satisfaction or whether it actually attracts the females. To the extent that these insects do make music, they also have excellent hearing, although their organs of hearing are located at places which seem strange indeed from the human standpoint. Crickets and leaf hoppers have their "ears" on their forelegs, grasshoppers on the abdomen. If the male's concert is transmitted by microphone to a room containing only females, the females gradually gather around the receiving apparatus. A cricket's chirping played from a tape recorder lures female crickets from their hiding place. And if two male grasshoppers, one of whom has been artificially silenced, are locked in cages and a female is placed in the room, she will go straight to the cage in which the fiddling male is housed, completely ignoring the mute male.

Some species of grasshoppers fiddle by vibrating the "string" of the forewing with the "bow," a rough peglike joint on the hind leg. Others rub a hard vein in the wing against the edge of the other wing, producing even louder sounds. Crickets do the same. Among the locusta, too, not all the females are mute. Female field locusts answer softly when the males fiddle, and so there develops a kind of alternating chant in the course of which the pair approach closer and closer.

For some years American scientists have intensively studied the love song of mosquitoes, not only for pure information, but in order to construct acoustic mosquito traps. By mosquito "language" the zoologists mean not the disagreeable buzzing of a female hunting blood, but a number of delicate sounds which we can hear only with the aid of amplifiers. Three such sounds in male mosquitos have been distinguished. The first expresses irritation, the second is a cry for help, and only the third plays a part in the sex life of the insect. The scientists call it the "wolf call," and maintain that amplified it resembles the whistle of boys for a pretty girl passing by.

The wolf call of a gang of mosquito youths has approximately the same effect on young mosquito females as the boys' whistling upon human girls: both scurry by, pretending not to have heard. If the passing beauty utters a certain cooing sound, however, the match is made. The male mosquito follows the cooing girl, draws her off into the bushes, and after the consummation returns to the gang. The female flies away and looks for the right place to lay her eggs.

Mosquito traps which imitate the cooing sound of the female have been employed here and there in mosquito-plagued tropical regions to lure the males away from the females and thus significantly diminish the numbers of the species in question. Biologists consider this method of combating insects far more sensible than the mass extermination wrought by DDT and other pesticides which wreak havoc upon countless forms of life. The acoustic traps specifically affect the one species of insect that is undesirable to man, and do not harm the ecology of a whole region.

Other sexual signals have been used for human purposes. In 1960 American biochemists succeeded in synthesizing the scent with which the female gypsy moth attracts males. The following year Adolf Butenandt, German biochemist and Nobel Prize winner, and his associates at the Max Planck Institute for Biochemistry in Munich, succeeded in analyzing and synthesizing the scent of the silkworm. Since the attracting scents of various types of butterfly are remarkably similar in chemical structure, differing only by the position of a few atoms, scientists will probably soon be able to create specific scent traps which, like the acoustic traps, affect only the males of the harmful insect without endangering other forms of animal life.

Already such sex traps prevent millions of dollars worth of insect damage annually. If more use were made of such devices, the earth might be saved from slow poisoning by insecticides. Hosts of loudspeakers may someday lure locusts into prepared death traps; tape recorders might free whole countries of flies and mosquitoes; scent machines might make possible the annihilation of the hordes of harmful moths whose larvae prey on vegetation. But the thoughtful man may also feel a twinge of dismay when he reflects upon this use of scientific cunning to turn the reproductive urge against its own end. As yet, few species respond to the man-made calls. But if someday science should succeed in making all creatures blindly obey its lures— what then? The utilitarians scarcely know moderation; they tend to condemn as harmful all creatures whose immediate usefulness is not apparent. And if they had their way, the whole earth might be as waste and void as at the beginning of time.

Let us hope, with the majority of biologists, that so much power will never lie within the hands of man. "Every new weapon gives rise to a new defense," Fritz Kahn has said, referring to the chemical methods of insect warfare. Even as we now have whole species of mosquitoes which have become immune to DDT and other insecticides, so tomorrow there may well be moths, locusts, and other harmful insects which will no longer walk into the sex traps laid by man. And that would be just as well; for a large-scale liquidation of the insect population would produce a natural catastrophe unparalleled in the history of the earth. Directly or indirectly, half of all the higher animals of land and fresh water live on insects.

FLIRTATION, COURTSHIP, AND WEDDING GIFTS

The American naturalist William Beebe undertook several expeditions on the yacht *Zaca* between 1936 and 1940. His purpose was to study living organisms in the bays and mangrove swamps of Central America. The results of one such expedition were set down in an essay on the courtship of fiddler crabs, which Beebe wrote in collaboration with Jocelyn Crane. Among these coastal crabs, which live almost entirely on land, the females possess two claws of equal size. The males, however, have one claw which grows into a monstrous, strikingly colored "fiddle," usually longer than the rest of the crab's body. "When scurrying rapidly along," Beebe and Crane write, "they reminded us of cowboys on horseback at full gallop, that lovely, smooth gait with the bellies almost touching the ground. Held high aloft, as the rodeo riders do their sombreros, the fiddlers brandished at full height the great claw."

Why did the crabs brandish their claws? The investigators of the mangrove swamps could not agree on this question. Some of them thought the crabs were beckoning to the females. Others objected; the males went on beckoning whether or not a female was in the vicinity. William Beebe and Jocelyn Crane determined to solve this problem. At first they too saw only the male, rather unimpressively colored, constantly waving its claw up and down, even though it was engaged solely in feeding. "Every little while, however, a wave of excitement would sweep over him and his masculine neighbors, who would all leave their lunch without a qualm and go racing about on tiptoe, with the great pink claws extended stiffly, and their small claws spread just as stiffly in the opposite direction, their whole attitude being one of alertness and intense excitement."

What had happened? After some time the two scientists discovered the cause of the agitation:

> . . . a female, so small and drab and inconspicuous that at first she escaped our notice. To the males, however, she represented the acme of interest, if only she were of adequate age, yet unburdened by eggs, and if she at least had definitely stopped eating for a moment and hence was open to persuasion. Even more desirable, apparently, were foot-loose flirts who provocatively wandered far from their holes, electrifying every male they passed. When a male succeeded in getting close to one of these, he would literally dance her along in the circle of his great nipper-arm, never touching her, but trying to tease her over to his hole.

Beebe and Crane soon saw that such dances formed only the opening stages in the courtship. "This method . . . seemed more a sport than serious flowers-and-candy courtship." Gradually the mood of excitement would seize the whole colony. The dances of the different species resembled graceful ballet, wild jitterbugging, and the "giddy Panamanian carnival dance, the tamborito, in which the woman dances first with one man, then with a succession of others. . . . So distinct were the dances that we could recognize different forms in a mixed colony." During the dances the males became more and more colorful. "Like good Latin Americans preparing for fiestas, the crabs literally dressed up before dancing, changing before our eyes from

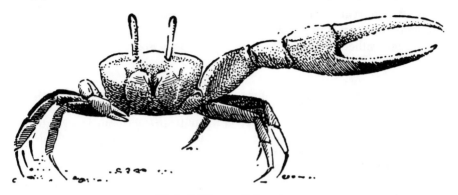

Male fiddler crab dancing.

dowdy browns and grays to the rose and white, purple and green or turquoise, magenta and blue of their respective clans." Beebe and Crane described the dynamics of a courtship as displayed by a newly discovered emerald-backed fiddler crab which now bears Beebe's name:

> He was in full display color, and for at least an hour had been try-ing vainly to attract the attention of a drab little female four inches away. He interrupted display only with the merest minimum of feeding, but she apparently paid no attention at all, redigging her hole and feeding busily, with never a glance in his direction. At last, however, she stopped feeding and appeared to see him for the first time. With this slight encouragement, he speeded up the tempo of his dance, pumping his great purple claw frantically up and down and adding extra clogging steps to the prancing of his eight green legs. The female sidled an inch or two in his direction, pausing for snacks as she came. Her suitor pranced still faster, and at last won her fascinated attention. Almost hypnotized she seemed as she watched, motionless, an inch away. He varied his dance, revolving slowly before her like a mannequin, so that his back of iridescent green faced her alternately with his purple claw. Finally she ap-proached within reach, he stroked her legs gently with his own, and she stroked his in return. They parted, briefly, he did one more pranc-ing jig, and then dashed suddenly down his hole, his bright claw vanishing last with a final, irresistible waggle. And at once the fe-male followed after.
>
> Five minutes later the male reappeared briefly at the mouth of the hole, kicked up a plug of mud, and deftly flipped it over the entrance with his last-projecting legs as a most eloquent "do not disturb." And we saw no more of them.

What Beebe and Crane had witnessed was only one of the many pretty courtship rites practiced in countless variations by a great many different types of crabs, spiders, and insects. Not quite so graceful, but rather similar, is the love dance of the scorpions as it was observed by Fabre:

> Brow to brow and with tails erect, two wrestlers stand on their heads, so that they are balanced only on the thorax, while the rest of the body is sticking into the air. Then the tails, stretched out in straight lines, rub against one another; one brushes over the other; their ends form a hook, intertwine many times, and release one another again. Suddenly the amiable pyramid collapses and both abruptly hasten away.

This was not an attempt at mating, but only a first tender flirtation. "To declare his passion, the scorpion stands on his head," Fabre observed. But a different type of scorpion dance was more serious.

> For the first time I observed two scorpions facing one another with six claws outstretched and fingers clasped. . . . With their tails prettily curled, the couples trot with measured steps along the pane. The male is ahead and walks backwards, without jolt or jerk, without any resistance to overcome. The female follows obediently, clasped by her finger tips and face to face with her leader.

If after a long trek, interrupted by frequent pauses and mutual caresses, the pair find a suitable hole, they consummate their marriage. We will have something to say in a future chapter about that bloody affair, as well as about the gruesome wedding customs of certain members of the next group, the spiders. Scorpions and spiders belong to the same class, the Arachnida, which is closely related to the most ancient arthropods we know, the trilobites that thronged the Paleozoic seas. The second great group of arthropods is formed by the crustaceans, the third by the tracheal breathers—the insects and millipedes. So much for the place of these animals in classification.

Courtship dances are extremely common among the spiders. There are two obvious reasons for this. In the first place the male spiders are usually much smaller than the females and therefore cannot conquer their giant brides by force; they are obliged to persuade rather than compel. And in the second place the copulation of spiders is an extremely complicated process which requires certain preliminaries on the male's part. Some of these preliminaries are included in the rites of courtship. In order to make this involved matter comprehensible, we shall first describe the mating of spiders in general outline.

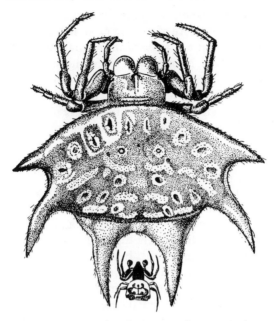

Sexual dimorphism in the spider Gasteracantha curvispina. *Above, giant female; below, dwarf male.*

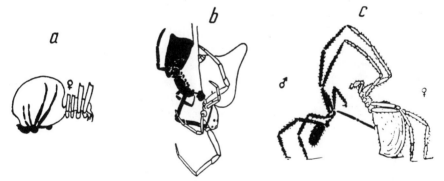

Three copulatory positions in different species of spider. The male must introduce his sperm-filled palp into the female's genital orifice in different and complex ways.

Male and female spiders possess genital orifices on the underside of the abdomen but they do not unite directly, as one might assume. The male spider has no penis. Instead, he employs his maxillary palps or feelers to transmit the semen. In order for a male spider to mate with a female, he must first spin a tiny web. He dabs this web against his abdomen, discharging a drop of semen onto the threads. Then he dips his palps into the drop several times, filling its bladder-shaped terminal joints with semen. Among the large tropical bird spiders this prelude to the adventure of mating often takes two to three hours.

The copulatory impulse is aroused in the male spider only after the palps have been filled. Members of different species have a great variety of ways to attract the females' attention. The males of web spiders add a thread to the female's web and pluck violently, in successive jerks, on this signal line until the owner of the web rushes up to see what is going on. Male wolf spiders beckon to the female with both palps, holding them high and at the same time taking a number of dance steps.

Male jumping spiders perform extremely droll dances. They are very small, often strikingly marked animals whose eyesight is excellent and whose hunting methods are rather catlike. They creep skillfully up to their prey, leap on its back and finish it off with a swift bite. But when the male jumping spider spies a female, it abandons its usual creeping movement. Instead, it raises itself high, beckons with its first pair of legs, and in this erect position runs in zigzags back and forth in front of the female, until at last it pauses and stands face to face with her. If the female remains peaceful and has not stirred, the male can venture to leap upon her and insert his semen-filled palp into her genital orifice.

In some species of spiders it is usual for the partners to hold hands during the prelude to mating. The male clings to the female's forelegs. This may look quite charming; actually it is a defensive measure on the part of the male. If he does not succeed in skillfully grasping the female's poisonous claws in time, the unscrupulous lady may drive her murderous weapons into his body. And if that takes place before copulation, the sex play has missed its function.

The members of the so-called stronger sex—but among spiders the males are invariably smaller and weaker—practice other precautions with the same aim. Among certain tropical web spiders, the male patiently waits on his rope bridge until an insect has flown into the female's web. He then dashes across his bridge into the web, wraps up the victim, and holds it out to the female—so that it serves half as a wedding gift, half as a protective shield. Less courageous males wait until the female has herself snatched the prey. In both cases, the male opportunely seizes the moment at which the female is consuming her meal to effect transmission of the semen.

A hunting spider, *Pisaura listeri*, goes a step further. The male catches a fly, wraps it in silk from its spinneret, and hands the package to the female as a bridal gift. The offering of this present can take some time, and can be repeated frequently, the male behaving like an infatuated youth waiting to see whether his girl will really accept his

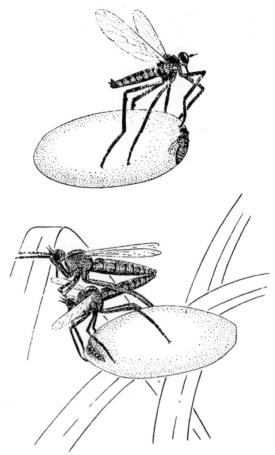

Male dancing fly passes over the female bearing a wrapped-up wedding gift, which she accepts.

flowers. The male spider is extremely agitated; his whole body quivers and he shakes his palps like arms outstretched in a desperate plea. Some *Pisaura* females refuse to be impressed and show the utmost indifference toward the tastiest fly. Others threaten the suitor and drive him away. Still others pretend to be fearful for their virtue, and scurry off. But when the fly is accepted, the male hunting spiders proceed much as do the web spiders. They crawl cautiously up to the feeding bride, introduce one or both palps into her vagina, and then hastily flee the scene of the consummation.

Insects as well as spiders have this custom of a bridal gift. But the function among the insects is a good deal more innocuous. The male flies who engage in the practice are not faced with having to save their own skins; they are simply satisfying the female's stomach during the act of mating. Bridal gift and wedding supper are an established ceremony among some three thousand species of dancing flies

(Empidae). The males of these flies dance above the surface of the water rather like midges but in addition some of them can spin. They spin delicate veils which they trail after them through the air. Apparently the veil dances they perform in sunlight are intended to attract the females.

Other male dancing flies use their spinning talents to prepare large balloons of silk. Inside these balloons are small dayflies or gnats which the males have captured and wrapped up to present to their brides. But the gift can also be presented without such balloons. The males of most species of dancing flies hold the captured insect cautiously between their legs without wrapping, and deliver it to the female. During copulation the gift is consumed either by the female or by both mates.

Various courtship customs, some tender, some chivalrous, some distinctly tempestuous, exist throughout the insect world. When a pair of crickets or grasshoppers have found one another (after their enticing song has accomplished its purpose) they feel one another with their antennae as parrots scratch one another's feathers before mating. Beetles, earwigs, hymenoptera, and diptera often perform characteristic rites as preludes to mating. And the mating flights and mating games of butterflies offer a fascinating spectacle for the behavorial scientist.

Most male butterflies are in a state of extreme excitement when they go hunting females. They fly at every butterfly that pauses anywhere near them and that even approximately resembles in size and coloration a potential mate. If the other flies away, the male butterfly swerves and looks for a new partner. But if after a brief flight the other settles down and buzzes with its wings, the butterfly knows he has found a willing female of his own species. The two then begin a courtship which in some species can take the form of wild gyrations, the male flying above the female, circling her and turning loops like a stunt pilot.

In some forms of the courtship the female settles down on a twig or a large flower, and spreads out her wings. Her scent organs are operating and seem to intensify the male's sexual excitement to the highest pitch. He flies in steadily narrowing circles around the female's position. Then he too alights, bows, fans her with his wings, taps her with his antennae and legs, and finally caresses a particular spot on her head which is apparently especially receptive to sexual stimuli. Among the many species of moths and butterflies there are innumerable variations of this pattern. The bright wings will be repeatedly opened and shut, until at last the male arrives at the climax of the proceedings: he circles around the female and presses his abdomen against hers.

Courting males are not always able to go about their performance undisturbed. Where love is, there is jealousy. Rivals invariably appear and try to cut in. Among the arthropods, however, sexual conflicts have a rather sporting character; it is rare to find them engaging in the bitter battles characteristic of fish, reptiles, birds, and mammals, which sometimes end in the death of the defeated animal.

ARMORED DUEL

One of the most diligent popularizers of entomology during the second half of the last century was Ernst Ludwig Taschenberg of the Zoological Museum in Halle, Germany. He wrote little homilies on the good and bad types of insects, for the use of gardeners and orchardists. He conceived the idea of displaying entomological posters in classrooms. His book entitled *Things that Crawl and Fly* attempted to dramatize the life of insects, in much the same way as his great French colleague Jean Henri Fabre had done.

One of Taschenberg's favorites was the stag beetle. The male of this beetle is equipped with two large horns which resemble the antlers of a deer. It is well known that the stag uses his antlers to fight his sexual battles. Consequently, zoologists since the days of Jan Swammerdam had concluded that the male stag beetles used their horns for a similar purpose. But no one had actually observed such duels. It had, however, been noted that the beetles, in licking up the sweet sap of various trees, would quarrel over their food and bite one another.

Taschenberg seems to have been among the first entomologists to succeed in obtaining dependable eyewitness reports of genuine tournaments of love on the part of the stag beetles. As Taschenberg described one of these contests, they were a good deal more serious than the disagreements over food:

> They had crossed their antlerlike mandibles over one another, so that these extended over the opponent's prothorax. Thus they struggled with one another, rearing high, their heads touching, until one of the warriors weakened and tumbled to the ground. Now and then a skilled wrestler would succeed in grasping his opponent around the abdomen. He would then hold him writhing in the air for

some time, and finally dash him to the ground. There was a crackling and snapping whenever the mandibles closed. However, the battle looked fiercer than it really was, for aside from a superficial bite in one mandible, no wounds were observed.

Stag beetles are excellent examples of sexual dimorphism, the difference between the sexes in the insect world. In the rhinoceros and Goliath beetles, which are distantly related to the stag beetles, the sexual differences are especially striking. The males are adorned with rhinoceros horns, antlers, pincers, knobs, forks, and other bizarre chitinous formations on their heads or prothoraxes. Most of these excessively large growths seem altogether useless; in fact the animals seem needlessly burdened by them. Darwin commented:

> The horns do not show marks of friction, as if used for any ordinary work. Some authors suppose that as the males wander much more than the females, they require horns as a defence against their enemies; but in many cases the horns do not seem well adapted for defence, as they are not sharp. The most obvious conjecture is that they are used by the males for fighting together; but they have never been observed to fight.
>
> The conclusion which best agrees with the fact of the horns having been so immensely yet not fixedly developed—as shown by their extreme variability in the same species and by their extreme diversity in closely allied species—is that they have been acquired as ornaments. This view will at first appear extremely improbable; but we shall hereafter find with many animals, standing much higher in the scale, namely, fishes, amphibians, reptiles, and birds, that various kinds of crests, knobs, horns, and combs have been developed apparently for this sole purpose.

Apparently the combativeness which Taschenberg ascribed to the stag beetles was not characteristic of the Goliath and rhinoceros beetles. Further observation seems to have borne out Darwin's guess that the monstrous chitinous horns of these species are pure luxury. Males with the biggest horns by no means invariably win the females. William Beebe observed this in the case of a number of Hercules beetles which he kept in the biological laboratory of Rancho Grande in the rain forest of Venezuela.

A new-caught Minor showed more vitality and activity than has any Major. Placed with five Majors and four females the small male mated with all the females in turn, and several times in succession with two of them, while the much larger beetles took time off from feeding to mate with only one or two. The matings of the Minor were as complete and successful as those of the Majors.

The horns can, therefore, scarcely have arisen by sexual selection. Probably the genes which govern the origination of such monstrosities are linked with other genes whose effects are helpful to the survival of the beetles. However, we do not know what markings or characteristics may be involved. The traits cannot be courage or sexual boldness, for the small-horned males certainly do not lack either of these qualities. The small beetle described by Beebe was always the first to attack the large one. "In several combats with the two Majors the Minor showed no lack of courage and rushed his giant opponents, but always to no purpose. He was invariably seized and carried off the field high in air, in the massive, toothed horns." This treatment in no way impaired his sexual activity.

Hercules beetles and other horned beetles also actually fight like stag beetles for the females—a procedure many zoologists besides Darwin have failed to see. Beebe describes the struggles of two Hercules beetles nearly equal in size, one of them black and the other olive in color. It became clear to him that the duel of the beetles can be broken up into quite specific phases:

> The Black rushes the contest. Throughout what we might call rounds, he seizes the other, raises him on high and stumbles about with him, and finally bangs him down. During all this, Olive is perfectly quiescent, putting up just enough defense to show he is not actively trying to escape. His very relaxation seems to preserve him from injury, as is so often the case in human contests or other activities. When slammed down for the fourth or fifth time, the lethargic Olive is suddenly obsessed by what appears to be a most unbeetle-like rage, and from now on the mêlée is full of reciprocal action. The little bulging eyes must see more than they appear to, for again and again, Olive avoids the scissors grip and snap of his dark opponent, and with what I can call nothing but skill, suddenly smothers Black, grips him, shifts his hold and rising so high that he seems on the point of overbalancing backwards, hurls down the bigger beetle, with his handicap of two grams, once or as many as three times. Whereupon the victor turns and scuttles off as fast as his six legs will carry him.

In such combats between two equal opponents, the winner openly enjoys the reward of victory.

> Twice Olive watched his vanquished rival kick as he swiveled around on his back, and both of these times made his way to the nearest female

and mated. Again twice his rage failed to cool and he continued the battle until Black was reduced to complete immobility, although ultimately he recovered fully. On these occasions Olive wandered away to a split banana, thereupon subordinating all other emotions.

At Rancho Grande, Beebe was also able to substantiate a fact that had long been thought a charming myth: that the giant beetles used their horns to seize the females and carry them away.

One day after a Major had speedily defeated and transported a small Minor, and flung him down according to schedule, the Major came upon a female and with no hesitation picked her up and walked off as if she had been of the tribe of Sabines. She was held rather awkwardly and soon one of her dangling legs tripped him and she was dropped.

In other cases the knight carried his abducted bride into the underbrush. But only in one case did Beebe see mating follow immediately upon abduction. The function of this phase of the courtship ceremony in the sexual mechanism of the Hercules beetles is still unknown.

Another group of insects are provided with weapons of an entirely different type which have given them an unsavory reputation. An old and altogether foolish superstition maintains that these creatures can creep into the human ear and destroy the eardrum with the pincers they carry at the rear of their bodies. Hence their name: earwigs. In truth they are quite harmless creatures who live on all sorts of vegetable and animal matter. Their exact place in the zoological system is not quite clear. Perhaps they derive from cricketlike or cockroachlike ancestors.

Pincers pinch. Some species of earwigs use these weapons for this purpose. They are even able to inflict lethal wounds on spiders with the tips of their pincers, but they are far too feeble to harm larger animals, let alone man. And in struggles with sexual rivals, jealous earwigs can do no harm whatsoever. They do present their backs to each other and make furious assaults with their pincers, but neither of the fighters is ever seriously injured. The stronger pushes or hurls the weaker aside and then seeks out the female; the loser puts a good face on the matter and abandons the arena.

For human beings, the sexual battles of certain species of animals have become sporting spectacles—which perhaps reveals sadistic traits in the human observers. Asian and Central Americans raise mettlesome varieties of domestic fowl, stimulate the fighting cocks with drugs and certain poisons, fasten sharp little knives to their spurs so that the combatants can horribly lacerate each other, and then bet heavily on the outcome. The Siamese have developed a brightly colored fighting fish, the so-called labyrinth fish of Southeast Asia. It too can be employed for murderous duels, and such fishfights enjoy almost the same popularity as cockfights. In the Mediterranean world, people find amusement in the sexual battles of insects.

The insect which is most easily stimulated to attack its rivals is the cricket. In nature every cricket has a dwelling hole of its own, in front of which it sits making music to call its mate. But when two male crickets whose territories overlap chance to encounter one another while seeking food or mates, they utter peculiar "competitive cries" and leap at one another, each trying to bite. These disputes on the borders of territories usually end in the weaker cricket's retreating to its hole. But showmen at Italian country fairs will put two male crickets into a narrow cage, where the loser cannot escape. The spectators place their bets as in cockfighting or fishfighting, and the battle goes on until one of the fighters is killed.

Possibly the most impressive weapons among the arthropods are possessed by the crayfish and crabs. We might imagine that such animals as the lobster, the river crab, the robber crab, and the shore crab would be able to inflict frightful wounds upon sexual rivals with their powerful claws. But in general these nippers serve them only for catching prey and dissecting their food. Only the shore crabs and the fiddler crabs have actually been observed in unquestionable sexual battles. Among colonies of fiddler crabs, in fact, it seems customary for periods of eating, courtship, battle, and hole building to follow one another in a fixed rhythm during ebb tide.

Male fiddler crabs fighting.

SEXUAL ACROBATICS

What happens after the courtship or the sexual duel? The ancient Indian textbook of love, the *Kama Sutra;* the prose dialogues of that brilliant Renaissance scapegrace, Pietro Aretino; the drawings of his contemporary and fellow countryman, Giulio Romano; and any number of similar works have attempted to compile all possible positions in the sex act of our own species. Most of the positions thus recorded sprang from pornographic imagination and have no place in real life. But even the most fantastic wish-dreams of erotomaniacs would not stand comparison with the multitude of sexual positions practiced by the arthropods. For the members of this phylum of the animal kingdom employ virtually every method of sexual union conceivable. Everything takes place that historians of morals have brought to light in the way of strange, sordid, and diabolic behavior among humans: rape, cannibalism, vampirism, abuse of children, murder of spouses, and the wildest acrobatic tricks in copulation. Also to be found are marital fidelity, tenderness, touching child care and a number of other traits to make up for the erotic chamber of horrors.

But it would be a complete mistake to apply our own standards of morality to animals. The water spider, which practices an ideal marriage is morally no better than the male wolf spider which, as it were, rapes the female in passing, or the female garden spider which after mating attempts to seize and eat the male. In speaking of the sex life of insects Fabre used such terms as "orgies," "atrocities," "perverse lusts," and "bloodthirsty habits." Nowadays we are aware that each organism obeys certain laws, and Nature does not in the least care whether or not we human beings like those laws.

Here is a scene that might have taken place in the primitive days of life on earth. A brownish creature which looks half like a worm and half like a snail scurries on two dozen stubby legs through the damp rain forest seeking another of its species—if possible one larger than itself, a female. If it finds one, it sticks a capsule filled with semen onto some part of her body. Then it goes its way. The sperm cells meanwhile penetrate the body of the female and swim through the abdominal cavity to the ovaries. This process is characteristic of many worms and other lower animals, as we have seen. The stubby-legged brown creatures who fertilize eggs in this way occupy a place in the animal kingdom midway between the annelid worms and the insects. They have been named by a witty zoologist the Peripatidae, the "walkers."

Male "walkers" do not go to much trouble to find a female recipient for their semen capsules. If they encounter other males, or even young of their own species, they fasten the sperm-filled cartridges to them. A shortage of females, moreover, can lead to all the males of a given territory descending on a single female. A biologist once counted no fewer than 180 semen capsules covering the entire body of such a female.

Millipedes are somewhat closer to the insects. They, too, are worm-shaped, but they breathe through genuine tracheae and are completely clad in chitinous armor. Most millipedes possess gonopods—appendages for copulation such as we have already encountered, in somewhat different form, among the squid and spiders. That is, several of the male's legs are modified for reproductive purposes. These legs are either in the center of the body or toward the posterior end, while the sex glands open into the anterior part of the abdominal cavity, usually at the third segment. Consequently, before copulation male millipedes must roll themselves up in a curious manner in order to fill the gonopods with semen.

The sex play and mating positions which follow this initial coiling are quite amusing. In some millipedes the males and females twist and wind themselves into tighter and tighter circles until the male at last winds a regular knot around the frontal part of the female's body, at the same time placing the semen where it belongs. In others the couples lie abdomen to abdomen and hold each other with all their many legs. In every case, however, the male does not transfer his sperm directly, but with the aid of his sexually modified legs.

Such auxiliary organs also occur in the males of many crustaceans: modified limbs which take the form of papillae or stilettos. They serve to attach sperm-filled tubes to the external genital orifice of the females. In the large river crayfish the procedure is accompanied with a violent sexual combat. This crayfish must grip the female with his claws and throw her on her back; otherwise his copulatory instruments cannot place the tubes of sperm in the proper spot. If the female defends herself, which frequently happens, the human observer sees what seems to be sheer sexual brutality.

An enormous variety of positions and methods of copulation is found among the arachnids. Not only spiders and scorpions, but a great number of tiny organisms frequently found as parasites of man, animals, or plants, are included within this zoological class—the ticks and mites. Approximately ten thousand species of mites live on land,

in the sea, and in fresh water. They are found even in the polar regions. Some devour protozoans, others eat plants, others are parasites
on vegetables, grain, trees, or seaweed, or in mussels, sponges, sea
urchins, insects, and warm-blooded animals. Their sex lives are as
variable as their habits.

There are water mites among which the males hold their partners
during the sex act with hooks, and in addition actually glue themselves to the females. Some male mites possess a penis; others transfer
the sperm in the fashion of spiders, by means of maxillary palps;
others, again, use a pair of legs, like the crustaceans. Still others follow a simpler method: they leave a capsule of semen near the female
and rely upon her to transfer it to the right spot.

Among ordinary ticks, sexual congress becomes a surgical operation. When the female tick has attached itself to a warm-blooded animal, the male approaches her, crawls under her body, and introduces
its proboscis into her vagina. By manipulation it widens the vagina.
Then it turns around and deposits a packet of sperm nearby. Since it
has no copulatory apparatus, it must use its proboscis and feelers to
push the packet into the expanded vagina—a task which requires considerable skill. The female, meanwhile, goes on serenely sucking
blood.

By human standards the tick's behavior is strange. By those same
standards the moth mite *Pyemotes herfsi* reaches the acme of per-
versity. Male moth mites act as obstetricians in order to mate with
the newborn females immediately after they have come into the
world. Abuse of children with incest into the bargain! But for moth
mites the procedure is entirely reasonable. Female moth mites are
parasites upon the caterpillars of certain moths and butterflies. Like
many parasitic arachnids and insects, they bear living, fully developed young who have already passed through their larval and pupal
stages within the mother's body. If males are born, they linger around
the abdominal orifice of their mother, bore into the mother's body,
and feed on her juices while waiting for the birth of their sisters.

When the front end of a young female appears in the mother's
birth passage, one of the males turns around, grips his sister with his
nipperlike hind legs, and pulls and pries her out of the passage. Such
obstetrical aid is given only to the females. But it is not at all essential,
as is proved by the fact that the first-born are often females. The
young female which has thus been dragged out is not released by
the male. Instead, he mates with her immediately. Birth and mating
require on an average four minutes; then the fertilized female leaves
the mother behind and seeks out a moth caterpillar; it must find and
attach itself to one within two days or it will starve to death. The

males, meanwhile, wait for the next forceps delivery so that they can mate with the next newborn sister.

Among parasites such extravagant behavior has its point; the males would otherwise find it too difficult to locate their sexual partners.

Equally appropriate is the extraordinary variety of copulatory positions among the true spiders. These follow from the habits and anatomical peculiarities of various species of spider. Most male spiders are, as we have mentioned, much smaller than the females. All of them perform copulation with their semen-filled maxillary palps and must therefore know precisely where the female genital orifice is located, in order to deposit their semen packets in the right place. In general this orifice is well forward on the underside of the female's balloonlike abdomen, and, moreover, is concealed under a kind of lid. Since mating may take place on the ground, on a plant, or in the female's web, according to species, and since the difference in size between the sexes is sometimes very great and sometimes small, the possibilities are legion.

There are male web spiders which adroitly and cunningly tangle the female in a cocoon of silk and so render her temporarily immobile. They can thus approach her safely and take time to find the vagina. The males of the garden spider pluck at their "love bridge" for a while, agitating it until the female comes to it to investigate. If she is willing and shows no instant inclination to eat the male, the following ceremony ensues—as described by Curt Thesing:

> Slowly, the female creeps toward the male and hangs by her hind legs downward on the bridge, turning her underside toward the male. This is the signal for him to proceed boldly toward her. He now begins vigorously feeling her body with his legs, a caress which as a rule the female quietly permits. This sex play sometimes lasts several minutes and actually seems to hypnotize the female. Suddenly the male thrusts his maxillary palp deep into the female genital orifice, whereupon the semen flows into a special seminal bladder directly alongside the vagina; there it will be kept, and later on, when the female lays her eggs, it will fertilize the eggs. Now, however, the male is wise to flee as swiftly as possible, or else he will be the bloodthirsty female's prey. In his hasty flight his palp sometimes breaks off and remains sticking in the female genital orifice, where it is known as the sign of mating.

The males of various species of insects likewise leave behind such signs of mating—the drones of the honey bee, for example. Bees practice genuine copulation, the male sex organ being introduced into the vagina of the queen bee. The drone's organ then breaks off, and the male bee bleeds to death. The broken organ serves as a plug, prevent-

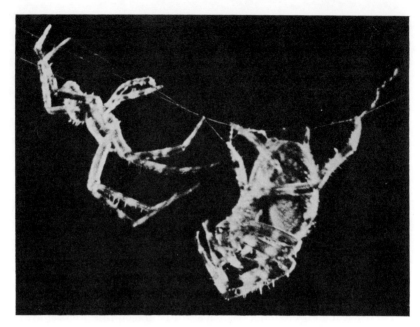

Spiders engaged in sex play on the "love bridge."

The huge spider female Nephila *carries the tiny male beneath her abdomen.*

ing the semen from running out of the vagina again. If this plug is removed, the queen lays only unfertilized eggs.

Not all female spiders have to be approached with such caution. Ground-dwelling spider females usually rear up if they are willing to be mated, and present their ventral side to the males—in which position the males can easily find the lidded opening of the vagina. Among crab spiders an intimate embrace takes place. The small male embraces the fat sphere of the female abdomen with all his legs, taking what sexologists call an "opposing" position. Among web spiders, too, the pair may unite head to head, or head to abdomen.

Finally, there are some species of spiders in which the males are so tiny that any preliminary sex play is out of the question. Among these are the tropical wheel-web spiders of the genus *Nephila,* whose females in some cases weigh six hundred times more than the microscopically small males. These dwarf males behave in a fashion similar to that of the male moth mites. Several of them live as parasites upon the abdomen of the huge female and mate with her whenever they feel like it. Presumably they are too inconspicuous even to be considered as possible prey by the colossal female. Moreover, *Nephila* offspring crawl around the mother after they hatch, so that the female might find it difficult to distinguish children from husbands.

In contrast to the spiders, insects do not need complicated positions or manipulations in order to mate. Their mating, with some exceptions, follows the general pattern of the sexual intercourse of vertebrates. It is genuine copulation, in which the posterior parts of the abdomen come into close contact. Male insects, however, possess a great variety of auxiliary organs which enable them to cling to or stick to the females during copulation. Corresponding provisions in the female sometimes facilitate matters for the male.

One example of conventional intercourse is offered by the *Dytiscus,* or water butt, a large predatory water beetle of European ponds, lakes, and seas. In 1915, Blunck and Heymons wrote the classical description of the mating procedures of *Dytiscus:*

> Restively, the males eager for mating dart about the water, but do not notice the females until they have approached within eight inches or a foot. Thereupon excitement grips the male. The feelers with which he first sensed the female wave back and forth; with rapid swimming movements the beetle races forward, then with lightning suddenness mounts the female and holds her fast. To do so, he presses the sucker pads of his forelegs against the side margins of her prothorax, while his claws embrace the sides of the female's thorax. The middle legs, stretched far back, grip the sides of the wing sheaths; the hind legs remain free, however, and the male is able to row with

them. With violent, jerky swimming strokes, the two linked beetles
rush through the water. But the male is not idle; he is using his
powers of persuasion upon the female, who for the time being resists
him coyly. His methods of coaxing are rather loud ticking or beating
sounds. Since he lacks any instruments for stridulation, he produces
these sounds by rasping the femur of his hind legs over the front edge
of the femoral ring. The female cannot resist the magic of these
sounds; she yields to the male. The pair separate again only after a
sexual union lasting for hours and even days.

Thus when water butts mate, the male mounts on the female's back
and the heads of the pair both point in the same direction. Every child
who has collected June bugs after their nuptial flight or observed
grasshoppers copulating is familiar with this position. Most human
beings regard it—not quite rightly—as the "normal" position among
animals. In beetles, if the mating lasts a long time, the male frequently lets himself fall over backwards and, with his belly up, his
posterior firmly glued to the female, allows himself to be dragged
along by his mate. This position, too, is familiar to those who have
observed June bugs. But many insects, for reasons that have to do
with the structure of their bodies or the shape of their sexual organs,
diverge from this "normal" position. Among butterflies, caddis flies,
and most species of bedbugs, the abdomens are united as in the beetles,
but the partners turn away, their heads pointing in opposite directions.
The female mole cricket mounts the male's back for copulation.

A curious reversal of the normal position is described by Fabre in
the case of the saber grasshopper *Decticus albifrons*. The beginning
of the sex act is similar to that of the mole cricket:

> The male is underneath, lying flat on the sand and towered over by
> his powerful spouse, who, with her saber exposed, standing high on
> her hind legs, overwhelms him with her embrace. No indeed: in this
> posture the poor Decticus has nothing of the victor about him.
>   Have not the roles been reversed? She who is usually provoked is
> now the provoker, employing rude caresses. . . . She has not yielded
> to him; she has thrust herself upon him, disturbingly, imperiously.

After a while, the scene changes:

> Master Decticus is on the ground, tumbled over on his back. Hoisted
> to the full weight of her shanks, the other, holding her saber almost
> perpendicular, covers her prostrate mate from a distance. The two
> neutral extremities curve into a hook, seek each other, meet, and soon
> from the male's convulsive loins there is seen to issue, in painful

labor, something monstrous and unheard of, as though the creature were expelling its entrails in a lump.

This lump extruded by the male saber grasshopper is a spermatophore or semen cartridge of rather remarkable form. It looks almost like a large packet of eggs. It remains hanging at the base of the saberlike ovipositor and after copulation the female drags it along, a heavy burden. She herself then completes the fertilization by curling up and, with her mandibles, cautiously squeezing the contents of the cartridge over her genital orifice.

Even this peculiar mode of copulation is relatively normal in the insect world. Among the real exceptions, the insects which mate in a totally outlandish fashion, are those flying creatures which nature lovers tend to regard as incarnations of grace and beauty: the dragonflies. The name is apt; lovely as these insects are in their vivid metallic color and artistic flight, they are truly dragons. Fritz Kahn has vividly described them:

> Gigantic double wings are attached to an airplane frame which is light and elongated and serves as a rudder. The head is the cockpit, its protruding and rotatable eyes providing the pilot with a panorama of the surroundings such as no human flier enjoys. An apparatus which permits the pilot to see the world on all sides, as the dragonflies see it, remains to be invented. Below the eyes runs the slit of the mouth, a veritable gate of hell which snaps instantaneously and with its sharp jaws acts like an airborne guillotine. . . . This protoplasmic fighter plane is so gluttonous that it does not take the time, like an eagle, to fly home with its prey, but consumes it in flight. And if a new victim crosses the dragonfly's path, it drops the half-eaten cadaver and chases after the new prey. Without a doubt the dragonfly belongs among the most beautifully and technically perfected types in the animal kingdom. It is saddening, but in keeping with the ways of Nature, that in each class of animals the most finished types are also the most perfect killers.

For mysterious reasons these master fliers and master hunters have made their sex lives extraordinarily complicated. In mating they assume a bizarre and involved posture. The male seizes his partner with the claspers at the abdominal end of his body, while the female, doubling up, arches her abdomen forward so that her eighth abdominal segment touches one of the foremost abdominal segments of the male. The whole process looks more like an acrobatic stunt than sexual intercourse.

The reason for this becomes more understandable if we compare

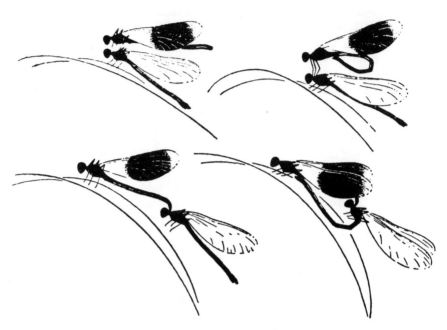

The acrobatic copulation of dragonflies.

the sexuality of dragonflies with that of crustaceans, spiders, and millipedes. These three groups of animals, as we know, employ gonopods —pseudo-copulatory organs. So do the dragonflies. Dragonflies are an ancient order among insects. Their ancestors—who were much like our present dragonflies, but could be as long as a man's arm—flitted about the horsetail forests of the Carboniferous Age some two hundred and fifty million years ago. At that time, perhaps, gonopods may have been employed by all arthropods. Gradually, most insects lost them; variations of them have survived only among the dragonflies and a few related orders.

The sexual apparatus of dragonflies is not quite the same as the gonopod of the crustaceans and millipedes and the maxillary palp of the spiders. Dragonflies have a bladderlike thickening at the second and third abdominal segment. This body zone contains a curious apparatus. It consists of a seminal vesicle and a semen transmitter. But the testes of the male dragonfly are in an altogether different spot— far back at the ventral side of the ninth abdominal ring, as is the case in ordinary insects. The dragonfly must therefore follow much the same procedure as the millipede who charges his gonopods and the spider who fills his maxillary palps with semen. He must double up his abdomen and bring it in contact with the third abdominal segment in order to discharge the sperm into the seminal vesicle.

In many cases this is done before the male has found and clasped the female; in other cases the charging of the seminal vesicles takes place only after the partners have joined. The mating itself, compared with the habits of other insects, is quite abnormal. The male darts after the female in flight and grasps her with his abdominal claspers so firmly by the prothorax that she can no longer free herself. But in this position the female's genital orifice, which is far back on the abdomen, cannot come into contact with the semen-filled copulatory organ of the male, since that is at the front of the body. That can only be accomplished by the acrobatics mentioned above—in which the female performs the active role. The female twists her abdomen until her genital orifice encounters the male's second abdominal segment. There the semen has meanwhile flowed from the vesicle into the intromittent organ, as it is called. As soon as the female's abdomen touches this organ, it straightens up like a penis and glides into the vagina. But that is by no means the end of intercourse. Thus joined together, the two dragonflies dart off in their ridiculous position to some suitable water plant. There the female protrudes her ovipositor and lays an egg in each of the stems. The female may proceed down the stem of a plant right to the bottom of the pond, dragging the male along with her. Diving dragonflies carry so much air in the hairs of their bodies that they can breathe under water for a short time. But not all male arthropods survive mating like the dragonfly.

CANNIBAL WEDDING

Scorpions seem to be very affectionate creatures. When they pair off, they apparently attain an intense and deep degree of infatuation. Jean Henri Fabre gave a lyrical description of couples crawling off hand in hand under a tile to prepare their wedding chamber: "The little forelegs flutter in feverish caresses. What are they saying to each other? How shall we translate their silent epithalamium into words?" Such tenderness, however, lasts only a few hours, until the mating is accomplished. Then, Fabre writes:

The idyl of the evening is followed, during the night, by a hideous tragedy. Next morning, we find the scorpioness under the potsherd of the previous day. The little male is by her side, but slain, and more

Scorpions at sex play. Photographs by Jean-Henri Fabre.

or less devoured. He lacks the head, a claw, a pair of legs. I place the corpse in the open, on the threshold of the home. All day long, the recluse does not touch it. When night returns, she goes out and, meeting the deceased on her passage, carries him off to a distance to give him a decent funeral, that is, to finish eating him.

In chapter after chapter of his *Souvenirs Entomologiques,* Fabre recounts such bloody nuptials. He reasoned that this cannibalism was an instinctive act which scarcely argued any special cruelty on the part of the female. "Each individual of a given species," a present-day zoologist, Wolfgang von Buddenbrock, states, "performs instinctive acts prescribed for the species; individual actions of the kind which in us are guided by reason do not exist."

The scorpion female, then, has to do her best to devour her husband after fertilization; she cannot escape this compulsion. However, the male has a fair chance to save his skin; whether or not the Agrippina accomplishes her murder depends upon his agility or lack of it.

This principle is clearly illustrated among the web spinners. We have already spoken of the danger facing the small male spider on his "love bridge" when the much bigger female approaches. Male spiders, however, have all sorts of stratagems to avoid being eaten. They wrap up the female before copulation; they put her into a kind of hypnotic sleep by their bites; and in addition they have a lively instinct for flight and will drop down on a rope of silk at the slightest threatening movement of the female. But the female's devouring instinct is often better than the male's instinct for self-preservation. In such cases the suitor becomes one more item in the lady spider's pantry.

The dilemma is simply solved by the wheel-web spiders, for example the *Argiope lobata.* In this species the puny male strains himself to such an extent in courtship and copulation that he is left utterly exhausted and breathes out his life immediately after the act. The *Argiope* female can scarcely be blamed for consuming her quietly deceased spouse for dessert. Fertilized carnivores are particularly hungry for protein and will not overlook anything that may serve them as food.

Philosophical entomologists attribute all cannibalism in spiders and insects to this protein hunger. After copulation the male has performed his function, has become superfluous and would die soon in any case. Why, then, should a prospective mother, whose body must produce vast quantities of eggs after fertilization, allow her former lover to go his way? The male can serve a dual purpose as inseminator and as supplementary food for the future offspring.

We need not decide whether this explanation covers all cases. For even among certain plant-eating insects the nuptials are followed by murder. "What shall we say," Fabre asks, "when the saddle grass-hopper, before laying her eggs, slits her mate open and eats as much of him as she can hold? And when the gentle cricket becomes a hyena and mercilessly pulls out the wings of her beloved, who performed so magnificent a serenade for her, smashes his harp, and shows her thanks by partially devouring him?"

Interestingly enough, the females of some species of grasshopper—whose males emit semen cartridges—refrain from eating the males after fertilization, but do eat the jellylike remains of these cartridges. Thus Fabre observed a female green grasshopper abruptly tearing loose the large tubule of semen that the male had deposited at the base of her ovipositor. She chewed it thoroughly, kneaded it, softened it, and finally swallowed it.

> At first I thought this banquet must be an individual aberration, so unusual and unprecedented did the insect's behavior appear to me. But observation taught me differently. Four times in succession I saw a female dragging the semen-filled wallet after her, and four times I observed her tear it off, work away at it for hours with her mandibles, and finally swallow it. This, then, is the rule. After the contents of the fertilizing vesicle have been employed for their purpose, the shell, which perhaps constitutes a powerful tonic and a wonderful delicacy, is chewed up and gulped down.

Perhaps the practice of eating such spermatophores gradually led to the devouring of the entire male. However, the eating of semen cartridges occurs rarely in the insect world, whereas nuptial canni-balism is found among a wide variety of insects besides the grass-hoppers and the spiders: among ground beetles, ant lions, and man-tises, for example. These are all predatory carnivores to whom the theory of protein hunger in the females might well apply.

Ant lions are fragile, large-winged, flying insects which somewhat resemble dragonflies. The larvae are more commonly seen than the mature insects, and their ferocity has earned the species its name. Ant lions build funnels in fine sand, and lurk at the bottom of these fun-nels with only their mandibles visible. They seize ants and other small insects which fall into the funnel. If the prey attempts to es-cape, the ant lion hurls loose sand at it so that it slips and slides back into the funnel. "This funnel," Konrad Guenther writes,

> is made with a mathematical precision which is a miracle of instinct. It is amazing to see how the larva, the moment it hatches from the egg, at once begins by alternately contracting and expanding its body to move around in a circle, so that its abdomen furrows the ground,

while the head throws the sand outward from the center. The circle is drawn tighter and tighter; and at last the funnel is finished, whereupon the larva buries itself at the apex with only its mandibles visible. The ability to dig the funnel is innate in the ant lion; it possesses that ability from the start and digs the funnel correctly the first time. If it had to practice for any length of time, it would starve to death before it caught its first prey. Moreover, there is no one from whom it might observe the art, or be taught. And all ant lions build essentially similar funnels.

The winged parents of these remarkable predatory larvae spend most of the day sitting motionless on the trunks of trees, their wings folded to form a roof over their heads. Only in the evening hours do they flutter uncertainly about through evergreen woods. Their bloodthirstiness appears only when they are in the grip of the sex drive. Various experiments have been conducted with them, all of which tend to show that both males and females can live peaceably with their own gender. But a fertilized female devours her husband; moreover, she will eat every other male she can catch.

Among ground beetles, which possess a good deal of economic value to man as devourers of caterpillars and other plant pests, the golden ground beetles are notorious nuptial cannibals. Fabre observed the mating of a pair and saw the female, as soon as this was over, launch an attack upon her partner:

A vain struggle to break away—that is all the male undertakes toward his salvation. Otherwise, he accepts his fate. Finally the skin bursts, the wound gapes wide, the inner substance is devoured by his worthy spouse. Her head burrowing inside the body of her husband, she hollows out his back. A shudder that runs through the poor fellow's limbs announces his approaching end. The female butcher ignores this; she gropes into the narrowest passages and windings in the thoracic cavity. Soon only the well-known little boat of the wing sheaths and the thorax with legs attached are left of the dead male. The husk, sucked dry, is abandoned.

Homo sapiens, with his notions of propriety, finds this horrible. But all examples of nuptial cannibalism are surpassed by the habits of the mantises, those "terrible predatory machines," as Fabre calls them. There are almost two thousand species of these strangely sinister creatures, their habitat ranging from the temperate zone to the tropics. They are often remarkably camouflaged in color and shape, are always lying in wait for prey, their forelimbs raised in that peculiar attitude of apparent prayer which has given them their name.

Those arms are in reality fearful weapons, at once traps, knives, harpoons, and saws. When they close on some unfortunate insect, the victim is hopelessly caught as if between the blade and sheath of a penknife that has snapped shut.

Among some Asian and African species the forelimbs astonishingly resemble the bright petal of flowers. An African traveler has described one such "devil's flower," as he called it.

> The limbs were spread wide apart, and head and thorax were directed downward, as if they were the stem of the flower. The delicately colored, lightly veined wings were unfolded slightly above the upward-slanting abdomen. In this position the insect, at the least approach, began moving abdomen and wings back and forth, obviously with the intention of presenting the appearance of a blossom shaken by the wind.

If a butterfly is so incautious as to visit this seeming flower, it is seized in a merciless grip and devoured alive.

Praying mantises bear a superficial resemblance to grasshoppers; but their large egg packets, which look like puff paste, indicate that they are more closely related to the cockroaches.

The way these uncanny organisms can prey upon even powerful creatures was witnessed by the zoological writer Rudolf Mell in Southeast Asia. One day he heard in his room the anguished cry of a frog. He investigated and discovered a praying mantis which had gripped an unfortunate frog in its arms and was beginning to eat it.

> It had already eaten a hole a good ten millimeters long and two millimeters deep. The blood was running down the frog's hind legs and dripping off its toes. The diabolic insect was not in the least disturbed by our presence; it merely glared out of its wicked wooden eyes at the lamp and went on eating. Yet the frog was by no means so small—its body perhaps fifty millimeters long, and its hind legs considerably longer. The praying mantis may have been some ninety millimeters long, but it was so thin that I would have dismissed as a ridiculous zoologist's fairy tale the idea that it could ever capture a frog, had I not seen it for myself.

Mantises of similar size are said to kill lizards and even birds.

It is scarcely surprising that these killers do not treat their males very tenderly. Almost all mantises devour their husbands after the nuptials. (In the terrarium, the mating of praying mantises can only take place if the female's terrible forelimbs are tied before she is introduced to the male. Otherwise the lady consumes the gentleman at his first tentative approach.) This insect's ravenous appetite is ac-

The cannibalistic nuptials of the praying mantis. The female throws her deadly arms around the smaller male.

After the meal—the remains of the male are on the left.

companied with an extraordinary hunger for love. Fabre observed
this when he brought more males to an already fertilized female:

> The Mantis, in many cases, is never sated with conjugal raptures
> and banquets. After a rest that varies in length, whether the eggs be
> laid or not, a second male is accepted and then devoured like the first.
> A third succeeds him, performs his function in life, is eaten and dis-
> appears. A fourth undergoes a like fate. In the course of two weeks I
> thus see one and the same Mantis use up seven males. She takes them
> all to her bosom and makes them all pay for the nuptial ecstasy with
> their lives.

This female bluebeard is reminiscent of certain semilegendary
queens who—if we may believe the ancient tales—would have their
favorites beheaded, hanged, or drowned after a night of love. But the
praying mantises go one step further: they sometimes do away with
their lovers during the act itself. Again Fabre is a reliable observer:

> I find, by themselves, a horrible couple engaged as follows. The male,
> absorbed in the performance of his vital functions, holds the female
> in a tight embrace. But the wretch has no head; he has no neck; he
> has hardly a body. The other, with her muzzle turned over her shoul-
> der, continues very placidly to gnaw what remains of the gentle
> swain. And, all the time, that masculine stump, holding on firmly,
> goes on with the business!
>   Love is stronger than death, men say. Taken literally, the aphorism
> has never received a more brilliant confirmation. A headless creature,
> an insect amputated down to the middle of the chest, a very corpse,
> persists in endeavoring to give life. It will not let go until the abdo-
> men, the seat of the procreative organs, is attacked.

Even such a seasoned entomologist as Fabre admitted to being
shocked by the mantis's behavior. "I have seen it done with my own
eyes and have not yet recovered from my astonishment."

NURSERY CARE

A beetle—the tumblebug or sacred scarab—is frequently depicted
on the monuments and temples of ancient Egypt. Stone scarabs were
placed on the chests of the dead; seals in the shape of scarabs were
given as presents; scarabs were set into rings, were employed as amulets—all with the aim of winning the sun god's favor. The cult of the

scarab was imitated by the inhabitants of Asia Minor and by the Greeks and Romans. Roman legionaries wore scarabs carved from stone on a string around their necks, as protection against wounds and death. To this day tourists in the land of the pyramids are offered scarabs as souvenirs. Most of these, of course, are modern forgeries.

Egyptologists have wondered why this particular inconspicuous black dung beetle should have played so important a part in the religious life of the Land of the Nile. The Egyptians, one explanation runs, considered it the symbol of the sun-god and identified the six projections on the scarab's head, which the beetle uses for preparing its balls of dung, with the rays of the sun. In any case, they believed that the tumblebug rolled its dung pills across the whole earth from sunrise to sunset, just as the god Ra rolled the star of day across the heavens in the same span of time.

The Egyptians considered the scarab a primeval creature born directly from the fertile, life-giving Nile mud. But why did this beetle form a ball the size of a marble out of dung and roll it busily, undaunted by obstacles, to some place it considered suitable for its purposes? The Egyptians gave deep thought to this question. They saw that the beetle finally buried its pill in a hole in the ground, and decided that the ball of dung had to lie in the darkness underground for twenty-nine days. But on the thirtieth day the scarab would exhume it and throw it into the Nile. There a new beetle would develop inside it, and after a time rise up out of the waters. Thus the Egyptians connected the pill—though in a vague and mythical fashion—with the propagation of *Scarabaeus sacer*.

Later observers approached the matter somewhat more realistically. They decided that every pill contained an egg, and was not thrown into the Nile, but left in its hole. The larva of the scarab then grew up in this cradle of dung and fed on the little sphere. It remained for Fabre to cast doubt on this theory. First he noticed that the scarabs he studied would often eat their own dung ball in the shelter of the hole. Consequently, it seemed unlikely that such pills contained any eggs. Moreover, he pointed out that rolling the balls over rough ground would probably damage any eggs. "How could the tumblebug's egg, so frail and sensitive under its thin shell, withstand such shocks in its rolling cradle? The spark of life which slumbers in the germ can be extinguished by the slightest touch. Why then would the parents have hit upon the notion of dragging it over hill and dale for hours and days? No. the matter makes no sense."

What really takes place can be seen from the conduct of thousands of other species of dung beetles. These beetles not only live on dung but also shape it into pear-shaped or cylindrical brood pills which

Sacred scarabs rolling dung balls. The Egyptians believed this beetle rolled its pill across the earth from sunrise to sunset just as the god of day rolled the sun in the same space of time. Actually, the pill is a cradle for an egg.

they bury in shafts deep underground. In each of these they lay an egg. The sacred scarab does the same thing. After a couple has bedded the ball of dung in the underground chamber, both work to shape it into a pearlike receptacle for the female's egg. Among some Indian dung beetles which make spherical brood pills, a coating of earth is deposited around these "cradles." As they dry out, the pills can become hard as stone. When they are uncovered during digging operations, people often do not recognize them for what they are. In older accounts they are sometimes referred to as stone balls made by the ancient natives of the region.

Because of the scarab's excellent provision for its young, most scarab larvae develop into complete beetles. And what applies to dung beetles applies to innumerable other arthropods. All the subtle courtship and nuptial ceremonies of crustaceans, spiders, millipedes, and insects would not serve their purpose if the parents did not take certain steps to assure that their offspring grow under the best possible conditions. The habits, precautions, and arrangements developed by these arthropods are so varied that the study of them has become a branch of science in itself.

Among the crustaceans, most are not in their final form when they hatch out of the egg. They must pass through one or even several larval stages. Hosts of crustacean larvae swarm in the sea or in fresh water; they require no especial care. Some large crustaceans, however, such as the lobster, the river crab, and the common crab, take steps to protect their eggs from the thousands of mischances which may befall before the larvae hatch out. They carry their "clutch" in a large ball attached to their swimming feet until the larvae hatch. The locust shrimp or sea mantis has predatory claws which give it a certain resemblance to the praying mantis of dry land. However, these sea creatures carry their eggs in front of them in their stomato-pods (mouth-feet).

Among the isopods, the eggs develop in a brood chamber on or in the female's body. Sometimes the entire female becomes a single brood sac, as in the case of *Danalia*, but most isopods carry the egg sac under the thorax. To the wood louse and other terrestrial isopods, this arrangement is particularly important because their larvae must grow up in water, like all crustaceans. Thus the brood chamber of the terrestrial isopods becomes a veritable aquarium in which the young swim happily about until they are able to lead the lives of adults.

Many female spiders likewise assume the care of large egg clumps. Anyone strolling in the woods or fields in the spring can see large wolf spiders bearing white or colored egg cocoons under their abdo-mens. Somewhat later the hatched young may be seen clinging in a dense throng to the mother and being taken for walks. The European water spider has a particularly appealing family life. The male of this species is in no way threatened by the female. After their nup-tials, the spider pair cooperate in spinning under water an airtight web consisting of two linked diving bells. The eggs are suspended from the roof of this underwater apartment, and the young spiders are tended by both parents.

Scorpions have no need of guarding their eggs since the young hatch out immediately after the eggs are laid. The infant scorpions at once clamber onto their mother and live on her back until the next molt. This spectacle delighted Fabre:

A black scorpion female carrying her offspring on her back.

They climb, first one and then the other, on the mother's back, hoisting themselves, without excessive haste, along the claws, which the scorpion holds flat on the ground in order to facilitate the ascent. Close packed one against the other, entangled at random, they form a continuous sheet upon her back. With the aid of their little claws, they settle themselves pretty firmly. I find some difficulty in sweeping them away with the point of a camelhair pencil without more or less hurting the feeble creatures. If I threaten the family too closely with a straw, the mother at once lifts her two claws in an angry attitude, rarely adopted in her own defense.

Should a scorpion's offspring be brushed off her back, she begins hunting for them, reestablishes contact with them, and again lets them climb onto her back. According to the observations of Fabre and other entomologists, "the offspring of others are as readily admitted as her own. One would say that she adopts them. . . . We have observed the same dark instinct in the tarantula, which is incapable of distinguishing her own children from those of others and will collect all those that are swarming around her feet."

The females of the scolopendra and other millipedes roll up around their eggs like giant snakes and hold them in a firm grip with the legs of the trunk. While incubating the eggs they take no nourishment and fall into an apathy from which they awaken only after the passing of several weeks, when the delicate whitish young appear. Earwigs guard their clutch in a small chamber in the ground; they lick and clean the eggs, eat those that have turned rotten, and at the least disturbance hurriedly carry their offspring in their mouths to some other place. Among most species of earwigs the females tend their young until the little ones are half grown. An earwig family presents a picture closely resembling that of the scorpion female and her young. All the offspring are gathered closely around the mother, often climbing onto her, and in case of danger the female spreads her nippers to defend them.

Such family idyls occur rarely among other brood-tending insects. Only a few of the solitary species of wasps and bees keep track of their larvae after they have hatched. The females of such wasps carry caterpillars into the nests. The females of the bee *Allodape* bring honey, and feed the larvae as a bird feeds its fledglings. In all probability the highly organized social insects developed gradually out of such brood-caring families. But the majority of insects have no traffic with their hatched young, having made provision for the next generation by other devices. The eggs may be laid in safe places or—as in the case of the scarab—deposited upon or within the necessary specific food. There is a whole gamut of variations, from the June bugs and grasshoppers which simply lay their eggs in the ground, to the flies which deposit their eggs in decaying meat, cheese, fruit, sewage, and even open wounds.

The caterpillars of butterflies are plant eaters. Virtually every species requires a specific type of plant for its food, and dies if it cannot obtain it. The butterfly female must therefore literally sense where it may lay its eggs and where not. It seems to orient itself not only by smell, but also by the color of plants. Several senses cooperate to avert a fatal error.

A number of insect larvae that live on plants grow up in galls. Galls are tumorous formations on leaves or roots; they used to be regarded as fruitlike formations or as boils caused by disease, until the seventeenth century Italian anatomist Marcello Malpighi demonstrated that they were caused by egg-laying female insects. The insect lays its egg in the plant tissues. A growth results from the irritation of the foreign body in the tissues. And in this boil-shaped brood chamber the larva grows. Gallflies, gall gnats, and gall lice are among these parasites. Man has no special liking for this family; the exception is the dyer's gallfly of Asia Minor and Syria, which used to be highly esteemed for the economic value of its galls, from which ink was once made.

Even more troublesome to man are those weevils which use apples and other fruits as brood chambers. The fruit lover who bites into a wormy apple is scarcely pleased to learn that the fruit has served as cradle for a weevil. And the forester curses those bark beetles which dig brood passages into standing timber; the larvae are capable of riddling whole forests. Other weevils nibble the leaves of certain trees, roll them skillfully into a funnel, conceal their eggs in them, and seal up the nursery with a sticky excretion from their bodies.

But when an oak-leaf weevil has laboriously carved a leaf into exact geometrical proportions, has rolled it up and deposited its eggs inside, there is no saying that the offspring will go unmolested. There are cuckoos among the insects too, who lay their eggs in a foreign nest. The cuckoo weevil approaches the funnel, bores a hole into it, and smuggles its own egg inside. And just as there are cuckoo beetles, so there are also cuckoo bees and wasps. The cuckoo bees wait cunningly until the females of solitary bees have built their brood cell, laid an egg, and filled the cell with nourishment for the future larva. Then they deposit their own egg in the cell. Their larvae grow so swiftly that—just like the offspring of the cuckoo bird—they crowd the rightful owner out of the brood chamber, condemning it to death by starvation. The cuckoo bumblebees are not so ruthless. Their fertilized females attach themselves to a bumblebee colony, live in it peacefully, and install their own eggs in some of the brood cells. The colony does not mind, and raises the young cuckoos along with its own offspring.

The methods of the ichneumon flies in laying their eggs and providing for their young form a chapter in itself. A bewildering variety of species of these insects, which from the human point of view are extremely useful, occupy all possible habitats. The females are perpetually seeking victims into which they can drive their swordlike ovipositors and deposit the eggs. The larvae of most species are carnivorous, feeding on the flesh of living insect larvae or spiders. Consequently the mother must inject her eggs into an animal of a particular sort. As soon as they have hatched, the larvae begin eating their involuntary host from within. With unfailing instinct they spare the vital organs, consuming the insect's fat and other nonvital parts, for the host must remain alive until the young ichneumons can set out into the world. By then the body of their host has been almost completely hollowed out, and collapses like a tube from which the air has been emptied.

Caterpillars and butterflies are generally considered to be the principal victims of this sort of parasitism. But the ichneumon fly also bores into countless other types of arthropods. It drives its ovipositor through hard wood in order to find the larvae of capricorn beetles and wood wasps which have burrowed passages in tree trunks. It dives into the water to attack the larvae of caddis flies at the bottom of ponds and ditches. It infects fly maggots and aphids and even battens on the larvae of larger ichneumons which in turn are living in other hosts. Each species has its specific host. And the tricks by which they outwit their victims seem as uncanny as the sly eating habits of the larvae who take care that their hosts do not die prematurely.

Sometimes a female gripped by the compelling necessity to lay her eggs will choose a rather dangerous victim. One investigator of ichneumons observed a fly which had fallen into a spider's web and with difficulty liberated itself. But to the scientist's surprise the ichneumon promptly flew at the web again, and was furiously attacked by the spider. Habermehl recounts:

> Looking closer, I discovered the eggs of the spider in a loosely woven cocoon. Evidently the ichneumon had been determined to get at these. A highly dramatic struggle now ensued between the spider, defending its eggs, and the ichneumon, impelled by the necessity to lay its own. Again and again the spider attempted to drive its poisonous falces into the fly and to ensnare it by tangling it in silk, while the fly stabbed at the spider with its sting and repeatedly freed itself from the threads of silk. Finally the spider appeared exhausted. It with-

drew to the edge of a leaf, while the ichneumon darted to the cocoon and drove its ovipositor several times into the spider's eggs.

Equally strenuous labors, though of a completely different sort, are undertaken by those carrion beetles which are known as burying beetles because of their special methods of providing for their broods. When they find a dead animal of suitable size, a mouse or a lizard, for example, they gather in large numbers around the cadaver and by great effort bury it in the ground. Fabre, who considered the burying beetle one of the most intelligent of insects, has given a precise description of such a burial:

> The carcass oscillates, while a cushion of sand, pushed out from below, grows up all around it. The mole, by reason of his own weight and the efforts of the grave diggers, who are laboring at their task underneath, gradually sinks, for lack of support, into the undermined soil. Presently the sand which has been pushed out quivers under the thrust of invisible miners, slips into the pit and covers the interred mole. It is a clandestine burial. The body seems to disappear of itself, as though engulfed by a fluid medium.

The burying beetle performs this sanitary mission for the same reason that the dung beetle buries balls of dung. If the burial spot is dug up after a while, the cadaver will be found changed into a pitch-like mush, swarming with the larvae of burying beetles. The larvae grow with extraordinary rapidity, for they must complete their development before the natural decay of the corpse removes their supply of food.

In 1933 the entomologist E. Pukowski discovered that these larvae can complete their metamorphosis into beetles only if they receive additional feeding from the mothers. Therefore the females prepare the cadaver in a curious manner by digging a crater in it and mixing the rotting flesh with their gastric juices. In this way the carrion is more or less predigested. But then, Pukowski tells us,

> the observer is presented with a surprising sight. As soon as the female approaches the crater, all the larvae raise the front of their bodies bolt upright, so that their legs snatch at the air. The beetle comes to a halt directly above the brood and with a throbbing motion of its forelegs beats on the carrion or sometimes on the larvae which gather around its head. Next, the female opens its mouth wide, and a larva quickly places its head between her mandibles. Perhaps the observer will see a tiny dop of brown fluid passing from the mother's mouth to the larva's. . . . The larvae beg with extreme insistence and follow the female on brief journeys over the carcass. They do this

with great agility, for they evidently can react at once to changes in the direction of the female's motion.

The male beetles, too, sometimes share in this feeding.

In sharp contrast to the useful sanitary activities and tender care of the young practiced by carrion beetles is the behavior of sand fleas. There are a number of such creatures who have the nasty habit of laying their eggs in the flesh of living vertebrates up to and including man. The fertilized females will bore into the facial parts of monkeys, dogs, sheep, and pigs, and, in the tropics, under the toenails of barefoot humans. There is a pretty copper-colored fly named *Lucilia silvarum* which preys upon the nostrils of unsuspecting toads and frogs. The unfortunate amphibians feel no pain when the fly lays its eggs, for it has been stung with a "tranquilizer." But when the larvae hatch out, the poor hosts go blind and are eaten alive.

The supreme practitioners of these cunning narcotic arts are the digger wasps, whose fascinating habits led Jean Henri Fabre to entomology. Digger wasps establish their brood passages in the ground or in dry wood. Before laying their eggs they fill the chamber in which the larvae are to grow with insects or spiders whom they have paralyzed by stinging the nerve centers. The venom they inject into their victims works in a manner similar to that of curare, the poison with which some South American Indians tip their arrows. It anesthetizes the skeletal muscles but permits the heart to continue beating.

A sand wasp attacks a caterpillar, paralyzing it with a well-aimed series of stings.

These wasps, endowed by instinct with knowledge comparable to that of an anatomy professor, may strike us as savage and murderous. They seem to belong among the most terrible predators in the insect world. But in reality the adults feed harmlessly on nectar or plants. They seek out their prey solely to feed their young—whom they will never see. For after they have dragged the paralyzed victims to their burrows, laid their eggs, and carefully closed up the entrances to the burrow, they fly away and leave their offspring to fate. The instinctive actions have been carried out automatically; afterwards the wasp is indifferent to the results of its work.

Every group of killer wasps has its own particular prey: beetles, bumblebees, honeybees, grasshoppers. Sand wasps drag caterpillars to their burrows; spider wasps are interested only in spiders. Fabre substituted a grasshopper which had been paralyzed by the sting of a grasshopper wasp for the June-bug larva which a scolia had stored as living provender. The larva of the scolia tried to eat its way into the alien feed, but after a few days the grasshopper had decayed and the larva were dead. This intense specialization among hunting wasps led Fabre at one time to doubt the theory of evolution. If there had been a common ancestor, he argued, whose larvae were once omnivorous, present-day wasp larvae should also be "unprejudiced eaters." For why should a once omnivorous animal restrict itself in such a way as to endanger its survival?

There are large spider wasps in tropical Asia and America which can overpower the mighty bird spiders and carry them off to their burrows. Konrad Guenther witnessed this in Brazil:

A bird spider sits in its upholstered tube, extends its legs and waits bloodthirstily for prey. Suddenly it sees something that fills it with consternation and it frantically retreats into the tube. The hunting wasp does not venture in, for there the spider would have the advantage. Instead, it restively flies back and forth in front of the tube; inside, the spider likewise darts back and forth and becomes more and more agitated. An unfortunate movement, and one of her legs emerges from the opening of the tube. The wasp instantly sees its chance; it savagely grips the legs and pulls the spider out. The spider, striking out in all directions, falls to the ground. The wasp is upon her at once, and drives its sting into her abdomen from behind. . . . Paralyzed, the bird spider collapses. Next comes the toilsome task of dragging the large creature to the nest.

To us there is something intrinsically moving about the way various animals will go to great pains to construct a nest in which their young can be shielded from the perils of the outside world. The egg

cocoons of spiders and the brood chambers of dung beetles and hunting wasps are really such nests. A highly artistic floating nest is built
by a certain water beetle. It makes use of a leaf drifting on the surface
of the water, and fastens to the underside of this leaf a saclike cocoon
which is provided with a chimney to admit air. Here the eggs are laid.
The Danish zoologist C. Wesenberg-Lund writes,

> When the larvae hatch, the cocoon serves as a splendid nursery—
> not especially roomy, but comfortable. Like the witch's gingerbread
> house it has the merit of being edible. The larvae eat the fine silk that
> surrounded them as eggs; even the walls are gnawed. They begin to
> creep out of their enclosure only when it has been reduced to the
> thinnest of shells. . . . The gray larvae clamber up and down the
> chimney, sun themselves on the roof of the cocoon, or bask on algae
> just outside their door. At evening or when danger threatens they slip
> inside. They spend several days in such a relaxed atmosphere before
> they leave their childhood home forever.

The architectural arts of insects reach their height in the nest-
building of two fundamentally different groups of insects: the hymenoptera—including ants, bees, wasps, and ichneumon flies—and the
termites. Together they exemplify, stage by stage, the gradual evolution of the individual nest into the populous colony. Individualists,
such as the wall wasp and the pill wasp, or the sand, mason, and leaf-
cutting bees, build handsome brood cells out of the most miscellaneous
materials. These cells are artfully constructed and lined. Mud, mas-
ticated wood, moss, leaves, flower petals, and wax may be employed
as building materials. The nests are placed in the ground, in hollow
trees, in bushes, in rotting wood, on embankments and walls, even in
empty snail shells. Fabre describes the simplest form of a hymenop-
ter's nest, that of the mason bee:

> After the mason bee has selected a stone, she brings a lump of mud
> in her mandibles to it and spreads a ring-shaped blob over the surface.
> The forefeet and mandibles are the mason's principal tools; with these
> she works the material, which is kept pliable by saliva. To reinforce
> the layer of mud, the bee adds sharp bits of gravel the size of a lentil
> to the soft mass—one bit after the other, but only on the exterior. This
> is the foundation of the building. Other layers follow the first until
> the cell has reached the desired height of an inch or so.

The wasps invented the mathematically precise hexagonal honeycomb. The bumblebees discovered that wax could be used for lining
the cell and that a mixture of honey and pollen, so-called "beebread,"
provided ideal nourishment for the larvae. Wasp and bumblebee fe-

males do not leave their nest after they have completed it and laid their eggs; they guard and care for the young. And the offspring also remain in the structure, enlarging it and contributing their services to the founder of the colony. Thus, from the solitary female's care of her brood, there arose the colony with its complicated division of labor, while the single brood cell developed into a hive.

Wasp and bumblebee colonies have to be founded anew each year by a fertilized female. Honeybees and ants, however, live in permanent colonies whose populations are constantly increasing. These insects have developed care for the offspring to a perfection we encounter on our planet only in two other social animals—the termites and man.

NATIONALIZED SEX LIFE

One morning the long-expected word of command goes through the hive, and the peaceful workers turn into judges and executioners. Whence this word issues, we know not; it would seem to emanate suddenly from the cold, deliberate indignation of the workers, and no sooner has it been uttered than every heart throbs with it, inspired with the spirit of the unanimous republic. One part of the people renounce their foraging duties to devote themselves to the work of justice.

This is how Maurice Maeterlinck begins his description of the massacre of the drones in his book *The Life of the Bee*. Of course Maeterlinck's approach to nature is outrageously sentimental and anthropomorphizing: the Belgian poet was a true child of his time in this respect. His three nature books—on the life of the bees, the ants, and the termites—have never been taken very seriously as scientific documents. But they were sincere efforts to tell a wide public about the extraordinary life patterns of the social insects.

The "work of justice" of which he writes is to be executed upon "the great idle drones, asleep in oblivious groups on the melliferous walls." The bees, too, end their weddings with a blood bath. But the slaughter is accomplished not by the queen herself, but by "an army of wrathful virgins," the sterile worker bees. Maeterlinck described the drama as follows:

Each one is assailed by three or four envoys of justice; and these vigorously proceed to cut off his wings, saw through the petiole that

connects the abdomen with the thorax, amputate the feverish antennae, and seek an opening between the rings of his cuirass through
which to pass their sword. No defense is attempted by the enormous,
but unarmed, creatures; they try to escape, or oppose their mere bulk
to the blows that rain down upon them. Forced on to their back,
with their relentless enemies clinging doggedly to them, they will
use their powerful claws to shift them from side to side; or, turning
on themselves, they will drag the whole group round and round in
wild circles, which exhaustion soon brings to an end. And, in a very
brief space, their appearance becomes so deplorable that pity, never
far from justice in the depths of our heart, quickly returns, and would
seek forgiveness, though vainly, of the stern workers who recognize
only nature's harsh and profound laws. The wings of the wretched
creatures are torn, their antennae bitten, the segments of their legs
wrenched off; and their magnificent eyes, mirrors once of the exuber-
ant flowers, flashing back the blue light and the innocent pride of
summer, now, softened by suffering, reflect only the anguish and dis-
tress of their end. Some succumb to their wounds, and are at once
borne away to distant cemeteries by two or three of their executioners.
Others, whose injuries are less, succeed in sheltering themselves in
some corner, where they lie, all huddled together, surrounded by an
inexorable guard, until they perish of want. Many will reach the
door, and escape into space dragging their adversaries with them; but,
toward evening, impelled by hunger and cold, they return in crowds
to the entrance of the hive to beg for shelter. But there they encounter
another pitiless guard. The next morning, before setting forth on
their journey, the workers will clear the threshold, strewn with the
corpses of the useless giants; and all recollection of the idle race disappears till the following spring.

These male bees who are put to death after having fulfilled their
function were engendered by parthenogenesis. Thus they had no father, but only a mother, like the plant lice and water fleas whose virgin birth had given Dutchmen of the era of Leeuwenhoek so much to
ponder about. But parthenogenesis among honeybees is a far more
remarkable phenomenon than it is among plant lice. The mated
queen bee can lay either fertilized or unfertilized eggs. From the fertilized eggs, females develop, either queens or sterile workers; the unfertilized hatch into drones. Until 1848 beekeepers had no suspicion
of this fact; they only wondered or were vexed when certain queens
fell into what is called "drone broodiness."

A queen becomes drone broody when she produces only drones.
Such queens are useless; the hive perishes from lack of female progeny. Pastor Johann Dzierzon of the Silesian town of Karlsmarkt however, was not satisfied with this simple observation. Around 1835 he

started a large bee colony, developed novel hives with removable combs, and promoted beekeeping with great energy. And since he was a keen observer he noticed that drone broodiness occurred only in certain queens, those who were too old or too infirm to undertake the nuptial flight. As an experienced beekeeper Dzierzon of course knew that the queen flies out with the males on the nuptial flight and is mated by one of the drones.

A queen, Dzierzon reasoned, becomes drone broody if for some reason she has not mated. She goes on laying eggs, but these eggs must be unfertilized. In order to confirm this theory by experiment, Pastor Dzierzon prevented several young queens from undertaking the nuptial flight. The result was as he expected: their eggs produced only males. He then examined the sexual organs of the queens more closely. Scientists had long since discovered the semen receptacle in

Queen bee surrounded by drones (a white spot has been placed on the queen for identification purposes). During the nuptial flight, the queen is impregnated by only one drone, who deposits millions of sperm in a pouch in her body. She returns to the hive, where for the rest of her life—usually several years—she lays fertilized eggs (which develop into sterile workers or queens) and unfertilized ones (which develop into fertile drones).

which the queen bee keeps the sperm she has received at mating. Entomologists and beekeepers, moreover, already suspected that the bee's eggs were fertilized only as they were laid, by passing the semen receptacle. Johann Dzierzon removed the semen receptacle from a fertilized queen. Holding it up to the light, he could distinctly see the milky sperm inside. But the receptacle of a drone-broody queen did not contain this milky fluid. Evidently, male sperm was unnecessary for the production of drones.

This discovery did the scientific-minded pastor little good. He ran into the same difficulties as had Sprengel: ecclesiastical superiors took offense at his dangerous revelations about sexuality in bees, and in 1869 he was dismissed. Other naturalists, however, confirmed his findings. As Bölsche puts it: "The queen has free control over the fertilization of her eggs. If she does not want to (i.e., if a certain definite instinct of her protests). she does not fertilize certain eggs in particularly large nurseries of the hive, and out of these unfertilized eggs every time, according to iron law, come genuine sexually potent drones, males."

Present-day geneticists have discovered a further curious detail about the process. Since the drones come from unfertilized eggs, they possess only a single set of chromosomes. If their germ cells divided before the spermatozoon matured as is characteristic everywhere in the animal kingdom, the sperm would contain only half the proper number of chromosomes. This would involve a reduction in the hereditary characteristics which would no doubt be fatal. Now as it happens two maturation divisions can be observed in the germ cells of drones; but this process, after the extrusion of certain inessential plasma particles, is reversed. The sex cells of other animals which reproduce parthenogenetically likewise do not halve the number of their chromosomes, but retain them all.

It is not only the queen bee who governs the sex of her offspring. The worker bees accomplish a similar feat. In emergencies they can raise a new queen. If no young queen is available when the old one swarms, taking with her a large part of the workers to form a new hive, remaining bees feed special food to worker-bee larvae in order to convert them into fertile females. This food, known as royal jelly. is secreted by special glands in the workers. Its high hormone content can make female larvae grow to sexual maturity instead of remaining sterile workers. A fad for this royal jelly started not long ago among certain members of the human species and aging ladies hope that this wonderful substance will give them back their youth and strength. It remains to be demonstrated whether royal jelly has these miraculous properties.

The colonies of social insects are, as one naturalist described it in rather high-flown words, "republics of love" which have put into effect a "nationalization of sexual relations." The queen's sole task is to be mated and to lay eggs. The males' sole purpose in life is the nuptial flight. The majority of the population consists of sexually atrophied, sterile workers who function as builders, food gatherers, and nurses. Colonies of ants and termites will include, in addition to these sterile workers, another class, the "soldiers," large-headed defenders whose reproductive organs likewise remain undeveloped.

Among bees and ants, these republics of love are Amazon states in which the males' role is severely limited. The workers and soldiers are all females. The whole apparatus of their states serves only the one purpose: producing progeny, caring for them, and sending them out to found new states. The honey-gathering and comb-building of the bees, the raiding expeditions, gardening, leaf weaving and slaveholding of the ants all serve that single aim. The sterile working females dominate the life of the state, and therefore control the egg-laying queens as well, these being condemned to a harem existence. In these nations of nurses, the individual counts for nothing.

An imaginative naturalist may choose to dramatize certain similarities between the social life of insects and that of men. Yet in reality such parallels are nothing but chance convergences that spring from the nature of social life. As the entomologist Karl Escherich cautioned half a century ago:

> It would be foolish to try to establish any causal connections among the common features which are presented by the social life of termites or ants and those of men. It would be utterly absurd to doubt for as much as a moment that such resemblances among men, ants, and termites are any more than simple analogies—even though these analogies may owe their origin to universal social laws still undiscovered.

Maeterlinck was tempted to attribute certain personal sensations to the bee queen, at least while she was laying her eggs. For in this act the egg passes the semen receptacle and is fertilized if a female is to develop from it. Possibly—so Maeterlinck thought—there is a pleasurable element in that process:

> It is not impossible that this slave-mother, whom we are inclined to pity, may be indeed a great amorist, a great voluptuary, deriving a certain enjoyment, an aftertaste, as it were, of her one marriage flight, from the union of the male and female principle that thus comes to pass in her being. Here again nature, never so ingenious, so cunningly prudent and diverse, as when contriving her snares of love,

will not have failed to provide a certain pleasure as a bait in the interest of the species.

Today professional naturalists do not permit themselves such speculations. Yet the social insects continue to intrigue investigators by the complexity of their life patterns. As one of the outstanding experts on bees in our time, Karl von Frisch, writes:

> Every attentive beekeeper comes to realize that bees must have some kind of communication. He will observe that a pot of honey can often stand out in the open unnoticed for days. But if only a single bee discovers it, within the briefest time dozens and hundreds of her hivemates will fly to the spot to gather this supply. They must have told their tale back home!

In the course of numerous experiments, von Frisch discovered the manner in which bees communicate. They perform dances of certain patterns, a sign language which conveys to their hivemates the exact direction of their find and its distance from the hive.

Bee language, then, is used to inform the others of the whereabouts of food. Innumerable other instinctive acts of the social insects serve to provide comprehensive and complicated care of the brood. Leaf-cutting ants bite off bits of leaves, carry them into their nests, chew them to spongy cakes, and use this medium for raising certain fungi on which they and their brood feed. Slave-holding ants steal pupae from other ant nests; the worker ants which develop out of these pupae are expected to care for the eggs and larvae of their masters. Many slave-holders, in fact, are incapable of feeding themselves; they must be nourished by their slaves.

The weaver ants of Ceylon inhabit extraordinary nests located at the tops of trees. These are made, as Karl von Frisch tells us,

> of leaves woven together. How this was accomplished was a great puzzle, since ants have no spinning glands. Only their larvae possess such glands, by which they make themselves their cocoons for pupating. But the larvae lie in their chambers, helpless little worms, and cannot crawl around among the leaves to serve as builders. The answer to the mystery seems utterly fantastic, but reliable naturalists have seen it with their own eyes. When these investigators made a tear in a nest, a procession of ants soon marched up to the disturbing rent and drew its edges together. Then, from the depths of the nest, other ants clambered up, grown larvae held in their mandibles. Apparently by pressure they forced the larvae to produce their thread. They directed the heads of the larvae first to one side, then to the

other side of the crack, and spun a silken fabric by using the larvae not only as living distaffs but also as shuttles.

Wonderful instincts, admirable orderliness, extreme ingenuity and at the same time an impoverishment of the individual, total subordination of sexuality to the community—that is the setup in the colonies of the bees, social wasps, and ants.

THE LOVE FACTORY OF THE TERMITES

The termite societies are even more totalitarian than those of the bees, social wasps, and ants. They seem to be the most elaborate of animal social forms.

A gentleman from Livonia named J. G. König, a great insect collector who spent many years in India, is regarded as the pioneer of termite study. In 1779 he published an account of the "white ants" of the district of Madras. Previously, virtually nothing had been known of these creatures. They were regarded, according to the whim of the naturalist, as relatives of the ants, the lice, or the ephemeral flies; they were execrated as harmful vermin; and people on tropical plantations did all they could to destroy the huge mounds built by the mysterious insects.

Two years after König's account was published, the African traveler Henry Smeathman dispatched a subsequently famous letter to the Royal Society in which he described the amazing social life of the "white ants." But entomologists were inclined to smile at his enthusiasm. Also, the wonders of the termitary were overshadowed for a long time by the astonishing facts that were being discovered about the life of ants and bees. Another reason for the lack of interest in the termites was that, as Karl Escherich has written in his survey of the history of termite research, "studying termites was a far more difficult undertaking than studying ants, if only because the researches had to be conducted chiefly in tropical countries. Then, too, it is much more difficult to get at termites in their huge, solid citadels, than at ants."

Smeathman's data were at last corroborated in 1855 by the American missionary Thomas S. Savage, the first to describe the gorilla. Five years later the entomologist Hermann Hagen began a detailed monograph on the termites, in which he objectively and conscientiously analyzed everything that had been reported on these insects since the days of ancient Egypt. Hagen's monograph, which summed up and evaluated many hundreds of observations by travelers in Africa, Asia, America, and Australia, created quite a storm in zoological circles. If what he said was true, then there was no correlation between the evolutionary rank of social insects and the complexity of their social organization. Bees, wasps, and ants are regarded as the highest of all insects, in evolutionary terms. But the termites, whose institutions in many respects greatly surpass those of the other social insects, belong to the lowest of the insects. According to Hagen, they are most closely related to the cockroaches.

Termites and cockroaches, Hagen pointed out,

> both live socially, are both uncommonly agile, both shy of light, both omnivorous. Their enormous and rapid reproduction, which makes them a nuisance everywhere, and their capacity for dissemination and acclimatization, emphasize the kinship. If we draw up a balance sheet of differences and similarities, it seems to me the differences are only those which serve to subdivide a group. Many of these differences, moreover, are outgrowths of the artificial social life of the termites.

In other words: termites are not "white ants" but community-forming cockroaches.

As we noted earlier, the salient difference between the higher insects and the lower ones is that the higher insects undergo complete metamorphosis. They spend their youth as maggotlike or caterpillarlike larvae, then pupate and go into a resting state during which they are transformed into the imago, the sexually mature insect. Among the lower insects, however, only an incomplete transformation takes place, called *epimorphosis*. Their larvae hatch out of the egg looking more or less like the adults of the species; they merely gradually increase in size with each molt and slowly develop into winged, sexually mature insects. As their last stage approaches they do not retire into a cocoon, but move about as nymphs, already winged but with their wings still concealed in special wing sheaths. After a last molt these nymphs appear in the complete imago form.

Toward the end of the nineteenth century it was determined that not only cockroaches, grasshoppers, earwigs, ephemerids, and other lower insects undergo epimorphosis, but also the termites. Hagen had been right. Such modern standard works on entomology as Klots's *Living Insects of the World* corroborate his findings:

In comparison to the high status of their social organization the termites are extremely primitive in their physical structure. No doubt they are closely related to the cockroaches and descended from a common ancestor of both. We may assume that some of these common ancestors—perhaps species close to the wood-eating roaches of the genus *Cryptocerus*—at a very early stage of their evolution developed a form of social life similar to that which we find among present-day termites.

There have since been any number of books on termites filled with miraculous tales, astonishing observations, and ingenious hypotheses. These include such factual accounts as the excellent treatises of Karl Escherich and Nils Holmgren; such excursions into natural philosophy as Maeterlinck's *Life of the Termites* and Marais's *The Soul of the White Ant;* and a number of science-fiction fantasies to the effect that the termites will eventually inherit the earth, or that humanity, as a consequence of the population explosion, will someday be compelled to go the way of the termites. By now everyone has heard about the termite, in one sense or another. While bees and ants are identified with industry and other virtues, the termite is regarded as the symbol of automatism, totalitarianism, and other sinister ways of life.

This somewhat unjust view of termite life probably stems from the fact that these insects are among the most destructive, especially in the tropics. Their columns of workers burrow into houses and gnaw the wood from within until beams collapse, furniture disintegrates into tinder, books and documents are eaten to shreds. Whole villages and parts of cities have succumbed to their depradations. Their termitaries interfere with agriculture and can only be removed by dynamite. And since man is apt to speak evil of those forms of life which prove a nuisance to him, he has made a dark legend out of the social life of the termite.

In reality, however, the termite colony is an organization dedicated to the care of the brood, like the societies of ants and bees. The chief difference is that—by our standards—it is better organized. It is a society which may represent, in the words of Karl Escherich, "the culmination of animal social life," but certainly not the anti-utopian utopias of Aldous Huxley or Orwell.

As for Eugène Marais's theory, it strikes practical zoologists as quite fantastic, even though it is founded upon an adequate knowledge of the facts. Marais holds that the termitary is "a single composite animal at a specific stage of development." In his widely read book, *The Soul of the White Ant,* Marais equates the rock-hard clay shell of the termite mound with the skin, the corridors with arteries and veins, the workers with mobile blood cells, and the royal chamber deep within the interior of the termitary with the heart, brain, and reproductive apparatus of this composite animal. The whole, he maintains, is directed by a group soul which exists outside any individual termite:

> The termite possesses no vestige of free will, or power of choice. The only quality it possesses is automobility—power of moving itself. It puts itself into motion, but when this motion will take place or what will be done with it, is decided, controlled, from without. . . . The whole behavior of the termite is determined from without by an influence—we may call it a thread by which he is firmly tied to the queen's cell. This invisible influence streams from the organism of the queen alone. It is a power beyond our senses; it can penetrate all material barriers, even such as thin steel or iron plates.

These are ingenious ideas, and deserve thought. But there is no firm evidence for the idea that the termite society is a composite animal nor for the idea of a group soul. Yet even without entertaining such speculations, we will find the reproductive system of the termites interesting enough. A society is founded when the termites swarm. Thousands upon thousands of winged, sexually mature insects fill the air, drift for days like clouds of smoke in the wind, and can darken a lighted room if they happen to enter it at night. These swarming males and females are sent out by the workers at regular intervals to find their mates. The Italian naturalist Filippo Silvestri observed this in the case of South American termites:

> When a scout has found the terrain safe, he slips further out of the mound, turns forwards and sidewards, and finally returns to the opening. Immediately afterwards a large number of workers, accompanied by a few soldiers, emerge and distribute themselves around the opening in the termitary. One of them goes back inside as if to give the last signal that exit is clear and secure. Immediately afterwards the first winged individuals set out. They run only a short distance and then launch themselves into flight. Slowly and heavily they move away, scattering in all directions. This goes on for several hours. But if a worker or a soldier becomes disturbed, some kind of alarm signal seems to be given, whereupon the entire guard withdraws and the swarming ceases until the danger seems to have passed.

This swarming is not a nuptial flight. Males and females do not mate in the air, as do bees and ants, or on the ground after the flight is ended. The function of those brief moments, in which the winged termites for the first and last time in their lives soar into the air, is the widest possible dissemination of the species. Those members of the flying host who are not destroyed by all sorts of enemies fall to the ground and cast off their wings. Only then do they form pairs. Each pair sets out on a walk, seeking a suitable place for founding a new nest. As they gnaw their way into a hollow in the ground or rotten wood, they gradually attain sexual maturity. "Thus," Escherich writes,

> the couples are not from the first kept together by shared love, as is the case among monogamous animals, but live together for a time as virginal maidens and youths. It is assumed that a secretion at the posterior end of the female attracts the male during the mating walk and continues to do so until the time of copulation. This "engagement period" probably has few analogies in the animal kingdom.

In contrast to conditions among bees, wasps, and ants, where females alone are the founders of the state, complete equality of the sexes reigns in the early stages of a termite marriage. Partners remain together, both build the first cells for the new nest, both care for the eggs and feed the larvae with a liquid secretion. And these larvae, the future workers and soldiers, are not exclusively females as among the ants and bees; some are male, some female. They grow into sterile workers quite slowly. Among some species it takes from three to six months, among others almost a year, before they are able to aid their parents. Only when sufficient workers and soldiers are available and when the nest has reached a certain size do the king and queen withdraw from the work of the colony and devote themselves exclusively to their sexual functions.

The greater part of the population of a termitary consists, as among the bees and ants, of workers and worker larvae. These take charge of most of the necessary activities. Even the growing larvae must work. In contrast to the helpless maggots of bees and ants, the larvae are completely mobile and resemble the grown workers. Alongside the working class is a soldier class, as among the ants. Termite soldiers function chiefly as engineering and construction troops. They repair broken places in the nest, stand guard, warn against danger, and repel weaker enemies. Many species will have several types of soldiers, each with his specialized task. There are large, medium-sized and small soldiers, some with normal heads, some with beaklike or saberlike snouts. The latter, the *nasuti* or "nosed" soldiers, utilize their snouts to spray enemies with a liquid which is apparently somewhat poisonous and also serves as a kind of glue for repairing the nest.

The workers often raise additional sexually complete kings and queens from existing larvae. These supplementary kings and queens

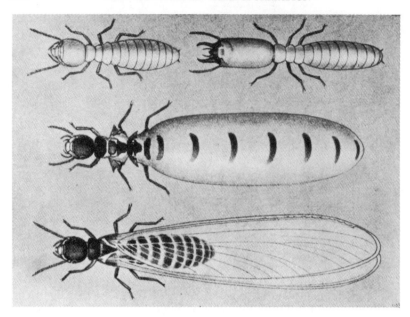

Termite castes. TOP LEFT, *worker;* TOP RIGHT, *soldier;* CENTER, *fertilized female (queen);* BOTTOM, *winged fertile male.*

are nymphs which achieve sexual maturity only by special hormone feeding. Finally, even soldiers can sometimes become active sexually and lay eggs. All the groups—workers, worker larvae, soldiers, young males and females and the royal couple—must be kept in numerical balance if the life of the nest is to proceed properly. If too few workers are available, all activities are impeded. If the number of soldiers is too great, that is also a serious danger to the community, since the soldiers, because of the special shape of their mouths, cannot feed themselves. If too many future kings and queens are produced, there will not be enough labor power to raise them and prepare them for swarming. And if the royal couple dies without there being substitutes available, the whole nest perishes. The workers alone are in a position to maintain the necessary balance. They are, as Escherich puts it,

> able to fill the ranks of the various castes from the different types of offspring; they can change worker and soldier larvae into supplementary sexual adults and, reversing the process, convert the larvae of kings and queens into soldiers. They see to it that the castes are always present in the proper numerical relationship. Where there are

too many in any group, the superfluous individuals are killed and
eaten; and where there are too few, the lack is quickly filled by
breeding.

Recent researches have demonstrated that termites mutually feed
one another and pass excreted drops of food on to others. Certain "social hormones" formed in the course of this process are fed to the
young and influence the growth and development of the larvae. The
rearing of termite offspring by means of these social hormones, pheromones, as they are called, is a highly complicated affair. It will suffice for our purposes to say that the young royal couple, during the
early period after the establishment of their nest, secrete pheromones
which check the sexual development of the larvae. During this period
only workers are produced. When there are enough of them, these
workers secrete other pheromones which promote the development
of soldiers and of winged sexual adults. The soldiers, finally, secrete
social hormones which inhibit the formation of more soldiers, so that
if there is a surplus of soldiers a large addition to the quantity of in-
hibitory pheromones sets up a strong bar against the production of
still more.

Some termite species erect gigantic structures of mud as hard as
concrete. Others live in tree nests the size of pumpkins, made of
chewed wood. Some raise fungi on their own excrement, both for food
and for regulating the interior heat of their nests; some carry protozoa in their digestive tracts which help them digest their principal
food, cellulose. We can scarcely undertake to describe all their diverse
social patterns and living conditions, but we must speak of the heart
of termite society, the royal chamber. For there the nationalization
of sexual relationships is most clearly evidenced. There, in the royal
chamber, subjects are turned out by mass production in a manner
unparalleled in the animal kingdom.

The royal chamber seems like a factory in which eggs are manu-
factured with machinelike regularity. Both founders of the society
are unusually long-lived. In some species the royal couple is said to
live from eight to twelve years. The queen, however, undergoes a remarkable change. She ceases to resemble a termite; she is transformed
into a monstrous sexual apparatus that looks like a sausage and in
some species lays an egg every two seconds. The average daily production of such a queen runs anywhere from eight to thirty thousand
eggs. Beside the queen sits the king, abdomen raised, almost as motionless as the gigantic female. From time to time he forces his way
under the huge, whitish body and attempts to mate with the giantess.

Workers swarm around the couple, cleaning them, feeding them, licking up their excretions and carrying away the laid eggs. Soldiers, their heads modified into huge weapons, form a protective ring around the busy horde, or see to it that the work goes forward in an orderly fashion. "When we consider," Escherich writes of this progenitive assembly line,

> that all the millions, perhaps even billions, of inhabitants owe their life to a single royal couple, and that constant losses resulting from the daily annihilation of thousands of individuals must be replaced, we can understand that the female, if she is to meet these demands, must do nothing but lay eggs, and that the male also can by no means lead an idler's life; he must keep himself in a state of readiness to supply the female with fresh sperm.

Aside from the water spider and some species of dung beetles in which the couples remain united to care for the brood, the termites are the only arthropods which lead a regular married life—a true marital partnership in our sense, in which the mates remain together for life. While male bees, wasps, and ants are killed after the nuptial flight, or simply die, the termite king remains permanently with his queen. But this rare case of monogamy in the insect world is accompanied with the most extreme disintegration of individuality. Sexual life has been transformed into the automated sex factory.

■

CHAPTER FIVE

COLD-BLOODED PARENTS

LADIES' CHOICE

To trace the evolution of sex among the vertebrates, we must once more descend to the stage where males and females simply discharge their sexual cells into the water and leave the rest to chance. That is the habit of the most ancient of the still living prevertebrates, our old friend the lancelet; many true fish follow the same procedure. Methods of reproduction among fish are, however, remarkably varied, and the behavior of the spawning fish toward one another evidences certain refinements in fertilization technique. One of the most colorful of these is what might be called "ladies' choice." The concept has a long and interesting history.

In 1898 an American zoologist, Charles Otis Whitman, introduced a new concept into psychology. Whitman had put aside all speculations about the animal *soul* and had instead confined his remarks to animal *behavior*. All previous animal psychology, he declared, had indulged in drawing outrageous analogies between animal and man. It was time to put an end to such anthropomorphic nonsense as the nineteenth-century idea that animals manifest love and hatred, honesty and falsehood, nobility and slyness, pity, gratitude, arrogance, gaiety, sorrow, vanity, meanness, and innumerable other human traits.

It was foolish, said Whitman and his followers, to pass value judgments upon animals, for such judgments are only projections of our human notions. The animal psychologist, they insisted, could do nothing but observe with cool objectivity all the various components

193

of animal behavior and compare these with one another—play, motion, instinctive actions, orientation, moods, affects, reactions to stimuli, capacity for learning, and the beginnings of thought.

In 1925 the American psychologist John Broadus Watson published a book entitled *Behaviorism*, which proposed applying this zoological method to the investigation of the human psyche. Watson, professor of psychology at Johns Hopkins University in Baltimore, took stern issue with his colleagues' habit of plumbing the human psyche by self-observation and then applying their discoveries to others. Such an approach was the source of too many errors, he maintained. The human psyche must be approached from outside; human behavior must be studied objectively under the shifting conditions of the environment. His extreme point of view did not, to be sure, win wide acceptance. But zoology has completely gone over to the approach that Whitman called for, and that Watson developed into a special field in psychology. Animal psychologists became behavioral researchers.

The phrase "behavioral research" was coined by one of the most ingenious and original minds among present-day biologists, the Austrian Konrad Lorenz. Lorenz himself is proof that modern behavioral researchers by no means approach animals with the coldness of psychotechnicians, as is sometimes assumed. Their emotional attachment to the objects of their researches is quite as strong as any felt by animal psychologists of previous eras. Lorenz once confessed that behavioral research demands "such direct intimacy with the living animal, but also such inhuman patience on the part of the observer, that theoretical interest in the animal would not suffice to make him persevere, were it not for the affection which enables him to see in the behavior of man and animal the kinship which that affection sensed."

One of the favorite techniques of behavioral researchers is decoy experiments. All kinds of animals are presented with decoys which more or less resemble their sexual partners, herd mates, rivals, enemies, or prey; the scientists then observe how the subjects react. Such decoy experiments are especially valuable to zoologists who wish to discover how the sexes recognize one another, how they find one another, and what stimuli determine the choice of a particular mate. Of course these experiments can only be undertaken with animals whose sight is excellent. The results are most interesting because they seem to substantiate a much-debated theory some ninety years old: the theory of sexual selection.

In 1871, twelve years after the publication of his *Origin of Species*, Darwin published a book which bore the provocative title *The Descent of Man, and Selection in Relation to Sex*. Among many species of animals, Darwin pointed out, the females prefer those males who are most magnificently adorned, that is, those who have donned the finest nuptial dress and have best developed their secondary sexual characteristics. The fact that male birds of paradise flaunt such vivid plumage, or that male hercules beetles and stags boast conspicuous horns and antlers, is due, according to Darwin's theory, to the females whose affections are stirred by such ornamentation. Hence, he concluded, such males have the maximum chance to reproduce their kind and the species is modified accordingly.

Darwin extended his idea of "ladies' choice" to human beings, but with certain important modifications. Human women would "choose not merely the handsomest men, according to their standard of taste, but those who were at the same time best able to defend and support them." Furthermore, while among birds of paradise the choice is entirely with the females, who pick out the handsomest of the courting males, among human beings the man also does some picking according to the taste set for him by his race and his times. Therefore, women as well as men would be modified by sexual selection over millions of years.

Darwin's contemporaries were shocked by what they considered the assertion that man had reached his present height of development solely as the result of various sexual maneuvers, and his doctrine of sexual selection was long considered a vague, faintly offensive hypothesis insusceptible of proof. Today's behavioral research has provided considerable factual evidence—although no proof—to support the idea of sexual selection among animals. Some of the most vivid examples are found among fish.

At spawning time, many male fish assume brilliant colors. Male bitterlings gleam in every color of the rainbow. Sticklebacks flash scarlet bellies and pale green backs. The underside of the male salmon glows a deep purple-red. The male paradise fish dons red and blue stripes and flaunts his frilly red fins. The nuptial colors of cichlids, cyprinodonts, labyrinth fish, and mahseer are appreciated by millions of aquarium-keepers. If two males fight for a female, the loser fades and soon looks rather drab. The winner, on the other hand, glows in even livelier colors, and the females ready for spawning follow him. These bright colors, then, are obviously intended for the other sex. They exert a strong allure.

Konrad Lorenz has described the nuptial splendors of the fighting fish:

In the fighting fish, this marvel of color is not continually present. For the little brown-gray fish that lies with folded fins in one corner of the aquarium reveals nothing of it for the moment. It is only when another fish, equally inconspicuous at first, approaches him and each sights the other, that they begin gradually to light up in all their incandescent glory. The glow pervades their bodies almost as quickly as the wire of an electric heater grows red. The fins unfold themselves like ornamental fans, so suddenly that one almost expects to hear the sound of an umbrella being opened quickly.

In 1937 one of the leading behavioral scientists of our time, Nikolaas Tinbergen, undertook a number of decoy experiments with fish in order to determine which characteristics and movements of the males aroused reactions in the females. It turned out that the female stickleback does not at all require an exact reproduction of a male in all his nuptial glory. A crude decoy colored red only on the underside is enough to lure her. When Tinbergen moved such a decoy back and forth in front of the female, keeping it in the male's courtship posi-

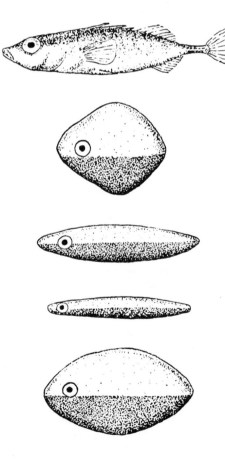

With the use of crude decoys like these, Nikolaas Tinbergen investigated the sexual behavior of sticklebacks. It turned out that the female was unable to distinguish between a decoy and a live male. If the decoy was painted gaily red on the underside and moved in characteristic courting movements, the female would respond by making herself ready for the next stage of the courtship.

tion, the female responded at once to this "key stimulus" by making itself ready for the next phase of the courtship.

Even stranger was the reaction of female pipefish. The males of these threadlike fish develop a yellow throat at spawning time. A spot of yellow color sufficed to lure the female. Tinbergen could even persuade his pipefish females to follow, with apparently intense sexual excitement, a simple yellow sphere which did not in the least resemble a male pipefish. The yellow color alone was the "key stimulus."

If several such decoys of similar shape and differing intensities of color are used, the female fish responds to the one which displays the male's nuptial colors with greatest intensity. Conversely, a male pipefish confronted with several female decoys courts the one with the thickest belly, which apparently signifies the greatest readiness for spawning. Thus it is the secondary sexual characteristics which attract the other sex. The animal which shows these characteristics most prominently has the greatest prospect of being chosen by a mate and reproducing itself. Similar decoy experiments with insects, reptiles, birds, and mammals bear out the same principle.

But color and ornamentation are not the whole story. The male must make proper use of his beauty, if he is to win his fair one's favor. He must court; he must carry out certain ritualized instinctive acts to which the female replies with her own ritual movements. This courtship ritual can easily be observed among aquarium specimens. If a male fighting fish, ready for mating, encounters a fish of the same species, he at once begins a "self-display dance," as Lorenz calls it, in which he swims excitedly around the presumptive mate, revealing every glowing spot of color and every iridescent ray in the beautiful fins. But as Lorenz writes: "To begin with, strangely enough, it is uncertain whether it will lead to love overtures and mating, or whether it will develop, by an equally flowing transition, into a bloody battle."

Many fish cannot tell whether the fellow members of the species they encounter are male or female. They find this out in the course of the ritual. If male meets male, the two go on with their self-display for a while. Then, if one of the two rivals feels too weak for a fight, he literally strikes his flag by laying his fins close to his body, allowing his colors to fade, and taking flight. If both are equally strong, the self-display often passes over into a bloody war dance which, in the aquarium at least, can end in the death of one of the opponents. Lorenz describes such a duel:

On account of their beauty, the fighters appear less malevolent than they really are and one is just as loath to ascribe to them embittered courage and contempt of death as one is to associate head hunting with the almost effeminately beautiful Indonesian warriors. Nevertheless, both are capable of fighting to the death. . . . When they are stimulated to the point of inflicting the first sword-thrust, it is only a matter of minutes till wide slits are gaping in their fins, which in a few more minutes are reduced to tatters. The method of attack of a fighting fish, as of nearly all fish that fight, is literally the sword thrust and not the bite. The fish opens its jaws so wide that all its teeth are directed forward, and in this attitude, it rams them, with all the force of its muscular body, into the side of its adversary. The ramming of a fighting fish is so strong and hard that its impact is clearly audible if, in the confusion of the fight, one of the antagonists happens to hit the glass side of the tank. The self-display dance can last for hours but if it develops into action, it is often only a matter of minutes before one of the combatants lies mortally wounded on the bottom.

These duels, however, are not fought for the favor of a particular female. They are territorial struggles. The fighting fish in rut will defend or conquer a territory where he wishes to build his nest of foam. The rutting cichlid fights to retain the spawning area he has chosen. The stickleback tries to rid his territory, not only of possible rivals, but also of females unready for spawning and even strange fish of approximately his own size. He fights for the territory in which he has built or plans to build his nest. And he goes on fighting long after the eggs have been laid and are being guarded. In every case, the male is concerned about possession of nesting territory.

But whatever his motive, fish are certainly not "cold-blooded" in the figurative sense of the term. Quite the contrary, Lorenz is right when he says: "I am familiar with many animals and with their behavior in the most intimate situations of their life, in the wild ecstasies of the fight and of love, but, with the exception of the wild canary, I know of no animal that can excel in hot-bloodedness a male stickleback, a Siamese fighting fish, or a cichlid."

The fact that such duels end fatally among ornamental fish is largely due to the confined space of the aquarium, where the loser has no chance to escape. Behavioral scientists have discovered that senseless killing of rivals is not common in the animal kingdom. Among many vertebrates, these duels end with a characteristic gesture of submission. The loser presents to the victor the most vulnerable part of his body, thereby indicating that he is abandoning the fight. At this point the stronger wolf, say, could easily bite through the throat of his antagonist, or the stronger turkey hack open the back of the loser's head. But this does not happen. The gesture of submission sets up an

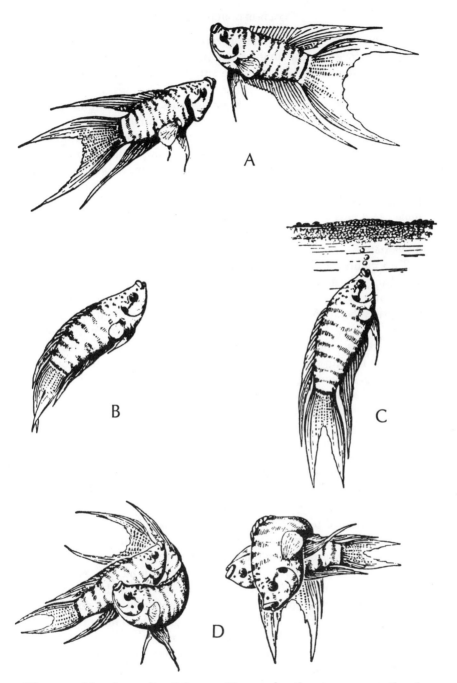

The courtship of paradise fish. TOP: *Two males threaten one another in self-display posture.* CENTER LEFT: *Male gesture of submission.* CENTER RIGHT: *Male building foam nest.* BOTTOM: *Mating beneath the foam nest.*

inhibition in the victor which prevents his continuing the fight. We may therefore assume that, when unconfined, the fish would normally end their battles with some similar gesture of submission and rapid retreat by the loser.

If the fish before whom the male assumes his self-display position is a female, she declares herself by another ritual which appears to be just as automatic. In many ornamental fish, the female folds her fins close to her body, as weaker males do. If the male does not appeal to her, she darts away. But if the resplendent male pleases her, she approaches him, as Lorenz puts it, "with shy insinuating movements, that is to say, in an attitude directly opposed to that of the swaggering male. And now begins a love ceremonial which, if it cannot compare in grandeur with the male war dance, can emulate it in grace of movement."

Two cichlids who have found one another go together to seek a spawning place, which, seemingly, they carefully clean with their lips. But it is not a real cleansing; it is, to use a pet expression of contemporary behavioral science, a "symbolic act" without specific usefulness. When the two fish clean stones and spit out sand, they are merely communicating to one another the fact that they are in the mood for mating and wish to perform the act of spawning together. The actual preparing of the spawning place takes place just before spawning, after a few more symbolic acts. Among fighting fish and other labyrinth fish, the male lures the female to the foam nest by swimming in graceful figures. The pair dance in narrower and narrower circles around one another, until at last the female is "embraced" by the male just beneath the center of the nest, and turned on her back. Both then simultaneously eject their sexual cells.

The most striking cases of ladies' choice in fish occur among the lophobranchii, among which are the sea horses and pipefish. Pipefish are snake-shaped pelagic fish whose snouts are elongated into a tube. Among these fish, the female wears the brighter nuptial dress. She darts alluringly around the male, coaxes him into all sorts of sportive games, rises to the surface of the water with him, and weaves her spell around him by swimming in circles. Such female displays and contacts stir the male just as the seductive arts and slow disrobing of an experienced courtesan do the human male. The female twines herself around the male's body, exciting him until his ejaculation of semen takes place at the same time as her release of the eggs.

Whether the female or the male is the more active partner, fish have the prerogative of picking and choosing their mates. The male stickleback builds an artful nest out of plant fibers and kidney secretion. It looks life a muff. Then the gentleman goes looking for his

Siamese fighting fish during spawning. As the female lays the eggs, the male catches them in his mouth and then deposits them in the foam nest above.

bride. He must not only drive away rivals, but also stir the interest of the females in order to bring suitable mates to his nest and persuade them to lay eggs. We may assume that the strong and handsome stickleback males attract the greater number of females, while male sticklebacks with less distinct secondary sexual characteristics have somewhat less success.

Among salmon, according to the observations of the American scientist P. T. Young, there can be no doubt at all about the fact of ladies' choice. First the salmon males fight for the spawning places. During these fierce battles the females calmly prepare a pit for the reception of the eggs. Then the female picks a handsome, strong, and successful male from among the champions and invites him to fertilize her eggs. As soon as she has begun laying her eggs, young males which have just reached spawning age hurriedly rush forward and pour their sperm into the pit. But these small, pale fellows do not satisfy the spawning female. If the mate she has chosen is caught or wounded in battle, the female promptly fetches another splendid old salmon before she continues her egg laying. Young saw a female salmon bring nine vigorous males to the nesting pit, one after the other. And when the ninth was also caught and taken from her, she coaxed a large male trout to the pit. Evidently his nuptial dress exerted a stronger stimulus upon her than the uninteresting colors of the young males of her own species. The trout in turn released its sperm upon the eggs—of course without result.

Lorenz considers it likely that fish actually recognize their chosen partners, differentiating them from others of their species. He once exchanged the females of two cichlid pairs which were in exactly the same phase of the reproductive cycle in two different containers. The result:

> The fish which had received the "prettier" female, the one to whom he had previously paid court, was quite content with the exchange, but the other, who had been landed with the formerly rejected female in place of his wife, was, not unjustifiably, furious and now attacked her much more relentlessly than he had done at first, in the presence of his wife. I am convinced that male number two, who had received an improvement on his wife, noticed the difference too.

"HOW FISH KISS"

A writer of clever hit songs once wrote a lyric containing the line, "Nobody knows how fish kiss." Evidently the lyric writer never owned an aquarium, or he would have thought better of that line. Since the keeping and breeding of ornamental fish is one of the most widespread hobbies in the world, we know more about the loves of fishes than we do about those of most other vertebrates. And certainly many ornamental fish kiss. The couples use their lips in the ceremonies of courtship in a surprisingly human manner. One species of labyrinth fish is known, because of this habit, as the "kissing gurani."

Fish offer all sorts of variety in their mating positions, methods of fertilization, and child care. Chars, barbets, and many other carplike fish engage in some preliminary courtship. Then, belly against belly, they dart toward the surface, simultaneously expelling eggs and semen. Plaice swim along in couples, side by side, at the same time releasing clouds of sexual products behind them. Among groundfish, males and females rub their bellies on the gravelly bottoms. Pike

The peculiar habit of this species of labyrinth fish has given it the name "kissing gurani." The kiss may last as long as 25 minutes.

couples rub against one another and increase sexual passion by blows of their tails. Other species expose themselves to tactile stimuli by swimming through dense growths of water plants. In spawning, salmon and trout dig deep pits while cichlids wind their strings of eggs around water weeds and other convenient objects. Those sharks which do not bear their young alive hang horny egg capsules on seaweed stalks or coral branches. Among the mailed sheatfishes and others belonging to the catfish family, the male attaches himself to the spawning female by means of clasping organs. There are even supposed to be sheatfish females which suck the sperm from the male and spit it out on the emerging eggs.

Thus far we have been speaking of true fish, which lay eggs to reproduce. Lower on the ladder of evolution but practicing human-style copulation, are certain classes not considered true fish by zoologists. One of these is the lamprey. This creature has been assigned to the distinct class known as Cyclostomata, or round-mouths, which are characterized by a funnel-shaped, jawless mouth. Some four hundred million years ago, at the beginning of the Silurian, the round-mouths inhabited shallow bays. There were many species, some heavily armored. It is assumed that the first jawed fish developed from them. Thus they are an archaic branch of the animal kingdom, of whom only the eellike lampreys and the still more primitive-looking hagfish are left. But the kind of sexual act practiced by the lampreys is quite

different from what one would expect of an animal on so low a plane
of evolution.

This was discovered as early as 1646 by an untrained Alsatian fisherman named Leonhard Baldner, one of the first students of fish life
in the waters of the Upper Rhine. Baldner referred to himself as a
man who had "earned his living on the water since his grandparents'
day." He lived by fishing, was a toll collector, and as "fence viewer
and forester" was in charge of the woods and waters of the Free City
of Strasbourg. From 1646 to 1666 he set forth the many observations
of animals he had made in the forests and on the waters in a book
entitled, *Right Natural Description and Depiction of the Water Birds,
Fishes, Four-footed Beasts, Insects, and Vermin which Are to Be
Found in the Waters near Strasbourg*. Naïve as it sounds, the work
has remained a treasure-trove for historians of zoology to the present
day.

Baldner wrote of the smallest European lamprey: "These lampreys
or lamprons have their spawn in March and April. They hang close
together to the stones; where the water runs fast they make deep pits
in which the pair put their bellies together to perform their lust, which
else I have seen of no other fish but the lampreys, since they spawn in
water which is not deep, so that it can be easily seen."

Over two centuries later, August Müller, a Berlin zoologist, made
intensive studies of the reproduction of lampreys, and fancied that his
own observations agreed with Baldner's account. Müller saw the
lamprey male attach himself tightly with his sucking mouth to the
neck of the female, then double his body around and press it against
his mate's abdomen. In this way, Müller thought, the male fertilized
the emerging eggs, as is the case with the majority of fishes. Modern
investigators, however, have ascertained that genuine interior fertilization takes place in most species of lampreys. During the embrace
the males discharge their sperm directly into the female's body, and
shortly afterwards the female discharges her fertilized spawn in various obscure nooks. The chances are that Baldner was well aware of
this actual copulation "which else I have seen of no other fish."
Baldner also had anticipated another discovery: metamorphosis in
the lamprey. This was rediscovered and interpreted long after him.

Ulisse Aldrovandi, the Italian zoologist of the seventeenth century,
put lamprey larvae among the worms. Thereafter, they haunted zoological literature under the name of prides or sand-pipers. As much
as a hundred years after Baldner, Linnaeus gave a special scientific
name to these supposed worms, *Ammocoetes branchialis*. But Baldner
had known that prides, which he called "blind lampreys," were the
larval forms of "seeing lampreys": "The seeing and the blind are else

of one kind, for the young from the beginning are all blind and hide themselves at once in the ooze, when they hatch from the roe. The blind lampreys have no roe until they become sighted."

Finally, August Müller was able to prove that Baldner had been right: lampreys undergo a regular metamorphosis. Yellow, toothless and tongueless worms hatch out of their eggs. These remain hidden in tubes of mud for several years. In the last year of the larval existence they metamorphose into fully developed lampreys within a few weeks.

Like the lamprey, the selachians—among which are the sharks, rays, and chimaeras—are also not true fish. Their skulls and spinal columns are not bony, but composed of pieces of cartilage. The gill slits are in the open. In the structure of the mouth and the internal organs they also differ considerably from the true bony fish. Since 1909, when the British ichthyologist Edwin Stephen Goodrich sketched a new genealogy for fish, zoologists have separated the sharks and their relations from other members of Pisces, and set up a special class of vertebrates for them. The selachians are a very old group and in many respects have remained remarkably primitive. But in regard to copulation they are, with some exceptions, more advanced than the overwhelming majority of true fish.

The males of most sharks, rays, and chimaeras are equipped with conic auxiliary organs which may be compared to gonopods—the false penises of squid, crustaceans, and spiders. These organs have developed out of the pelvic fins. In copulation they are introduced into the female cloaca in order to widen it. During this act the male adopts a characteristic position, embracing the female's whole body like a huge ring. When he has widened the female's genital orifice by spreading it with his copulatory fins, he extrudes a genital papilla from his vent, thrusts it into the female vagina and releases his sperm. Thus female selachians are mated and internally fertilized like the females of higher vertebrates.

The development of the offspring varies from species to species. Some sharks and rays lay eggs which are enclosed in a horny case with curious tassels. After the young have hatched, these cases are often washed up on beaches in huge quantities. People prize them as souvenirs of the seashore. In some species of selachians, the young hatch out inside the mother's body and are born alive. Finally, the man-eater and some other sharks form a placenta in the uterus. According the findings of several investigators, the young are cared for by the mother for some time after birth. If we saw a blue shark mother taking her offspring for a swim we would find it hard to believe that her place on the genealogical tree of the vertebrates is so lowly.

Since the selachians have virtually all the equipment necessary for sexual union and reproduction as performed by the higher vertebrates, it is difficult to understand why the true fish, which stand much higher on the evolutionary scale, should have taken a step backwards—to egg-laying—in procreation. But probably external fertilization is in the long run more favorable to aquatic animals than internal fertilization and live birth. The former method leads to mass production of eggs and hence to mass increase and mass dissemination of the species. All the same, the methods of the sharks are employed by some Teleostei, the true bony fishes.

Among most true fish the couple pays no attention to their offspring after spawning. The spawning ground is abandoned, and if the parents later happen upon their eggs or the hatched young, they regard their own progeny as a welcome addition to their diet. This is common, but so many species of fish deviate from this type of behavior that the deviations cannot be regarded as exceptional. There are fish which build nests and care for their offspring, fish which keep their offspring on or in their bodies, or even couple and bear living young. There are some species of sharks in which the female develops a kind of placenta for the nourishment of the embryos that strikingly resembles that of the higher mammals. Every type of behavior toward progeny can be found, from cannibalism to loving devotion.

Of the first type, the hard-hearted parents, a familiar example can be found in many homes. Practically every child who sets up a warm-water aquarium at first peoples his tank with viviparous cyprinodonts. These guppies, platys, mollies, and swordtails, as they are known in the ornamental fish trade, are sturdy, easy to care for, and prolific. The plump-bellied females periodically bear brisk, live young which must be caught and placed in a different vessel to save them from the sometimes cannibalistic adults. And the aquarium-keeper has the pleasure of seeing the small, more colorful males almost constantly dancing and darting around the females, like a swarm of hummingbirds around a blossom. The keen observer may even think he can see actual copulation taking place from time to time.

In reality, however, the apparent penis of the cyprinodont male is a gonopod. The anal fin has become an extended affair provided with a hook and a channel by which the sperm travels from the sexual orifice to the tip of the organ. The males do not introduce their gonopod into the female's body. Rather, the organ darts forward, quickly touches the female's cloaca, and attaches to it a packet of sperm which the female, presumably by some kind of suction, draws inside itself.

The spermatozoa remain fresh and vigorous in the oviduct. Thus such fish can go on bearing several sets of live young for some time after the death of all available males.

In recent times cyprinodonts have proved ideal experimental subjects for those biologists who are interested in the problem of sex inversion. By introduction of hormones, transplantation of seminal glands, and similar experiments, male swordtails have been transformed into females, and vice versa. Sometimes this inversion takes place without the intervention of an experimenter. If the ovaries of a female swordtail are so affected by age, sickness, or an invasion of parasites that they no longer supply female sex hormones, the fish undergoes a fundamental change. It grows slimmer; the typical pregnancy spot above the ventral fins disappears; the caudal fin acquires that swordlike tip to which it owes its name; the anal fin is transformed into a gonopod and the sex glands produce sperm. Henceforth the transformed female can court and mate with its sisters. If the hormone chemistry of the body is subjected to a less complete change, the affected fish becomes a hermaphrodite. If on the other hand the sex glands are completely destroyed, as by excision, the female develops into a pseudo-male which has male secondary sexual characteristics but is incapable of fertilizing females.

There are also, among fish, genuine hermaphrodites which have not been converted into this anomalous state by disease. In two groups of marine fishes, the dentate perch and the curling bream, specimens are frequently found with both fully formed ovaries and functioning testicles. A hermaphrodite perch has been observed to practice self-fertilization in the aquarium: presumably lacking a mate, it first laid its eggs and then released a cloud of its own sperm over them. But these are special cases. Hermaphroditism does occur now and then among the vertebrates, but in a free state self-fertilization does not.

A number of other fresh-water and marine fishes besides the cyprinodonts are vivaparous and follow a similar method of transmitting the sperm. In some species, however, the young develop in the shelter of the mother's or even the father's body, although normal external fertilization has previously taken place. The behavior of a flat-headed sheatfish, native to the waters of northeast South America, and looking remarkably like a frying pan, is especially bizarre. This fish, which bears the name *Aspredo caevis*, spawns on the bottom of rivers, as do many fish. The female deposits her eggs and the male fertilizes them. But then the mother rolls back and forth over the eggs until they are all stuck fast to her underside. Thereupon her skin grows over the spawn and wraps every egg in a cup-shaped case which remains firmly attached by a stem to the mother's body. The stems are supplied with blood vessels through which the mother feeds the embryos with her own body juices.

The mouth, too, can be used among fish for incubation. This happens particularly among two groups of fish whose "kissing" provides much amusement for fish fanciers—the labyrinth fish and the cichlids. A number of especially beloved aquarium specimens belong to the family of labyrinth fish: macropods, fighting fish, threadfish. Normally, the male labyrinth fish build a foam nest on the surface of the water, formed of bubbles given extra tensile strength by their saliva. They lure the female beneath this nest, by dances and ceremonial kisses, and persuade her to release her eggs. Then they guard the eggs and care for the hatched offspring for a while.

This sportive spawning was first described in 1889, by a fish breeder named Benecke who observed the macropods:

> First the male, then the female seized its mate's upper lip. And once they had taken a firm grip they seldom let go in less than ten to forty seconds. Their game was played with such vigor that shreds of skin dangled around their mouths, and for several days the male had a small sore on his upper lip. I could only regard this behavior as kissing of extraordinary intensity. . . .

Afterwards, the female was embraced by the male in the manner of the fighting fish and prompted to release her eggs. Once that was done, the male promptly drove away by brute force the sweetheart he had courted so tenderly. If the narrow confines of the aquarium make escape impossible, the anxious father slashes his mate's fins, tears open her flanks, and kills her. The instinctive behavior of pairing has been superseded in the male by the overwhelming instinct to care for the brood.

All labyrinth males that build foam nests have the habit of capturing in their mouths precocious progeny who escape too soon from their paternal care. They then spit them back into the nest. From this custom several labyrinth fish have developed the practice of carrying the young around in their mouths for a considerable time. In a number of species the eggs are brooded in the mouth in the most literal sense. Moreover, the father's or mother's mouth remains a dwelling and refuge for the young as long as they are small. For this reason these fish bear the descriptive name of "mouthbreeders."

This method has been developed to its highest degree by none other than the cichlid—the same fighting fish who was so wild and even bloodthirsty in the courting period. Now a tame husband, he and his wife present an exemplary married pair.

Among the cichlids which do not practice mouth breeding, husband and wife build a nesting pit or clean a stone on which to lay the eggs, and they stay together to look after the growing brood. Both mates care for the eggs, employ their fins to fan fresh water to them, keep the nesting place clear of dirt, and take turns standing guard over the nursery. This marriage grows even more idyllic when the young swarm about the nesting pit and follow the parents in a loose flock like a band of chicks following a hen. If some danger nears, the parents give a signal with their glittering caudal fins or some other part of their bodies, and at once the young dart back into the pit. They are carefully put to bed at night. But since some youthful cichlids are rash and frivolous, and tend to disobey the warning signals and continue to loiter outside the pit, the father becomes stern. He snaps up the naughty ones, holds them in his mouth for a moment and then blows them into the nest.

The labor of Sisyphus, one would think. For while the father is spitting a single baby into the nest, dozens of others may escape. But that, as Lorenz has discovered, does not take place.

> The baby sinks at once heavily to the bottom and remains lying there. By an ingenious arrangement of reflexes, the swim bladders of the young "sleeping" cichlids contract so strongly that the tiny fishes become much heavier than water and remain, like little stones, lying in the hollow, just as they did in their earliest childhood before their swim bladder was filled with gas. The same reaction of "becoming heavy" is also elicited when a parent fish takes a young one in its mouth. Without this reflex mechanism it would be impossible for the father, when he gathers up his children in the evening, to keep them together.

Since the parent often has to guard a troop of sixty to two hundred babies, one part of its mouth swells into a sac through whose stretched, transparent skin the swarm of young fish can plainly be seen. Naturally, the parent has little opportunity to feed during this period. It becomes quite emaciated, and is presumably glad when the young grow into independence and return to the mouth sac only in time of danger, or in order to sleep.

Cichlids are among the most intelligent of fish. Behavioral scientists have placed them in a variety of situations in which they were required to prove that they were able to think, to find a way out of an impasse. Lorenz witnessed one such conflicting situation in the case of the jewelfish *Hemichromis*, which is not a mouthbreeder but which does gather the young in its mouth to carry them to the nest. A jewelfish male had seized a worm which was too big to swallow at once.

West African black-chinned mouthbreeders spawning. When the couple have cleaned out a nesting pit, the female (with darker markings) deposits her eggs which may be seen in this photograph against the dark background of the pit.

The female then swims away and the male moves over the pit to fertilize the eggs. Both swim in a circle, returning to the pit and repeating the procedure.

In this species, it is the male who picks up the eggs and hatches them in his mouth, though the female may pick up any eggs that he has over-looked.

The spawning over, the male will carry the brood in his mouth until the little fish are hatched, some 23 days later. During this period he will take no food and his mouth will swell to enormous proportions. The photo-graph clearly shows the eggs in the male's mouth (left).

Cross section of the mouth of an egg-carrying mouthbreeder.

As he was about to chew, he saw a stray baby. The instinct to care for the brood forced the father to take the baby into its mouth also. "The fish had in its mouth two different things of which one must go into the stomach and the other into the nest. What would he do? I must confess that, at that moment, I would not have given twopence for the life of that tiny jewelfish."

But the father fish behaved like a human being whose instincts are suddenly blocked:

> It stops, blocked in all directions, and can go neither forward nor backward. For many seconds the father jewelfish remained riveted and one could almost see how his feelings were working. Then he solved the conflict in a way for which one was bound to feel admiration: he spat out the whole contents of his mouth: the worm fell to the bottom, and the little jewelfish, becoming heavy in the way described above, did the same. Then the father turned resolutely to the worm and ate it up, without haste but all the time with one eye on the child, which "obediently" lay on the bottom beneath him. When he had finished, he inhaled the baby and carried it home to its mother.

It was a truly impressive demonstration of intelligence for a fish. "Some students, who had witnessed the whole scene, started as one man to applaud," Lorenz concludes his account.

THE GREAT NUPTIAL MIGRATIONS

The sea and its abyssal depths are crisscrossed by a network of innumerable migratory roads. Periodically, swarms of fish travel along these, impelled by hunger and by sex. They rise from the abysses to the surface, swim along the coasts, and head out to the open sea; they return from the expanses of the oceans to the coasts, follow the plankton-rich currents and seek out shoals in which to spawn. Many of these piscine migrations have not yet been investigated. A crude map of the migratory trails has begun to emerge only since marine biologists began marking fish with metal or plastic disks.

There is an obvious reason for many species of fish to gather in tremendous migratory schools at spawning time. A reproductive act in which thousands and hundreds of thousands of males and females participate can assure a given species that most of the eggs laid will be fertilized. Moreover, the hatched young need special plankton food which they can find only in certain specific areas of the sea. The pelagic (oceanic) fish are drawn to such banks, coasts, and abysses at spawning time. And man profits by this habit, for he follows the paths of herring, cod, tuna, and sardines and scoops them by the millions into his fishing boats. The great power of the cities of the Hanseatic League was based on the profits from migrating fish. The exploitation of vast schools of fish is to this day essential to the economies of Japan, Norway, Iceland, and many other countries. Some say that the pursuit of fish brought Breton cod fishermen to the American continent before Columbus.

Migratory fish often reproduce in astronomical numbers. To be sure, only a small percentage of the fertilized eggs develop into sexually mature adults, and in addition ruthless modern methods of fishing have made serious inroads into the numbers of certain species. Nevertheless, fishermen continue to report "mountains" of herring and cod—closely packed masses of spawning fish which swim in several layers one above the other and sometimes fill an area of a square mile and more. It is no fish story that at times fish can be dipped out of the water in pails and shoveled directly into the boat; nor is it a fable that such mountains of fish have sometimes capsized small boats.

Similar spawning migrations take place in fresh water. Even more astonishing is the habit many fish have of spending their early youth in brooks or rivers, then going down to the sea to grow up, and returning in great schools to their birthplaces in fresh water at spawning time.

Sturgeon are just such drifters between river and ocean. They deposit their eggs in the river sands. There the young fish live for about two years, browsing through the ooze for all sorts of small animals until they reach a length of twelve to sixteen inches. During this time they gradually drift down to the open sea. After approximately eight years they begin feeding along the bottom in shoal waters, before reaching sexual maturity. In the course of their ten years of youth they gradually grow to four or five feet in length. These huge fish gather in the mouths of rivers, mount the streams, and look for sandy or gravelly places in the river bed—where a single sturgeon female can deposit as many as six million eggs.

The egg production of a kindred species, the giant sturgeon, is even greater. This monster spawns in the rivers that flow into the Adriatic, the Black Sea, and the Caspian. In 1769 a great sturgeon was caught in the Caspian Sea which measured thirty feet in length and weighed 3,000 pounds. The roe in this one female's body amounted to about eight hundred pounds. Such colossi have become extremely rare, because of intensive fishing. Since men regard the eggs of sturgeon—caviar—as an exquisite delicacy, and since, more-over, sturgeon are extremely sensitive to the pollution of water by in-dustrial wastes, these imposing fish are gradually disappearing from most European rivers.

An even more impressive spectacle is afforded by the spawning migrations of the salmon. Salmon likewise spend the earlier part of their life in fresh water and grow to sexual maturity in the ocean. At spawning time each salmon, with an obstinacy and purposeful-ness that tempts us to believe it possesses a sixth sense, seeks the river in which it was born. In reality it is guided by its sense of smell. It smells the chemical composition of the water and follows the track of this scent which it has known from infancy. Migrating salmon overcome seemingly insurmountable obstacles.

"When the salmon wants to leap rapids and weirs," writes Bern-hard Grzimek, animal psychologist and Director of the Frankfurt Zoo,

> it swims upward at a slant, with great speed, and then, stretched out at its full length, shoots like an arrow through the air. It is said to attain heights of as much as seven feet above the surface of the water. It is amazing how persistently these fish will repeat their attempts at jumping—which, however, are frequently not especially purposeful and are often carried out in a completely wrong direction. Quite often they hit rocks or hurl themselves out on dry land. Salmon also jump on other occasions, for example when they are in the mouths of riv-ers, but they do so in quite a different fashion. For then they bend sidewards, so that the caudal fin almost touches the head, and spring out sidewise.

All accounts agree on the vast hordes of salmon that assembled in the spawning grounds before industrialization and the technological rationalization of fishing. In Alaska at the beginning of the twenti-eth century it would have been a waste of labor to fish for the spawn-ing salmon, or to catch them with small ring nets. Instead huge mill wheels with nets stretched across them were placed in the river, so that with each turn they would fetch up a whole swarm of salmon and toss them to land. A single set of such salmon wheels is said to have conveyed forty thousand fish from a river on a single day.

Conditions were similar in the vast rivers of Siberia. The Russian traveler Aleksander Theodor von Middendorf wrote of this in 1875:

> Thronging incessantly, the *keta* salmon, gathered in millions, rushes up the mountain streams. The water boils with them, and takes on the taste of fish; oars are useless, and when the boat drifts along the shallows near the bank, the outermost rows of fish are forced onto

Atlantic salmon leaping a river rapid. Salmon have been known to reach a height of as much as seven feet above the surface of the water.

the dry land, where they perish miserably. But the main procession continues to rush onward, working against the raging stream, struggling through rapids, climbing into the mountains, forever upstream, until the water gives out. Already the dorsal fins, even the backs of the fish, are protruding from the watery element. Men, no longer armed with nets or harpoons, but simply with sticks, as well as bears, dogs, birds, wreak merciless slaughter on the endless horde. But the survivors are not deterred. Where the water is insufficient, they throw themselves on their flatter sides, now to the right, now to the left.

After spawning, Middendorf continues, the fish loses its sheen:

It darkens, turns greenish gray; the ventral scales rub off; the fins appear bloody; the whole lower half of the body turns dark purple, reddish blue, and finally black and blue, with repulsive markings climbing jaggedly up the sides like the half-gangrenous, scorbutic sores on mistreated warm-blooded animals; their whole bodies look raw, covered with proud flesh. But still the salmon strives to go upstream, until his last strength fails. At length, in late summer, the last of the water has receded from amid the tumbled stones in many places of the mountain brooks, and the air is poisoned with the rotting corpses of fish.

Thus the sexual migration becomes a death march. But why do the salmon migrate at all? Why do they not stay either in the sea or in the rivers? There are various theories about this. According to one, salmon were originally pelagic, but when they reached spawning age became "too fat and therefore too buoyant for sea water." This prompted them to make their way to the less buoyant fresh water to reproduce. At the same time, the argument continues, the young of most species of salmon, aside from trout, blue char, and other small salmonoid fish, do not find enough food in fresh water. For this reason they migrate back to the inexhaustible feeding grounds of the ocean, where they can stuff themselves until they reach sexual maturity.

Another theory reverses this argument. It holds that all salmonoid fish were originally river dwellers, but that for thousands of years— or perhaps only since the Ice Age—the larger species gradually adapted themselves to moving down to the sea. Since, however, in their tender youth they cannot yet endure sea water with its far higher mineral content, the adult salmon must return to fresh-water spawning grounds.

Both theories are sheer conjecture. The true reason may be entirely different. The nuptial voyages of fish still present innumerable riddles to marine biologists and ichthyologists. The deepest mystery of all remains a nuptial journey which is perhaps the most unusual and romantic in the whole realm of vertebrate animals—the migration of the river eels to the depths of the Sargasso Sea.

THE MYSTERY OF THE EELS

When zoology began to flower as a science in the eighteenth and the nineteenth centuries, naturalists finally laid to rest the age-old fable that eels did not practice the usual methods of reproduction, but were forever arising anew by spontaneous generation. The new generations of scientists amused themselves by citing, as curiosities, the quaint stories about eels to be found in Aristotle, Pliny, Albertus Magnus, Konrad Gesner, and other great early naturalists. But until 1897 zoologists had not the slightest idea how and where river eels actually reproduced.

There was no denying that the believers in spontaneous generation, from Aristotle to Izaac Walton, were right about one fact at least. No one had ever caught eels about to spawn; no one had ever seen the spawning ground of any eels; not a single eel that was cut open had either eggs or sperm in its abdomen. Consequently, simple folk persisted in the belief that eels must have emerged from some type of worm. The favorite candidates were the intestinal worms of the black goby, an ooze-dwelling fish. In Sardinia the people actually believed that a beetle was the true progenitor of the eel.

Rewards were offered for sexually mature eels. Expeditions set out with the specific aim of catching them. All in vain. In the midst of this ambitious activity, no one paid heed to a discovery that had been made by the German naturalist Johann Jakob Kaup in 1856. Someone had sent to Kaup from the Straits of Messina small, translucent fish shaped like a willow leaf. He thereupon wrote up a description of these "willow leaf fish" under the name of *Leptocephalus brevirostris*. And science was content. It catalogued the "willow leaf fish" along with other known animals and delved no further into its origins and its nature.

Forty years later, in 1895, two Italian oceanographers named Grassi and Calandruccio began investigating *Leptocephalus* more closely. They too fished in the Straits of Messina, where peculiar currents prevail. These currents bring deep waters to the surface, and frequently carry deep-sea fauna along with them. The "willow leaf fish," the Italian scientists first concluded, must be such deep-sea creatures carried up above their normal depth. But Grassi and Calandruccio were in for a surprise. One day they caught even slimmer little fish which were equally glassy and translucent. Quite obviously these were related to *Leptocephalus*. The "willow leaf fish" seemed to be turning into an eel no thicker than a match. In a flash of inspiration the two scientists realized that *Leptocephalus* must be the larval form of the eel.

But then where did the eels spawn? Where did these willow-leaf larvae hatch? And why had no eels capable of spawning ever been discovered? Since Grassi and Calandruccio regarded *Leptocephalus* as an abyssal creature, they concluded that adult eels must descend to the depths of the sea to reach sexual maturity and reproduce. A number of observations fitted in with this theory. In the first place, it had been known for some time that eels, after reaching a certain age, would make their way toward the sea; this impulse apparently struck male eels at the age of five to seven years, female eels at the age of nine or ten. In the second place Grassi and Calandruccio had fished a number of unusually sizable eels with extraordinarily enlarged eyes out of the sea. These eels, moreover, showed some slight development of sexual organs. Large eyes are, as both men knew, characteristic of deep-sea fish. But where in the sea did the eels begin their dive to the depths in order to reproduce? There was no trace of any such place in the Mediterranean.

An International Commission for Oceanographic Research took the matter in hand. In 1903, one of its associates who was covering certain portions of the eastern Atlantic came upon masses of migrating eel larvae which were considerably smaller than the willow-leaf larvae of the Mediterranean. These larvae were swimming steadily eastward, toward the coasts of Europe. Larvae of the American river eel were likewise found in the middle of the Atlantic. They were migrating westward, toward the coasts of America. In the light of these findings, the Commission sent the Danish zoologist Johannes Schmidt on an expedition with instructions to trace the path of the eel larvae systematically back to its point of origin.

Schmidt's research, which continued from 1904 to 1926, belongs among the great achievements of zoological study. He made expedition after expedition in his celebrated ships, the *Thor* and the *Dana*, drawing concentric circles around the eel larvae. He was aided by the crews of many naval and merchant vessels who took samples of the plankton in various parts of the Atlantic. The area of search was steadily narrowed down. By the beginning of the First World War the situation had been clarified to the following extent: west of the British Isles, eel larvae averaged 75 millimeters in length; near the

Canary and Cape Verde Islands they were only 60 millimeters; and in the vicinity of the Azores between 35 and 45 millimeters. Similarly, the size of American eel larvae diminished from the eastern coast of North America to the Bermudas. Therefore the spawning ground of both species of eel must lie between the Azores and the Bermudas—probably in the depths of the Sargasso Sea.

In 1921 Schmidt's four-masted schooner *Dana* was cruising in a region southeast of Bermuda, its keel plowing through great masses of Sargasso seaweed. There, at last, at approximately the sixtieth degree of west longitude and the twenty-fifth degree of north latitude, the great discovery was made. In twenty-five places Schmidt fished up out of the seaweed swarms of tiny "willow-leaf larvae" no more than ten millimeters in length, evidently just hatched from the egg. Not long after Schmidt brought up the first eel spawn ever found.

During the next five years more details were added to complete the picture. European and American river eels spawn in a very limited area of the Sargasso Sea, between 55° and 68° west longitude. They do not, however, spawn on the bottom, which is thirty thousand feet deep in that region, but at depths between 1,700 and 3,300 feet. The eggs float at that depth because of the buoyancy given them by a droplet of oil inside them. If they sank into the cool depths, the embryos would die, since they need a temperature of between 61° and 63° F. in order to develop.

For three years the young eels live as "willow-leaf larvae" in the sea. During this time they are gradually dispersed by the Gulf Stream over a large part of the North Atlantic. They must travel some six thousand miles to their destinations on the coasts of Europe. The American river eel, on the other hand, though born in the same spawning grounds, has an easier time. Its larval period lasts only a year, and its route to the mouths of North American rivers is far shorter than the long journey of its European cousin. Why, zoologists have asked themselves, do not all the young eels migrate from the Sargasso Sea to America? No one knows. Perhaps tens of thousands of years ago completely different temperatures prevailed in the Atlantic abysses. Possibly both species of eels spawned in a region equidistant from America and Europe.

"But when in the course of geological evolution," write Klaus Günther and Kurt Deckert in their book, *Wunderwelt der Tiefsee*, "the warm 63° temperature in the depths of the Atlantic declined and retreated further to the west, the European eel also had to shift its spawning ground further and further to the west, since it obviously could not adapt to the changing conditions." But, the argument continues, since the larvae of both species are endowed with altogether different reactions to certain conditions of light, salinity, current, and temperature in the ocean, the European eel larvae continue to make their way to the coasts of Europe in spite of geological changes.

The larvae make use of the Gulf Stream, although it remains a mystery how they keep their direction unerringly over so many thousands of miles. For that matter, how do the sexually mature eels succeed in finding, with uncanny accuracy, that spot in the whole vast ocean which alone can be counted on to provide their brood with the right temperature and sufficient food? There are no signposts, no currents, no changes in the mineral content of the water, to point their way. And it is absurd to imagine that they recall the invisible road to the Sargasso from the time of their birth and larval period.

Hitherto, only a single plausible answer to this question has been found. It is suggested that the eels, on their sexual migration, develop a special temperature sense, a "positive thermotaxis," as it is called, which compels them to swim toward precisely that part of the ocean in which the proper temperature prevails. At the same time, as their "deep-sea eyes" develop, they presumably acquire a "negative photo-taxis"—a tendency to flee from the light which prompts them to seek the regions of the ocean below the 1,600-foot level. But whether these theories are correct or adequate explanations, we do not know. The eel remains to this day a most mysterious fish.

LILLIPUTIAN HUSBANDS

One of the strangest and most grotesque denizens of the dark abysses of the sea is the deep-sea angler fish or deep-sea devil. These fish are clumsy, solitary predators equipped with lanterns or other lures with which they beckon to their unsuspecting prey. If some organism not too large attempts to snap at the bait, it vanishes immediately into the gigantic maw of the "devil." Since the angler fish are extremely sluggish and reluctant to move from any given spot, it seems as though they must have difficulty finding suitable mates at spawning time. But not very much is known about the reproductive habits of the creatures of the abysses. The exploded organisms which the dragnet brings up can scarcely tell the researcher much about their sexual secrets. And there is small likelihood that the sparse observations through the glass ports of bathyspheres would reveal something of the intimate life of the eccentric deep-sea dwellers. As yet, most of the fauna of the depths have surrendered few of their secrets.

They are scarcely accessible alive, and their dead bodies are difficult to interpret.

As early as the second half of the nineteenth century, scientists noted that their nets brought up only female angler fish. Almost every expedition obtained new species, among them impressive specimens nearly two feet in length. But there was never a male among them. Was it possible that these creatures were hermaphrodites? But the most careful dissection provided not the slightest evidence of this.

Among another group of deep-sea fish, the *Aceratiides*, the case was exactly the reverse. Only males were discovered. Now the aceratiides are, compared with the anglers, tiny creatures no more than an inch or two in length. In appearance they are totally dissimilar, possess no lures or lanterns, and instead of the gigantic maw of the angler have a strikingly developed nose and curious pincerlike jaws whose function no one could fathom. It never entered the minds of even the most imaginative zoologists to connect the male aceratiide dwarfs with the female anglers.

Then, one day, Johannes Schmidt aboard the *Dana* fished up from the depths of the Caribbean Sea the most amazing monster he had ever seen. It was an angler female to whose abdomen three aceratiide males had fastened themselves with their pincers. The males had not only dug their teeth into the angler; they had actually grown into her and attached themselves to her blood circulation. The angler was breathing for them and feeding them. The aceratiides were evidently parasites.

Parasitism is scarcely an unusual phenomenon among marine animals. The fact that fish could be parasites caused no great stir among zoologists. Certain museum specimens of angler fish, either dried or preserved in alcohol, had shown bodily appendages which eluded explanation. It was a relief finally to have found a satisfactory explanation of these. Evidently these anglers, too, had had aceratiide parasites.

But the number of cases grew with suspect frequency. And in every case the large anglers were female and the parasites males. Moreover, the parasitic lilliputians were often attached very close to the female's genital orifice. Could this be sheer chance? Gradually the reason dawned upon the scientists. The so-called parasites, often only a twentieth the size of the huge females, must be male anglers; they simply attached themselves to the bodies of their mates and had no need to worry about either sex or food.

Nowadays it has been definitely established that all aceratiides are really male angler fish, though it has not yet been determined which types of aceratiides belong to which species of anglers. The male an-

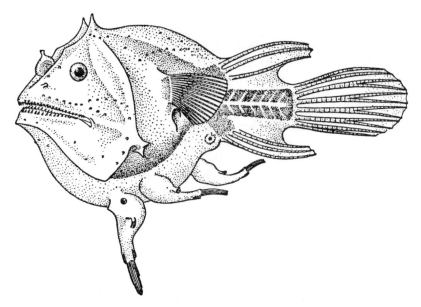

This female deep-sea angler, caught by the Danish research ship Dana, *had three ingrown males attached to its body.*

glers as a rule swim agilely through the water; they are far more lively than the clumsy female. With the aid of their highly specialized noses they seek the females by scent. And when they have found a giant mate ready for spawning, they take hold of her temporarily, fertilize her eggs, and then—in many species—let go. Since there is a considerable excess of females among the deep-sea anglers, the practice is also quite sensible.

It is not yet clear why the lilliputians of some other species of angler abandon their untrammeled sex life and from their earliest youth attach themselves to the females, often several at a time, in order to become permanently intergrown with them—a lifetime marriage with no possibility of separation. The parasitic males do not always locate, as was first thought, around the female's genital orifice. In attaching themselves they make grotesque mistakes. They grab hold with their pincers wherever they happen to strike. Angler fish have been found who wore their lilliputian husbands on their heads or on the operculum, the gill lid. Since the ingrown males are nourished by the females, the males' organs of digestion atrophy in favor of the enormously developed sexual glands.

It is possible that the apparently permanent marriage is broken up again at some time. Some marine biologists believe that the attached and ingrown dwarf males may be cast off by the females after they have fulfilled their reproductive duties, and that they can return for a while to their free-swimming existence. For how otherwise do the many other females who lack attached males ever achieve fertilization of their eggs? But if this happens, no one has ever seen it.

Dwarf males parasitic upon or inside the bodies of the females exist in the marine worm *Bonellia*, in some Cirripedia, and in a large number of Rotifera. Zoologists had not previously suspected the existence of such a curiosity among vertebrates. The deep-sea angler fish represents, as one marine biologist has put it, "a degree of specialization not even approximately achieved in any other species."

THE PREGNANT FATHER

For another case of bizarre reproductive habits, we must look at a small, curiously shaped fish which amazingly resembles the knight in chess. This is the sea horse, a dweller in the upper strata of the seaweed jungles. In the sea horse, Nature seems to have turned everything topsy-turvy. For the male, not the female, is the child-bearer.

Of course, it is no genuine pregnancy but a peculiar method of brood care, for if it were otherwise the male would not be a male. All the same, when the sea-horse male scurries through the tangles of seaweed with enormously swollen abdomen in which the babies twitch and kick, the observer cannot help being reminded of a woman great with child, or of a female kangaroo carrying its young in its pouch.

Two sea horses ready for mating put on the tenderest and most charming of courtship spectacles. As among the closely related pipefish, the female is the active partner. In her resplendent wedding dress, far showier than the modest male, she dances around her mate and grasps him with her prehensile tail. Both swim through the water, head against head, in a close embrace, like human lovers. They sway to every side, rock back and forth, and then rise to the surface of the sea. Thereupon something altogether extraordinary happens. The male puffs up his abdomen so that it presents a kind of sac, and the female protrudes a sort of penis from her body.

This female "penis" is actually a prolonged genital papilla, usually of a striking orange-red hue. With it, the female gropes about along the male's body and tries to introduce it into an opening in his abdominal sac. An observer of this process cannot help feeling that the male is being fertilized by the female. But what is taking place is not breeding in the proper sense of the word, but only a transmission of eggs. The female wants to deposit her spawn in the male's pouch. Again and again she thrusts her organ into the opening in the pouch and drops one egg after another inside. This act apparently exerts an irresistible stimulus upon the male. For at the same moment that the female's "penis" enters his body, he pours his sperm into the brood pouch.

After a while the couple terminate their embrace. The female swims away, but the male sea horse has been "impregnated" and must now undertake the nourishing and raising of the brood. He continues to behave like a female. The embryos develop in his brood pouch. They hatch out there. And as the small sea horses grow, the father's abdominal region swells like a balloon. At last the "difficult hour" approaches—the hour of birth.

The expulsion of the young from the pouch is an ordeal for the sorely tried father—a true delivery. For the opening of the pouch is

Among sea horses, the role of the sexes is partially reversed. The female "impregnates" the male with her eggs, and the male must bear the children.

small and the offspring numerous. The male doubles up, plainly suffers pain, and breathes easier when the last of his children sees the light.

MALE CHILDBED AND MIDWIFERY

A number of primitive as well as civilized peoples, ethnologists tell us, have preserved the strange custom of couvade, or male childbed, even down to our own day. Among the Bakairi and other Indian tribes of South America, among the Burmese at the time of Marco Polo, among some of the inhabitants of Southeast Asia and Oceania, when a woman had a child, the father behaved as the woman normally would. He went to bed, kept to a restricted diet, was made to undergo all sorts of painful trials, and assumed charge of the infant. Ethnologists believe that the purpose of these rites was to establish a close relationship between father and child.

Among the vertebrates who first left the water to make their home upon the dry land—the amphibians—there are hundreds of species of frogs in which the fathers care for their young or even carry them in special brood pouches. Couvade is common among such frogs, with the difference that the father does not just *pretend* to be undergoing confinement; he actually does so. When Darwin on his voyage around the world visited the coastal forests of southern Chile, he discovered tiny frogs, less than an inch long, which jumped about in the grass as gaily as grasshoppers and sometimes stood comically on their hind legs. Their heads were as amusing as their behavior: they narrowed to a point like an elephant's trunk. Therefore the animal was named "nose frog"—*Rhinoderma darwini,* as the zoologists have baptized it, in honor of the discoverer.

But the frog's fame is due not to his nose and his comical hopping, but to his way of rearing his brood. Darwin had observed that the underside of some nose frogs looked curiously swollen. If such a frog was slit open, a dozen tadpoles or fully developed small frogs tumbled out. Consequently, these specimens were thought to be females. Zoologists wondered at the existence of viviparous frogs, for such a method of reproduction is not common among the batrachians—the frogs. But the true secret of *Rhinodermi* remained hidden from them for some time. At last it was suggested that the "pregnant" frogs were not females, but males. This sounded so improbable that at first few were willing to believe it. But a staff of competent amphibian specialists set off for South America and began studying the *vaquero,* as the nose frog is known in Argentina, with the thoroughness of detectives. They made the following discoveries.

When a female frog has laid her twenty or thirty eggs, several males gather around the spawn, fertilize it, and guard it for some two weeks, until the tadpoles begin to move inside the eggs. Then the males suddenly fall upon the spawn and each tries to swallow as many eggs as possible. But the greedy fathers are not cannibals. They do not permit the eggs to slide into their stomachs, but into a large throat sac which extends from their chins almost to their thighs. There the spawn grows into the father's tissue and is nourished by the father. The young remain in the male's body until they have completed their metamorphosis and become finished little frogs. They are nourished by substances in the male's blood and finally leave the brood pouch through the father's mouth.

Males among the tree frogs or tree toads do not have quite so hard a time: the females usually stick their fertilized eggs to the male's back. There the tadpoles develop, without coming into contact with water, aside from occasional rains.

"If the tadpoles happen to be dislodged prematurely from the father's back," Doris Cochran writes of them (in *Living Amphibians of the World*) "they are entirely helpless in the water. But at a rather advanced stage they are ready to leave their parent's protection, and when he immerses himself and them in some suitable bit of water, they swim free and enter upon a life of independence."

The Seychelles frog, which lives on an archipelago in the Indian Ocean and spawns in the water-filled funnels of big leaves, exemplifies another variant of male delivery. "The tadpoles," the German herpetologist Franz Werner tells us, "crawl by movements of their tails onto the father's back. They fasten themselves there with the aid of a sticky secretion exuded by the male's skin. In this way they go through their entire metamorphosis out of water."

The male of the European accoucheur toad not only serves as a moving kindergarten, but also as a faithful midwife. At spawning time, he draws the eggs, which are arranged in long strings, from the female's cloaca, fertilizes them, and then winds the strings in figure eights around his hind legs. Once he has provided one female with obstetrical assistance, he oftens seeks out a second, third, and fourth, until he has eggs strung up to his thighs. With this burden, the accoucheur toad moves about through wet grass and among dewy weeds, thus keeping the spawn moistened. Meanwhile the tadpoles develop inside the eggs. When the time for hatching approaches, the father hops to the nearest suitable pool and there slides the strings

Male accoucheur or "midwife" frog with strings of eggs on his back.

off. The tadpoles hatch, swim away with merry flicks of their tails, and do not see their devoted parent again.

All these techniques represent adaptations to life on dry land or in the treetops. Normally, the eggs and larvae of amphibians develop only in water—in keeping with the piscine inheritance. But quite a few frogs build homes for their eggs outside of water, sometimes accomplishing true architectural feats.

Among the tree frogs which practice brood care, the female takes care of the spawn and the young by herself. The male, however, contributes important services in the preliminary phase. African and South Asian frogs find a twig hanging over water, exude a slimy fluid over it, and then both sexes vigorously beat the fluid into a foam. They discharge eggs and sperm into this foam nest. The mother guards the nest, holding it in an embrace with her arms and legs until the larvae have hatched. The next strong rainstorm washes the foam nest from the twig and carries the tadpoles into the water. If the reproductive instincts of these frogs did not drive them to make their cradle directly above a pond or an irrigated rice field, the larvae would fall to the ground and there dry out and perish.

Male and female of the fragile, attractive maki frogs choose a leaf high in the treetops, but directly above water, and glue it into the shape of a funnel. They then fill the funnel with spawn. If one funnel is not big enough, the pair go together to another leaf and likewise convert it into a cradle. This species does not guard the eggs. Nor do the tadpoles wait for rain. After a week they crawl out of the leaf nest of their own accord and drop into the water.

Remarkable mud nests are built by the most popular tree frog of Brazil. Because of its loud, metallic-sounding mating calls, which can be heard almost everywhere in the rain forests and even on the margins of the cities, the natives call is *ferreiro,* the "blacksmith" frog. Emil Göldi, a Swiss by birth and one of the most eminent naturalists of Brazil, has given us a graphic account of the way the blacksmith frog builds its nest:

> We saw first a faint movement in the water; then a quantity of mud rose to the surface, carried by a frog of whom only the two hands were visible. Diving again, after a moment the frog brought another mass of mud to the surface. . . . This was repeated until a circular wall had been reared. But what most amazed us was the manner in which the frog used its hands to smooth the interior of the mud wall like a mason with his trowel. The parapet of the wall received the same sort of careful smoothing, while the outside was neglected. For leveling the floor the frog used its abdomen, throat and hands. The resulting heap might well be compared with the crater of an extinct volcano, or with a large, water-filled soup bowl about a foot in diameter.

Only the female does the mason work, but both parents guard the eggs for several days after spawning. It is said that some blacksmith frog females continue to sit steadfastly in the nest even after the tadpoles have hatched, in order to frighten away possible predators. Such reports are quite credible, for the blacksmith frog is one of the largest and strongest of all tree frogs, attaining a length of four inches or more.

Among the marsupial frogs of the American tropics, the male offers obstetrical assistance but the female raises the children in a brood pouch on her back. Just how the eggs enter the sac is not quite clear. It appears, however, that the male helps somehow to put them there. The young are fed by the mother's body and crawl from the pouch after they have completed their metamorphosis and are fully developed small frogs.

William Beebe has called the emergence of these frogs "one of the most remarkable births among all jungle creatures." He writes:

> The opening on the lower back of the frog widened, forming the center of a narrow open spindle, as if one should bend apart the thin

slats of a venetian blind. A tangle of thickened tissue pushed out. The
frog in the gap was suddenly hustled out by succeeding impatient
brethren. He struggled free, did a slide down his mother's bent thigh
and somersaulted to the ground. Here he righted himself, looked
around and then scraped at his eye where something had lodged.
Two scrapes made all well, but no sooner did he gather his feet together and sit upright exactly as his mother had always sat, than
he was knocked head over heels by a brother who rocketed into him.
Both rolled over and over, then righted, almost touching noses and
staring into each other's eyes. . . . Out of the bulging membrane,
eyes and snouts began to appear, and sometimes four frogs would
start a terrific squabble as to which should be born first. The supply
seemed unending. There poured out a perfect stream of infants all
eager to enter the world and begin their adventures.

But the most striking form of paternal or maternal brood care in
amphibians is displayed by that Surinam toad whose "most curious
transformation" Maria Sibylla Merian described as long ago as 1705.
This toad—pipa as it is called by the inhabitants of Surinam and also
by the zoologists—has a thoroughly preposterous shape. It looks, as
Doris Cochran puts it, like a rectangular, somewhat burned potato
pancake, covered with lobes and fringes; it has no tongue and extremely small eyes, wears tactile hairs on its finger tips and huge
webs between its hind legs, which makes it an excellent swimmer
and diver. Moreover, it lives exclusively in the water and is incapable
of locomotion on land.

Maria Sibylla Merian took an interest in the Surinam toad because
she thought it produced neither eggs nor living young, at least not in
the normal manner. Instead "the young pipas grow out of the mother's back." It is understandable that Madame Merian's contemporaries should have burst into laughter at this ridiculous tale. But subsequent travelers to South America in fact observed that the back of
pregnant pipa females would be covered with what seemed to be a
honeycomb of cells. In each cell lay an egg or an embryo. And if the
toads were kept in captivity for some time, the lids of the cells would
spring open one day, and out of them would clamber small, fully
formed toads.

The French naturalist Constant Duméril and other zoologists had
in the meantime discovered the brood pouch of the marsupial frogs. It
seemed likely that the Surinam toad also might use its alveolar cells
as brood chambers. But then how did the cells arise? How did each
egg come to be in a special cell? This problem was not clarified until
1895 when Philip Lutley Sclater, then the leading British zoologist,
and his colleague Bartlett, head of the London zoo, carefully studied

The peculiar-looking "burned potato pancacke"—a female Surinam toad
—has an even more peculiar way of hatching her eggs. During mating,
the male smears the fertilized eggs on her back, a protective layer of skin
grows over them, and at the end of the incubation period, fully formed
little toads hatch from their dorsal brooding chambers as shown in this
19th-century drawing.

a number of Surinam toads from the beginning to the end of their
reproductive act.

Sclater and Bartlett saw that the couples copulated in normal frog
and toad fashion. The male mounted the female, gripping her tightly,
and waited for the eggs to emerge and fertilized them. But suddenly
the female's cloaca pushed out in the form of a tubelike sac and bent
upwards. The male seized this tube, swollen with spawn, pushed it
beneath him, squeezed the eggs out by pressing with his abdomen,
and gradually spread the entire spawn over the female's back. Then
he released her and swam off. The extruded cloaca, which looked in-
flamed, shrank rapidly and was retracted into the female's body.

During the following days the skin of the female's back grew over the eggs, one by one—probably, it is now assumed, as the result of a hormone stimulus exerted by the spawn upon the mother's body. Soon each egg was thus embedded in a cell ten to fifteen millimeters in depth and precisely rectangular in shape. A secretion formed lids over these cells. The young matured for eleven to twelve weeks, fed by the proteins formed in the tissues of the mother's back. When the incubating period was over, heads and legs of baby toads eager to be born could be seen protruding from all the cells.

Why the Surinam toad practices so complicated a method of caring for its brood has remained a mystery to zoologists. African relatives of the pipa which lead precisely the same underwater life, and whose offspring are no less imperiled by all sorts of enemies, have developed no such habits. These clawed frogs, *Dactylethra*, reproduce in the usual fashion by attaching their spawn to a variety of water plants. The tadpoles look very much like fish, and the parents pay attention to them only when they can catch and eat them.

The clawed frogs, however, became important to reproductive biologists in another respect. Around 1940, South African medical researchers discovered that they were ideal animals for diagnosing human pregnancy in its early stages. If the urine of a pregnant woman is injected into the cloaca of unfertilized *Dactylethra* females, certain hormones in the urine cause the frogs to lay eggs within a few hours —a much shorter time than in the familiar rabbit test. If the woman is not pregnant, the hormones are lacking and the frog females lay no eggs.

Since the frog test provides prompt and certain information immediately after impregnation, clawed frogs became indispensable in every gynecological clinic. However, it has since been discovered that all species of frogs react in the same way and can be used for the same purpose. Consequently, in Europe and North America the expensive *Dactylethra* was dispensed with and replaced by easily available native toads.

THE FIRST LOVE SONG

The science of biology would do well to erect a monument to amphibians, out of respect and gratitude. For it owes a good part of its most exciting discoveries to the innumerable experiments it has made with members of this class of the animal kingdom. Spallanzani, we will recall, first demonstrated artificial insemination with frogs. Frogs were also the first vertebrates which lent themselves to demonstrations of artificial parthenogenesis. In 1930 the French biologist Eugène Bataillon pricked unfertilized frog and toad eggs with a fine glass needle moistened with blood, and thereby stimulated the eggs to begin cell division. The tadpoles that emerged from these eggs were fully viable.

Nowadays biologists subject frog eggs and sperm to various forms of radiation in order to produce artificial anomalies or mutations. The secrets of change of sex and the formation of twins are being studied by experimentation with frogs, toads, and salamanders. Pituitary hormones are injected into tadpoles in order to enlarge their brain cells. Frogs serve as experimental subjects for research on industrial poisons and radiation damage. From the development of the eggs and larvae of amphibians, evolutionists have learned important facts bearing on the crucial question of how fish developed into land-dwelling vertebrates.

Amphibian eggs make ideal subjects for experimentation because —aside from the numerous special cases—they do not mature inside the mother's body, but are laid unprotected in the water. Reptiles and birds also lay eggs, of course, but these eggs, which develop under dry conditions, are protected by a hard shell which inhibits the work of the experimenter. As for amphibian larvae they are also convenient to the biologist because they swim about freely in water and can therefore be easily observed, inoculated, irradiated, and operated on. No vertebrate above the amphibians has a larval stage. Finally, adult amphibians are also dear to experimental science. They are not only extraordinarily tenacious of life; they also possess certain peculiarities which make them invaluable to the student of reproductive biology.

Among these peculiarities is hermaphroditism in toads and frogs. Among young frogs, especially, the sex is by no means finally determined. Along with indisputable females and males there is a high percentage of individuals that possess incipient sexual organs of both sexes, and are apparently undecided on which way to go. Most of these hermaphrodites gradually develop into males as they approach sexual maturity; some become females. Among certain species of toads there are no true males at all, only hermaphrodites—which, however, engage exclusively in male sexual activity. If they are castrated, the female characteristics, hitherto rudimentary, develop further; ovaries, oviducts, and female sex glands are elaborated, and within a short time the eunuchs have become true females capable of reproduction.

Here, then, we have a phenomenon similar to that which exists in the swordtails. But the toads and frogs prove far more convenient than swordtails for studying the problems of the origin of sex, the determination of sex, and chemical reversal of sex. What has been discovered is certainly no boon to the masculine element. Unfavorable conditions of life and nutrition generally favor the development of males; favorable conditions promote an increase in the number of females.

Not only biologists, but musicians and composers have a special debt to the amphibians. For when this class of animals began occupying dry land, somewhere between two hundred and three hundred and fifty million years ago, in the Carboniferous Period, living organisms began to express themselves in music, in love calls. Not that crustaceans and fish are mute but we cannot hear the sounds they produce because they are either outside the range of our hearing or drowned out in the water and inaudible from shore. Among insects, as we know, there are some passionate musicians. But in the Carboniferous Period chirping grasshoppers and crickets, humming mosquitoes and flies, screeching cicadas and click beetles did not yet exist. The Carboniferous continents were a silent world—in so far as sounds produced by living creatures are concerned. The only animal sound that mingled with the crash of thunder, the howl of winds, the roar of the sea, and the rumble of falling rocks may have been the metallic swish and hum of giant antediluvian dragonflies.

We do not certainly know, of course, whether the primitive amphibians of the Carboniferous Period already possessed vocal cords, but it is quite possible. Amphibians existed before that time. When they conquered all the continents during the Carboniferous Period, they had already assumed an amazing variety of forms—from tiny creatures only a fraction of an inch in size to gigantic armored monsters. And all the characteristics that distinguish present-day amphibians must already have been present then, at least in elementary form. Genuine batrachians, true frogs or toads, it is true, first appeared only in the Mesozoic Era; but we can scarcely imagine that the as yet unknown ancestors of frogs who lived in the earlier Paleozoic Era did not jump and croak. How otherwise would they have met for mating?

Three orders of Amphibia still remain out of the large numbers of primordial representatives of the class. They are the Gymnophiona, Urodela, and Anura—respectively, the wormlike, tailed, and tailless amphibians. The wormlike and in many respects still primitive Gymnophiona produce no sounds. Not very much is known about their reproductive life. Some species are viviparous. In others the females lay their eggs in holes they have dug in the banks of rivers, then wind themselves around the clutch and guard it until the larvae hatch out. The larvae must then seek water in order to continue their development as tadpoles.

The Urodela also—the newts and salamanders—do not raise their voices in a love call. Those among them which are not wholly mute produce only a soft croak, squeak, or peep and only when molested. Males and females find one another without the aid of music, usually by means of their sense of smell. Probably the females ready to spawn emit a specific scent into the water. Then the males, often decked out in splendid nuptial attire, with rippling dorsal crest, swarm to the scent-impregnated spot in the water, court the female by lashing their tails and showing their splendid colors, and try to block her way. It is assumed that they also give forth a scent to stimulate the female. Eventually the female moves slowly toward one of the males, thereby showing him that he is her choice. The male crawls out on land with a waddling gait; the female follows. After some time the male contorts his body and places a conical spermatophore wrapped in jelly on the ground. The female approaches it, presses her cloaca upon the cone, and allows the sperm to enter her body. In some cases she takes up the entire packet of semen. It may, however, happen that the proud lady changes her mind in the course of the walk and in that case she pitilessly devours the male's cone of sperm. Aside from his excited courtship dance, the male newt remains quite passive. He has no way to prevail upon the female to allow him to fertilize her. He can only hope that the proud mistress who has chosen him will accept the offering of sperm.

In certain Urodela which are still quite primitive in an evolutionary sense—the mud eel, the giant salamander, and the canine-toothed newt—the process of fertilization is like that among fishes, the female laying the eggs and the male then coming along and releasing his sperm over them. In some species of canine-toothed newts the male is said to engage in midwifery like the accoucheur toad, in that it uses its hind legs to pull the packets of spawn out of the female's body. The female of the mud devil, an American giant salamander, pastes her long strings of eggs to a stone where they will not be swept away by swift currents.

For a long time zoologists believed there was a second exception to the general rule among urodeles. The land salamanders, which bear living young, seemed to mate in the manner of the higher vertebrates. Salamander couples were often found in what seemed to be a highly intimate sexual union. The male embraced the female's body with his legs and tail, twisted himself, and pressed his cloaca firmly against the female's. It was hard to think of this performance as any-

thing but genuine copulation, although male salamanders—like all
amphibians with the exception of the Gymnophiona—possess no organs of copulation. Only at the end of the nineteenth century did a
herpetologist named Zeller come forth with the announcement that
land salamanders in coupling perform no differently from the newts.
The male expels a cone of sperm which the female takes into her
cloaca. But in the land-dwelling urodeles the female does not have to
find the spermatophore; it is delivered by the male right at her door,
so to speak, since the sexual orifices of the two salamanders are
pressed close together.

While the courtship of salamanders is a silent, almost impersonal
ritual, that of the frogs is a passionate, deafening concert. In the salamanders the female alone is active, in the frogs the male performs
virtually an act of violence. Like male crickets and grasshoppers, male
frogs make music that lures the female, but they have at their disposal
an incomparably richer set of tonalities. Everyone who has attempted
to describe the song of the frog resorts to onomatopoeic terms. Each
species of frog has its own call: they croak, squawk, grunt, bleat,
thrum, chirp, and whistle; they ring like small bells, knock like ham-
mers, clang like struck iron. And they produce all these sounds by
means of the same simple method which enables human beings to
speak: they make their breath pass over vocal cords.

When the males at breeding time have noisily proclaimed their desires long enough, the spawn-filled females come hopping or swimming along. Thereupon the males are seized by a rapist's fury.
Theirs is no tender courtship; they do not indulge in the games or
dances of fish and salamanders. Their sole impulse is to mount upon
the female's back and fasten their arms around her in a seemingly
irresistible embrace. And if they do not succeed, frogs will seize upon
other species, fish, bits of driftwood, even the human hand.

A male frog fortunate enough to mount and grasp a female has by
no means solved all his sexual problems. For now the unsuccessful
rivals come along, try to displace him, or also seize upon the courted
female. The violence of these struggles often leads to the death of the
females from exhaustion or internal wounds.

Nor does the embrace itself bring the male frog release from his
sexual drives. Often he must sit for days upon the female before the
actual copulation can take place. Sometimes couples hop in tight embrace over fields and paths before the female condescends to seek out
a pool suitable for spawning. And all around the pair, while they celebrate their nuptials, sounds the infernal racket of the disappointed
rivals. The male frog does not seek to inject his sperm into the female's body. As Spallanzani long ago showed by his famous experi-

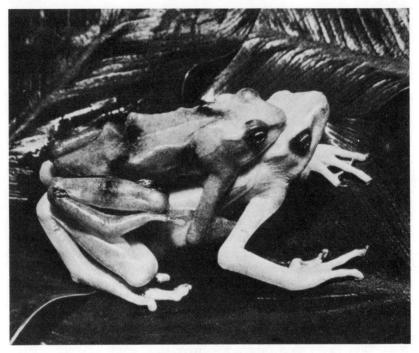

Frogs pairing in the jungle foliage.

ments of putting breeches on frogs, the bullfrog practices external fertilization. This means that he must wait until the spawn comes welling from the female's body, in order to release his semen at precisely the right moment.

Many male batrachians help matters along, however. As a rule they offer obstetrical aid, although the form of this is not so obvious as it is in the accoucheur toad and the Surinam toad. By the force of their embrace they literally squeeze the clumps or strings of eggs out of the female's body. This pressure can be so powerful that—according to the observations of the French naturalist Héron-Royer—the male's thumbs sometimes bore deep holes in the female's abdomen. This prolonged sexual furioso climaxes in an eruptive discharge of the sex cells from both partners, followed by profound exhaustion. Here is an act of passion comparable to that among the higher animals, at least for the males.

Among the Dactylethra, those African clawed frogs which were the first to be used in the pregnancy test, the male performs an additional act of violence in order to render the female submissive to his will. Male Dactylethra are considerably smaller than the females. The difference in size is such that the male would scarcely be able to hold a fully mobile female long enough to squeeze the eggs out of her body. Accordingly, after the little fellow has embraced the female, he spins her around several times until she actually loses "consciousness." Then he proceeds with the rape of his now helpless mate.

EVOLUTION OF AN ORGAN

As we have seen, the male frog has no organ for copulation, and the female no vagina. The sexual products are discharged from the cloaca, through the same orifice as the excretions of the intestines and the kidneys. Fertilization takes place outside the female's body. And the hatched young must pass through a larval stage before they take on adult form. But all male mammals possess an organ for transmitting the semen, and most female mammals have a sexual orifice distinctly separated from the opening of the intestines and the urinal passage. Mammals practice internal fertilization; the embryos pass through their entire metamorphosis inside the mother's womb and are born as complete, though small, replicas of their parents.

The vertebrates developed these characteristics and habits step by step in the course of two hundred million years. The penis was "invented" by reptiles, rejected by the majority of birds, and rediscovered by the mammals. Among the lowest mammals—the spiny anteaters and the duckbills—the cloaca has continued to function as the female sexual orifice. In the marsupials, however, the practice of conceiving and giving birth through the anus is finally abandoned. Among the marsupials, also, living birth—which was the rule only among certain fish, amphibians, and reptiles—became established once and for all. Above the level of the marsupials it has become the unvarying practice for children to be released from the mother's body only after they are fully formed.

If we were to ask a contemporary zoologist where the lower vertebrates leave off and the higher vertebrates begin, he would unquestionably draw the line between the Amphibia and the reptiles. For the reptiles have much in common with birds and mammals, but only a little in common with the Amphibia. Reptiles are covered with scales or other horny integument as birds are covered with feathers and mammals with hair. They practice internal fertilization and deposit their offspring almost entirely on land. They do not pass through any larval stage. Their eggs are protected by shells, like those of the birds. And most male reptiles possess a genuine organ of copulation.

This organ has an interesting evolutionary history. Some sort of apparatus for introducing the sperm directly into the female's body exists among countless invertebrate animals—many worms, snails, and insects have true sexual members. Squid, crabs, and spiders, on the other hand, transmit their packets of sperm with the aid of false organs of copulation. This is also true of the viviparous fishes. Male amphibians lack all such equipment, true or false. But Nature has undertaken two experiments on the amphibian level, one of which has proved to be fraught with consequence. The subject of both experiments is the male anus. In the first case, among a number of land salamanders the male's anus inverts *over* the female's, so that the packet of semen will be deposited precisely in front of the female genital orifice. But the reverse experiment proved far more effective: the male thrusts his anus *into* the female's. Here was a technique with many potentialities.

The only amphibians which mate in this manner are the primitive wormlike caecilians. Bölsche describes their copulation in his somewhat extravagant style:

> Despite their snake form, the aforesaid caecilia has no tail of any kind, but the anus is placed exactly on the posterior tip of the body. Since this anus is at the same time a genuine gateway of love, our blind burrowing friend pushes out the wall of its anus in the form of a long pointed cone, till the anus itself looks like a genuine copulative member. And this it now thrusts deep into the anus of the female burrower, as a really ingenious pederast, in whose case the maneuver still fulfills its real purpose.

With a little imagination we can easily construe the next step. A tubelike extrusion in the wall of the anus is wetted with sperm and immediately thereafter turned inside out like the finger of a glove, so that the inner surface is on the outside. When the inverted tube is thrust into the female opening, the droplets of sperm clinging to it accomplish the fertilization. After copulation the finger of the glove is drawn back into its original position.

In all probability many primordial reptiles practiced this method of copulation; it is still in use among lizards and snakes, although with some variations. In the first place, male lizards and snakes protrude not one but two "glove fingers" from the anus, although usually only one of them performs its function. In the second place the organs are provided with notches from which the semen can drip. And in the third place these organs of copulation are really terrifying in appearance, for they are covered with spines, warts, or hooks. The male uses these to hook himself firmly inside the female's body. Two paired lizards can scarcely be separated, and when a snake in the act of procreation flees, it drags its firmly attached partner along by the anus.

We do not know whether the female feels pleasure or pain when these barbed tubes penetrate her body. The sex act of lizards, at least, seems to resemble a rape, as among frogs. Not that the amiable preliminaries suggest anything of the sort. When the lizard male first seeks out a female, he behaves like a courting fighting fish. He shows off, raising himself high on his legs, drawing his head back and displaying all his resplendent coloration. Rivals are driven away with furious bites. Then the male follows the female in a characteristic mating procession, moves closer and closer to her, licks her, and suddenly digs his teeth into her flank or neck.

The love bite seems very rough. But it is an indispensable part of the ritual. Actually, the act is not genuine rape. For if the female is unwilling, she flees rapidly, and in that case she is never pursued. If on the other hand she tolerates the bite without trying to run away, she thereby shows her acceptance of the mate. The male must then slide his abdomen underneath the female in such a way that the anal slits meet. It can then introduce its spiny "glove finger" without difficulty.

Among snakes the procedure is considerably tamer. Some nonpoisonous species practice the love bite also, but most snakes merely twine around one another, the male groping with the tip of his tail for the female's cloaca. We can easily understand that poisonous snakes do not bite during copulation: if they did the males would soon have exterminated all the females. Aside from this matter of the bite, the copulation of snakes differs little from that of lizards. Among vipers and adders we will sometimes see a whole knot of males and females in sexual congress. The reptiles which have thus transformed themselves into a Gorgon's head are attached in pairs, anus to anus, and if disturbed cannot extricate themselves from their tangle. They can do no more than extend their heads from the knot, hiss and strike at the disturber. Courageous foresters and rangers have sometimes amused themselves by gathering up the whole hissing lot in a canvas bag and carrying them away.

Unfortunately, paleontologists can tell us nothing about the genitalia and copulatory methods of the prehistoric saurians, (dinosaurs, ichthyosaurs, etc.), for soft tissues, unlike bones, do not petrify, and hence are not preserved over the ages. Certain injuries to skull and jaw bones, however, offer evidence that some giant saurians must have

Sex play of the common adder.

engaged in violent mating struggles. We know, too, that there were both oviparous and viviparous saurians. Numerous eggs of land saurians have been found in the Mongolian and South African deserts. And embedded in the slate of the Swabian Jura mountains, where a great arm of the sea extended during the Mesozoic Era, scientists have found the skeletons of female ichthyosaurians with fully developed young inside their bodies. Some primordial reptiles may have mated in salamander fashion, without the aid of a male copulatory organ. The only surviving saurian, the New Zealand tuatara lizard, does so today.

We might also consider crocodiles and tortoises as living survivors of primordial times. They existed in the Mesozoic Era, in the age of the giant saurians, and have lived on in scarcely altered form. Since both birds and mammals evolved from the early Mesozoic reptiles, the sexual mechanisms of crocodiles and tortoises can tell us much about the development of sexual union. Among these animals, the primitive form of the mammalian penis arose. And this primitive member functioned in much the same way as that of the mammalian male.

Male crocodiles and turtles possess a wartlike or cone-shaped fleshy protrusion on the anterior wall of the cloaca. Ordinarily this organ lies hidden inside the cloacal slit. In sexual excitement, however, blood pours into the genital region, filling the cone-shaped appendage. The organ swells, erects, and protrudes like an outstretched finger from the male's cloaca. This is true erection, the process which makes possible sexual intercourse in the scaly lizards, in many birds, and in all mammals. According to the definition of sexual biologists, erection is the product of an accumulation of blood, resulting from certain nerve stimuli, in the erectile tissues of the male penis. If we abide by this definition, the protrusion of the copulatory tubes in lizards and snakes cannot be called genuine erection, whereas the swelling of the copulatory organ in crocodiles and turtles does meet the requirements.

Here, it would seem, all that the male human being needs in the way of sexual equipment is already present. But the crocodile's copulatory member differs from that of the mammals in one significant respect. It does not have an internal tube down which the semen can flow; it has only a deep longitudinal groove on the outside. Thus the sperm runs from the male's to the female's body like water in an open rain gutter. This would seem to be a somewhat impractical arrangement, for if the sexual union were not quite close enough, many of the precious male sex cells could easily be lost. Nevertheless, the method worked and became established. Those birds that possess male organs (ostriches, ducks and geese, bustards, the hocco, and others) have the same type of groove as the crocodiles and tortoises. Only among the mammals did the "gutter" become an internal channel.

Much as crocodiles and turtles resemble one another in the structure of their genital apparatus, their behavior is altogether different when in the grip of the breeding impulse. The manners of crocodiles are crude, to say the least. They open wide their maws showing rows of fearsome teeth; they roar and fight. The male throws the female on her back and overpowers her, belly against belly. After the act is completed, some accounts say, the male crocodile may be courteous enough to turn her over again. But that is as far as he goes.

The hearts of male turtles, on the other hand, are full of tenderness and affection. These animals engage in courtship and nuptial play which seem inconceivable in animals of such clumsiness. The engagement ritual of the mud turtle and water tortoise is particularly charming. If a male mud turtle meets a female at breeding time, it swims slowly toward her until their heads almost touch. The two then make a succession of quivering movements with their forelegs. Their heads are stretched forward and then withdrawn; excitement mounts, and in a good many species the ceremony becomes a veritable swimming dance. Even very small terrapin which are not yet sexually mature greet one another by such quivering dance movements. Probably the sexes recognize each other by specific gestures.

The male turtle can mate only if the female is ready and plainly indicates that she is. For she must thrust the posterior part of her body with the cloacal cleft partly out of her shell. If she does not do so, all courting will be in vain. As a rule, the quivering dance suffices to arouse the sexual impulses of the female. After a while she drops to the bottom of the water, extends her tail from the shell, and in this position awaits the male. He then hastily clambers on her back and bends his own tail down so that he can introduce his copulatory organ into the female's cloaca. The pair often remain united for hours at a time. It is said that in the large marine terrapin the males may ride on the female's shell for days on end.

Now and then there is a prudish tortoise female who withholds herself from her suitor. The male has an infallible technique for overcoming such primness. He snaps once or twice at the head or legs of his prospective mate. The female then withdraws these parts of her body into her shell, obeying an irresistible reflex. And since turtles at mating time are especially fat, the hind end automatically protrudes. In mud turtles this is a common trick; among land tortoises it is the rule. The land tortoise, ordinarily clumsy, is agile and passionate at breeding time and so the male pursues the female with surprising speed, snaps at her legs, tries to mount her. The female primly runs away from the suitor, but is coquettish enough to wait for him if he slows down and appears to be on the point of abandoning the race. If she proves too coy, the male will sometimes inflict several battering-ram blows against her shell; in the larger species these maneuvers produce a thrumming noise. Similarly, jealous rivals ram and bite one another. It may take days before the male is at last in a position to mount the female's shell. Even then he must guard himself against competitors who try persistently to drive away the fortunate lover, or even to lift the united couple and throw them on their backs.

The zoologist Karl Escherich describes how a Moorish tortoise crooned a love song during courtship and copulation.

> The male ran back, climbed on the female with his forelegs resting on her shell, stretched his neck forward as far as possible, and with mouth wide open produced sounds which resembled the distant cries of a baby; they consisted of a long-drawn-out Aaaa, aaaa which was audible at a considerable distance. The female's behavior was quite remarkable. At the sound of these cries she likewise stretched her head forward and then moved it jerkily, in a regular rhythm, to the right and left, as if listening to determine where the singer was.

Other tortoises peep, groan, moan and utter a sound like a cat's meow in such situations.

The males of many species of tortoise use the spiny tips of their tails to stimulate the female's genital region. While riding on the female's back they strike their tails almost continually against their mate's cloaca. These blows obviously intensify the female's sexual excitement, and after a series of such blows she extends the hind end of her body as far as possible out of the shell.

RACE WITH DEATH

The reproduction of turtles has entered world literature in the work of the playwright Tennessee Williams. In his drama *Suddenly Last Summer*, there is a scene in which Mrs. Venable, the decadent cosmopolitan woman infatuated with her son, describes the tragedy of the turtle's birth:

> Once a year the female of the sea turtle crawls up out of the equatorial sea onto the blazing sand beach of a volcanic island to dig a pit in the sand and deposit her eggs there. It's a long and dreadful thing, the depositing of the eggs in the sand pits, and when it's finished the exhausted female turtle crawls back to the sea half-dead. She never sees her offspring, but we did. Sebastian knew exactly when the sea-turtle eggs would be hatched out and we returned in time for it. . . .

Mrs. Venable then describes how the just-hatched sea turtles scramble out of the sand pits and start their race to the sea:

> And the sand all alive, all alive, as the hatched sea turtles made their dash for the sea, while the birds hovered and swooped to attack and hovered and—swooped to attack! They were diving down on the hatched sea turtles, turning them over to expose their soft undersides, tearing the undersides open and rending and eating their flesh. Sebastian guessed that possibly only a hundredth of one per cent of their number would escape to the sea. . . .

This estimate is decidedly too pessimistic. For every female diamondback terrapin and green turtle lays from a hundred to a hundred and fifty eggs. The animals would long ago have become extinct if at least five per cent of the offspring did not escape the perils which threaten them after hatching on the beach and during their first few weeks of aquatic life. But otherwise, all of Tennessee Williams' facts are correct. The baby sea turtles' rush to the sea is literally a race with death. And today these large marine turtles, as well as the gigantic tortoises that have survived on a few tropical islands, are threatened with extinction. For rats, dogs, pigs, and man have joined their many age-old enemies. Their eggs are collected for eating, adult tortoises are caught and made into soup, and all sorts of ornaments are made out of their shells.

When the first carnivorous mammals—inconspicuous creatures the size of rats—appeared on earth during the Mesozoic Period, the great reptiles ceased to be the uncontested rulers of the earth. The small, scurrying mammals could do no harm to them directly, but they could eat the eggs of the most enormous saurian. And they apparently did so with pleasure. The American explorer Roy Chapman Andrews discovered many clutches of saurian eggs in the Gobi Desert, and saw that in many cases they had been cracked and sucked dry by small mammals. A similar fate must have befallen the eggs of giant reptiles in other regions of the earth.

Thus the gradual extinction of the saurians could have been due to the rise of the Mammalia. "It is quite probable that such may have been the case," writes the American paleontologist Edwin H. Colberg, "but how important this factor may have been in causing the ultimate complete decline of the dinosaurs is a question of considerable uncertainty." Possibly the saurians passed from the face of the earth just like other organisms which reached and overstepped the peak of their evolution and specialization, so that they were no longer able to adapt to changing conditions.

It is, however, significant that those primitive reptiles which were exempted from the general disappearance of the saurians were those which buried their eggs carefully and in some cases guarded them until the offspring hatched. The primitive tuataras, turtles, and crocodiles care for their brood; the same is true of the "recent" reptiles, the lizards and snakes. Perhaps such care is a heritage from the days in which rodentlike predators scurried about in the night and greedily fell upon the eggs of saurians.

The simplest reptilian nest is a pit in the ground. Chameleons and various other lizards—those that do not bear living young—dig a hole in the ground, lay eggs in it, and cover the eggs with soil. Iguanas are fond of using ant nests or termitaria for this purpose. The practice is a useful one, on two accounts. In the first place the nests are pleasantly warm, and in the second place the offspring hatch out to find ideal food right at hand. The same practice is followed by various snakes. Other species of snakes lay their eggs on heaps of leaves or piles of manure, which keep the eggs moderately moist and at a proper incubating temperature. Pythons can actually incubate their young. They twine themselves around the clutch of eggs, and their

Spotted rock snake incubating eggs. She acts as her own nest.

Young Indian pythons hatching.

muscular activity maintains a temperature of from three to five degrees above that of the environment.

The strangely archaic tuatara lizard of New Zealand, mentioned above, lives in the cave colonies of petrels and finds deep shafts in which to lay its eggs. It heaps them in several layers, covers them with grass or leaves, then blocks up the entrance to the shaft with a mixture of grass and earth. That this most primitive of all living reptiles goes through such a careful procedure is probably due to its close association with the petrels. For the birds are enthusiastic egg eaters, but they cannot get at these delicacies in their safe-deposit vaults.

The way a female turtle digs a pit for her eggs has been described by Bernhard Grzimek as follows:

> At the spot the turtle female has chosen, she inserts her rather long tail, its tip held stiff, into the ground, and then moves her body back and forth so that the tail drills into the earth and makes a conical hole. Then she alternately digs with her right and left hind feet, in a shoveling motion, thus producing a hole which widens out inside and is almost egg-shaped. As soon as the first egg emerges from the anal opening it is cautiously caught by the hind leg and guided to the ground. The other hind leg performs the same service for the second egg. Each egg is covered with a thin layer of earth. . . . Finally the turtle buries the eggs and smooths the ground by moving her shell over it, crawling back and forth until no one can find the location of this important cache.

The female of many species of turtle employs her tail to dig a pit for the eggs, guiding each egg as it emerges with her hind foot, and finally smoothing the earth of the hiding place by moving her shell back and forth over it.

Sometimes, however, the ground is quite hard. Fresh-water turtles have learned to solve this problem. They possess two large bladders which are connected with their intestines and which in some species extend almost from the lung to the anus. These anal bladders, as they are called, are constantly filled with fresh, oxygen-rich water, and enable the animals to breathe partially through their intestines. When a mud turtle wishes to establish an egg pit in hard ground, it first softens the earth by discharging the water of the anal bladders over the spot. As it digs with its tail it lets more liquid run into the hole. As soon as the anal bladders have been emptied, it returns to the water, refills them, and then continues its work.

The most affectionate reptile mothers are found among those of the class which to our minds are its most savage and fearsome members, the crocodiles and alligators. They not only bury their eggs in sand or swampy ground and cover them with a layer of reeds, but also care for the eggs after laying. Female alligators even lie on the nest, fend off enemies, and help the young to hatch. When hatching time has come, the baby alligators inside the egg make squawking sounds. This is the signal for the mother to remove the heap of reeds and dig out the eggs. Once all the babies have hatched, she leads them down to water like a duck with her brood of ducklings.

Among the South American caymans the mother is said to continue to lead a model family life. The females display active affection for their young for a long time, and defend them furiously. The British traveler Sir Robert Schomburgk attests to this. An Indian in his expedition once crawled out on a tree trunk projecting over a Brazilian river, killed a young cayman with an arrow, and drew it out of the water. At that moment the mother bobbed up in the midst of the other young, uttered a loud roar, and tried to attack the party. "The hitherto calm surface of the water," Schomburgk writes,

> suddenly became an agitated mass of billows, since the cayman lashed it continually with her crooked tail, and I must admit that the incredible boldness of the animal made my heart beat twice as fast. . . . After we had exhausted our supply of arrows, I thought it wise for us to retreat as cautiously as possible. Obstinately, the mother followed us as far as the shore; but she came no further, for on land the cayman is too timid to be dangerous.

The activity of birds in building nests, hatching their eggs, feeding their young, has always struck the human race as the finest symbol of self-sacrificing parental love. But as we have seen, the reptiles are far from indifferent toward their young. In the next chapter, we shall see to what extent birds deserve their reputation, as well as how their families are brought into being in the first place.

CHAPTER SIX

■

MARRIAGE AND FAMILY

IN THE NEST

WHY DO BIRDS SING?

When we hear birds singing in the spring, we more or less assume that they are singing of their love and their joy in being alive. But this belief, time-honored as it is, is open to question.

The first ornithologist who refused to accept the songs of birds at face value was Bernhard Altum. Born in 1824 in Münster, Westphalia, he became a Catholic priest and developed such an interest in birds that at the age of thirty-one he returned to the university to study the sciences. He became one of the leading ornithologists of Germany, gave lectures on zoology, and in 1863 published a book which at the time aroused a great deal of controversy, but whose conclusions are nowadays coming to be accepted. Its title was *Der Vogel und sein Leben* ("The Life of the Bird"), and it shocked people's sensibilities because Altum contended that the behavior of birds was governed solely by instinct. The ornithologists of his day held the opposite view: birds could love and hate; they were endowed with judgment, reason, free will, and a rich spiritual life—like man. Bird lovers protested loudly when Altum uttered his heresies.

No doubt Altum went too far in his efforts to reduce birds to pure instinctual machines. He was by no means in sympathy with the tendency of nineteenth-century naturalists to obscure the borderline between animal and man. He wanted to demonstrate that the crown of creation was a being entirely different from even the highest animal. And so he ridiculed those sentimental bird lovers who made much of the devotion of birds for their fledglings. "The so-called love

248

of offspring is the urge to feed birds of such and such a shape, uttering such and such cries, fluttering their wings in such and such a manner and opening their beaks wide, but it is not love." Modern behaviorists would agree that Altum described this feeding urge correctly. But they would add that man, too, in tending his children is to a large degree reacting instinctively to an innate "baby pattern."

In man this instinct to care for the young applies not only to his own babies, but to all young animals which have large eyes, look plump and soft, and make clumsy movements. At the sight of such creatures every normal person is stirred to tenderness and affection. But those young animals which do not fit into the human baby pattern—unfeathered fledglings in the nest, for example, and blind, newborn rodents—are regarded by most people as ugly. In bird mothers, on the other hand, and in rodent mothers, only such "ugly" creatures arouse the fostering instinct; such creatures correspond to *their* baby pattern. So in the realm of child care, at least, the gulf between man and animal is not so wide or deep as Altum thought.

Altum had some equally hard things to say about the singing of birds. Birds, he said, do not sing because they are in love, but because they wish to define the limits of their territory. "Only birds that have a breeding territory sing well." The song proclaims to other male members of the species that the place they are approaching is already occupied. The cock does not crow to please the hens, but to inform other cocks: "Here I am and here I intend to stay." Similarly, the male finch or lark trills, not to delight his female, but to set acoustic boundary posts around his property.

After many years of research, first on wrens and then on other songbirds, ornithologists were able to show that this view is absolutely correct. Female wrens pay virtually no attention to the energetic and almost continual singing of their males. They are far more interested in the round, artfully constructed nests of moss of which the little singers offer them a rich selection, and they wander from territory to territory to pick out the prettiest nest. Many other species of birds have been observed to behave in the same way. Bernhard Grzimek has put the matter succinctly: "Male songbirds wage their battles mostly with song, not with blows. If one blares more loudly and vigorously than another, after a while the other male usually takes himself off of his own accord."

Sometimes, however, the singers' contest degenerates into a genuine fight. In that case, not the best singer but almost always the first and legitimate owner of the territory proves to be the victor. David Lack once undertook an experiment with two robins in order to determine the rules of such combats. Each of the males had his own territory. Lack caught one male, placed it in a cage, and left the cage in its own territory. Soon the owner of the adjacent territory arrived and began to sing. The caged male, however, hurled at him a bellicose song of such volume that the intruder hastily quit the field. Now Lack carried the victor in his cage into the territory of the defeated male. At once the situation changed. The male who had fled only minutes before evidently felt so strong on his own ground that he furiously attacked the cage. And the former winner was so uncertain in the alien territory that he did not utter a peep, let alone a challenging song.

Among wrens, a territory is as large as a good-sized kitchen garden. In a small park there may be anywhere from five to ten wren territories. Each territory is full of nests. The male wren may build as many as a dozen nests of moss and wet leaves in the course of a season. A number of years ago a Dutch student of zoology named Kluiver was strolling through the park of his university, which was divided by invisible boundaries into several wren principalities. It occurred to him and some of his fellow students to band all the wrens and follow their comings and goings. They observed that the males remained faithful to their stations, while the females strayed from territory to territory. If a male wren succeeded in seducing a female with the aid of an especially attractive nest, so that she mated with him and laid her eggs, he promptly lost interest in her. She wandered away and perhaps conferred her favors upon the ruler of the adjacent principality. The male continued to meet his obligation to care for the fledglings, went on singing lustily, drove away more rivals and captivated more females, so that in a good many cases he might have to care simultaneously for three nests of hungry youngsters. Wrens, then, are both good fathers and polygamists whose marriages are anything but exemplary.

Among the majority of songbirds, however, monogamy is the rule —at least for the duration of a breeding period. The male and female recognize each other and do not tolerate any other bird of their own species in the vicinity of the nest. Those who really know birds, however, warn us against passing moral judgments upon avian marriages. It is scarcely to the point to speak of monogamy or polygamy. The "monogamists" differ from the "polygamists" not because of the number of their mates or the alternation of mates, but because both parents are necessary for incubating and raising the offspring. The couple remain together for this reason. If, on the other hand, only one of the parents cares for the offspring, several mates are possible, or the mating may be an entirely casual affair.

Birds other than the songbirds proper also possess the gift of voice.

Birds do not produce their sounds in the larynx, as mammals do. Instead, at the spot where the windpipe forks into twin bronchial branches they have a highly complex singing apparatus made of muscle fibers—the syrinx. With this instrument many species can not only produce a variety of definite tones, but can also alter their song at will. Such conscious variations reach their apex in imitation, or mocking, as ornithologists term it. The expression dates back to the days of moralizing zoology, when people naively thought that mocking birds were making sport of those they imitated.

Actually, mocking birds have merely incorporated the sounds of other animals and of nature in their songs. Shrikes, starlings, blue throats, and jays, as well as mockingbirds proper, belong among the imitators. Raptorial birds and parrots which repeat human speech are also "mockers." In any case, many songbirds do not possess an innate knowledge of the proper song for their species. The young must learn how to sing from their parents. "It is easy to demonstrate this," the German ornithologist Oskar Heinroth declares,

> by rearing a male finch in solitude from a very early age. Such a bird invents a song which does not in the least resemble that of a member of its species that lives in freedom. No one acquainted with the finches would take it for a finch song. Man may make clever use of the imitative talents of young male songbirds by whistling songs to them; these songs are then reproduced with amazing fidelity by bullfinches, blackbirds, starlings, and various other species.

Birds, then, are the best musicians in the animal kingdom. And any animal that possesses such a tonal range as they do is bound to use its voice not only to scream challenges to the world at large, but on many other occasions—whenever it has something to say. The young speak up; the parents coax the band of fledglings; the finding of a good place for feeding is announced; warnings of danger are given; couples greet one another; a bird will inform other members of its species just how it feels at the moment. The syrinx—the tonal apparatus of the bird—is used so frequently that it inevitably plays a special part in courtship. But, strangely enough, the so-called songbirds use it in this way less than others.

The courtship song of the capercailzie or cock-of-the-woods is among the most famous. Hunters and writers on hunting have described it in the most romantic terms. The sound of it is supposed to rouse the feelings of a hunter to fever pitch. Gentler bird lovers, who are not bent on shooting the lovesick cock so they may deck their hats with his showy feathers, have also given rapturous descriptions of this song. A rather more sober account of the capercailzie's courtship was set down in the midst of the Romantic era—in 1822—by Pastor Christian Ludwig Brehm, a far better ornithologist, incidentally, than his son Alfred, author of the popular *Brehm's Tierleben*.

"The cock," wrote Pastor Brehm in his three-volume book on birds,

> extends his head in courting, holding it at a tilt; he raises the feathers of his head and throat and produces smacking sounds which succeed one another more and more rapidly until the principal cry rings out and the "slurring" begins. The slurring consists of hissing sounds that much resemble the whetting of an iron tool; they are produced several times in series, with the last tone drawn out. Usually, right at the beginning of the cry, more rarely at its mid-point, which consists of rattling sounds, the cock raises his tail, spreads it in the shape of a fin, and stretches his somewhat lowered wings out from his body. When he rattles, he sometimes makes prancing motions on his branch; in slurring he erects almost all his feathers and quite often turns in a circle. But the courtship song does not always follow this pattern. Some capercailzies stop their rattling before the principal cry, others afterwards, still others in the middle of the slurring; still others produce only a few rattling notes. In fact we sometimes come upon a capercailzie who alternates regular with irregular courtship songs on one and the same morning.

Capercailzies and heath cocks do not sing in order to drive rivals away from their territory; their aim is to attract hens ready for mating. If the song accomplishes its purpose, the cock briefly pays court to the hens, mates them, and goes his way. The hens have to take care of the offspring alone. As Heinroth puts it: "Aside from mounting, there is no connection between male and female." Among other species of fowl, however, the cock surrounds himself with his harem, stays with them after mating, and helps to raise the chicks.

Male fowl, whether they are good or bad husbands and fathers, are considered fierce fighters at mating time. The sport of cockfighting is popular the world over. Man, with his breeding methods, has increased the bellicose propensities of fighting cocks, but blood flows in the sexual duels of wild species also. Hesse and Doflein describe a free-for-all among a number of heath cocks:

> Now all the cocks bowed and whirled and hopped around like mad. Now and then one leaped two feet up into the air. Suddenly two flew at each other, attacking with beaks and claws. Feathers flew, and one of the warriors, defeated, left the scene of the battle to try his luck in another mating territory. Other cocks hissed at one another, ran circles around their antagonists, and waged sham battles. This went on four hours, from four o'clock in the morning until

nearly eight o'clock. Meanwhile many hens had assembled in the vicinity, making their presence known by a soft clucking.

Such sham combats are also practiced by the males of American prairie fowl. They puff out their crops so that the colors make an impressive display and turn—to quote Adolf Remane—"in jerky movements that seem almost mechanical around and alongside one another. This dance does not, however, take place in front of the inconspicuous females." During this ritual they utter curious rumbling sounds. The females put in only brief appearances on the dance floor. They are mated in passing, as it were; the cocks seem far more interested in their mass ceremony than in their sexual duties.

The courtship patterns and love songs of birds are of such amazing variety that only a few examples can be cited here. Ganders make sham attacks on any other birds, winding up the performance by a screeching cry of triumph. If the goose for whom the braggart is putting on this act joins in the cry, the marriage is celebrated. Drakes utter a particular grunting whistle when they catch sight of a female, and assume all sorts of display postures which show off their fine plumage. Pigeons coo and make throaty sounds. Ravens bow, fluff their feathers, and produce croaking nasal tones. Turkey cocks in their mating dance utter a curious gobbling noise; their dark-red wattles swell alarmingly, so that they look and sound as if they are going to have a fit of apoplexy any moment.

It seems perverse to say that in the turkey's gobbling and the gander's trumpeting there is more amorous yearning than in the finch's song, the blackbird's warble, or the lark's chortle. No doubt the song with which the songbird fills the air in order to mark out his territory does incidentally call the female's attention to the singer. Moreover, wedded pairs will call one another at lower registers. But during the breeding season and after the nuptials, any further singing that goes on is due to the male's determination to keep strangers out of his private property.

There is, however, some connection between the songbird's singing and his desire for a mate. For the principal singing period comes just at the time when the sex glands are swollen and the body well supplied with sex hormones. Incidentally, birds are virtually sexless outside the breeding period. Before it and afterward, their sex glands shrink to such an extent that they are hard to find.

THE PEACOCK SPREADS ITS TRAIN

The sex hormones also account for the different dress worn by male and female birds at breeding time. Feathers which contain no pigment are just as white as unpigmented hair. The horny tissue of which they are made is honeycombed with numerous air-filled cavities. When pigment flows into these capillaries, or they are coated by an outer layer of pigmented and unpigmented cells, the initially colorless plumage acquires a great variety of brilliant patterns. And since birds undergo periodic moltings, many species can change their dress from season to season.

For a time zoologists believed that it was the activity of the male hormones that caused male birds to put on such resplendent nuptial plumage. Present-day theory holds that just the opposite takes place. Male display is the normal dress of birds; the female sex hormones, however, come into play at breeding time to give the female her drab dress. For while the mothers are incubating their eggs and caring for the young, they must wear protective coloration. (There are male birds, too, who put on a modest summer dress after breeding. What influences this phenomenon has not yet been determined.)

A great many observations and experiments have strengthened the hypothesis that the female, not the male, deviates from the normal dress of a given species. Castrated cocks and drakes retain their brilliant colors but if the ovaries of a domestic hen or a pheasant are removed, she grows male plumage at the next molt. Evidently a sexless bird ends up with male plumage; hormones produced by the ovaries prevent such plumage from developing in the female. If female sex hormone is injected into a poulard which has put on male plumage, she will recover her original hen coloration.

We are all impressed by the magnificent iridescent colors of peacocks, pheasants, birds of paradise, hummingbirds, drakes, kingfishers, and many tropical songbirds. The effect of iridescence is due, writes Heinroth, "to what are called interference colors. These are produced by minute colorless plates, one ten-thousandth of an inch thick, which are set so as to reflect the light just as it is reflected in a soap-bubble. . . In feathers a dark pigment lying beneath the little plates makes the effect possible."

The function of fine attire is to show off. Bright colors and ornamental feathers are at least as important in the courtship of birds as mating calls. Cock pheasants parade before their hens and exhibit their glowing ruffs. The courtship of the Argus pheasant is particularly striking. This large and showy Southeast Asian fowl is named after the many-eyed giant of Greek legend whom the goddess Hera appointed to watch over Io because the secondaries of its wings are adorned with some four hundred eyespots. In courtship the cock extends his outspread wings in such a way that his head seems circled by a magnificently vivid basket. At the same time he rocks his body back and forth and adds a succession of bows to his courtship dance.

The peacock's train with its myriad eyes is composed not of wing feathers but of elongated tail feathers. Peacocks reached Europe at the time of Alexander the Great, and ever since then naturalists, writers, and moralists have tended to use this bird, with its green and golden iridescent feathers, as the symbol of pride and vanity. Thus Leonardo da Vinci noted in his *Bestiarium*, which he used as the basis for allegorical paintings: "The peacock is always contemplating the beauty of its tail, spreading it out in the form of a wheel and attracting to itself by its cries the attention of the surrounding animals."

Leonardo was probably aware that this was only a moralistic legend. The peacock cries in order to stake his claim to his territory. And he spreads his tail in order to put the hens into the mood for mating.

Rear view of peacock flaunting its tail. For a time zoologists believed that it was the activity of the male sex hormones which caused him to put on the splendid nuptial dress. Present-day theory is that the resplendent male dress is the "normal" one for both sexes but that the female sex hormones give the female her protective drab coloring. If the ovaries are removed, the female will grow male plumage.

The cock has a simple way of determining whether the hen is responding to his suit. After he has spread his tail, he turns its less imposing reverse side toward her. If the hen wishes to continue enjoying the full beauty of the tail, she must run around the cock so that the "eyes" are before her once more. The cock then rattles his tail feathers and once more presents his rear to the hen. This test of love goes on for some time, until the hen has been sufficiently overwhelmed by the magnificence of the tail and would like to experience the cock's sexual performance as well. Thereupon she crouches invitingly.

Here is another example of the phenomenon of "ladies' choice" which caused Darwin to formulate his doctrine of sexual selection. The males woo by displaying their ornamentation, and the females choose the handsomest. Among the magnificent stone grouse of South America, the males step forward one by one in their red-orange and black plumage and parade themselves upon the stony courtship ground. The ceremony is very like a human beauty contest, when young ladies walk across a stage, displaying all their charms, until one of them is crowned Miss Universe.

There is a snipelike sandpiper known as the ruff, one of the brightest of his clan. Like the cock pheasant, he sports a large, beautiful feathered ruff around his neck. This fighting sandpiper has been given an amusing scientific name: *Philomachus pugnax*—"pugnacious lover of fighting." At breeding time the males fence almost continually, in order to ingratiate themselves with the females, the reeves. These combats, however, are harmless and bloodless.

The ruff chooses a tournament ground and waits until the occupant of the adjacent territory is ready for a fight. When the time comes, the warriors erect their ruffs, spread their ear tufts, and furiously cross beaks. They stamp their feet, clatter their wings, and whirl around one another like two balls of feathers. The duel quickly kindles the fighting spirit of the other males who have assembled at the breeding ground. Soon vigorous combats are in progress all over the area. Each duel is ended by the surrender of one of the rivals. At once the victor stops fighting. The birds' beaks are so soft and their ruffs so thick that they can hardly hurt one another.

All this while the reeves stand around in a circle watching the show with obvious interest, like spectators at a boxing match. In strict keeping with the principle of sexual selection, the handsomest and strongest of the ruffs has the best chance to obtain a mate. The reeves run after the champion, pick at him very gently, and then crouch on the ground in mating position. Sometimes the victor will go away with the female he prefers. But often he quickly mates right in the dueling ring and then resumes fighting.

North American sage grouse during strut. The male of this species is characterized by two yellow air sacks on the throat which inflate to enormous proportions during the elaborate courtship and push the neck feathers up to hide the head.

Thanks to their light, air-filled bones, their feathers, their wings, and the system of air sacs in their lungs, the birds have conquered the air to a greater degree than any other animals. They even play in the air as part of their courtship. Raptorial birds will indicate their eagerness to breed by circling one another, plummeting straight down, soaring again, and displaying all their aeronautical feats. Male lapwings turn loop-the-loops like stunt pilots, uttering wild screeches of jubilation. Snipe, which can plunge like dive bombers, go in for a strange sort of music-making. As they drop they utter a low sound, half bleating, half growling. Just how this sound is produced has not been definitely ascertained. The surmise is that it is made by the tail feathers, which are spread wide in flight, and vibrate rapidly as the bird drops through the air.

The tiny, iridescent hummingbirds are even greater masters of aerial acrobatics. The very first naturalists to describe American birds were enchanted by the beauty of this family, by their speed and agility, their dances in the air. "Among all living creatures," the master of French naturalists, Count Buffon, wrote two hundred years ago, "the hummingbird is the most beautiful in form, the most exquisite in coloration. Precious stones and metals cannot be compared with this gem of Nature. The little bird is her masterpiece."

Although the hummingbirds are not considered songbirds, the males are diligent singers. In addition, they fight furiously with one another. These flying gems are able to fly vertically up and down, forward and backward. Their wings move so rapidly that they become invisible. Smaller species of hummingbird can make from sixty to eighty wing strokes per second—which will propel them through the air at fifty miles an hour. During courtship flights the speed of the wing strokes can rise to a hundred and even two hundred per second. They describe the most breath-taking arabesques in the air, darting in circles and arcs, soaring vertically into the sky, dropping like stones toward the ground, braking their fall with perfect airmanship just in front of the female, which sits on a twig watching. The males remain suspended in the air, wings quivering, until the female invites one of the males to take a seat beside her.

Hummingbird females accept mating only after they have built their nests: pretty bowl-shaped structures made of the finest plant fibers and spider web, pasted together with saliva. The males, on their courtship flights, must therefore look to see whether a nest is ready. After copulation the males of most species desert the females and look for a new courtship ground, often in the immediate vicinity of the first. There they seek to win the favor of another bride.

Posed in flight, a female ruby-throated hummingbird hovers over her nest to feed her chick.

THE DANCE IN THE BOWER

   While Buffon regarded hummingbirds as the loveliest of all birds, there is a different group to which ornithologists of earlier centuries would have given the beauty prize. For a long time, these birds were known only through their preserved skins, and in incomplete form, the natives having trimmed away the feet. This gave rise to the belief that these fantastically beautiful birds lived ethereal lives, never touching the ground, and feeding only on the dews of heaven. Perhaps they had even come directly from paradise. To this day they are still known as birds of paradise.

   An amusing legend was devised concerning the loves of these birds. Konrad Gesner, the sixteenth-century zoologist, decided that birds of paradise mated in the air and raised their offspring in the air also. The male, Gesner imagined, had a concave back and the female a convex belly. After mating, the female—while flying—laid its eggs in the male's hollow back, sat on them there and incubated them while both birds hovered in the air. To keep the two of them firmly lashed together, the male wound his two long, thin tail feathers around the female's body.

Such a theory was not incompatible with the quaint natural history of the time. It was an honest attempt to deal with the known data. The few mutilated skins of paradise birds which reached Europe during Gesner's time scarcely indicated the true nature of the birds. We can forgive him for developing a myth originally invented by Spanish and Portuguese sailors. But even three hundred years later scientists still knew virtually nothing about these remarkable birds of New Guinea. Of course it was no longer believed that such large birds, which are distinctly poor fliers, lived and reproduced in the air; but the courtship of the males and the function of their luxuriant ornamental feathers were still a mystery to zoologists.

From 1858 to 1862 Alfred Russel Wallace, who arrived at the theory of evolution independently of Darwin, was busily exploring northwestern New Guinea and the Aru Islands. In his book on these travels he described his feelings upon first seeing the bird he had hitherto known only from descriptions:

> The remote island in which I found myself situated, in an almost unvisited sea, far from the tracks of merchant-fleets and navies; the wild luxuriant tropical forest, which stretched far away on every side; the rude uncultured savages who gathered round me—all had their influence in determining the emotions with which I gazed upon this "thing of beauty." I thought of the long ages of the past, during which the successive generations of this little creature had run their course—year by year being born, and living and dying amid these dark and gloomy woods, with no intelligent eye to gaze upon their loveliness—to all appearance such a wanton waste of beauty.

Wallace was the first person to report the courtship of paradise birds. He observed that the males lured the females by means of beautiful display dances. But how could this be explained? he asked himself. Do birds have esthetic feelings—like man? Darwin weighed the question and emphatically affirmed that they had. Such ornamental plumage, Darwin maintained, was either meaningless or disadvantageous in the struggle for existence. If the birds of paradise had nevertheless carried ornamentation to such an extreme, it must be because it pleased the females. Thus Wallace's descriptions of the birds of paradise served as a crucial suggestion which led Darwin toward his theory of sexual selection.

A modern American zoologist, Thomas Gilliard, has described the courtship rites of several species:

Birds of paradise courting. Water color by W. A. Weber (from Natural History Magazine).

Four different male paradise birds in courting position. After Stresemann.

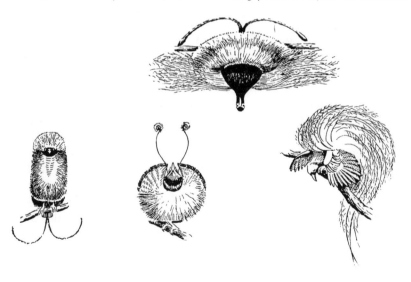

The great tails and other extraordinary plumes are used in courtship display. Capes, veils, whips, fans, fleshy caruncules, serve to transform the birds into odd and startling shapes. Some seem to become elongated, round, angular, or even flower-like, and often they bear no resemblance to birds. Others suddenly open their mouths to reveal jade and opal-colored surfaces, or they pirouette with giant capes that have a dashing look. One species (*Pteridophora*) lashes the air with relatively monstrous head plumes; four others (*Parotia*) cavort on low limbs and on the ground in deep forest, spreading their apron-and-cape raiment in symmetrical circles about their bodies, with almost the precision of a bullfighter. Two species (*Diphyllodes*) perform like gymnasts on thin, vertical saplings growing from the floor of deep forest. Others (*Paradisaea*) elevate lacelike cascades of plumage over their backs or hang shimmering from limbs.

A large, long-legged bird of the southeastern Australian bush, which looks somewhat like a pheasant but is related to the songbirds, is almost the match of the paradise birds in terpsichorean talent. It is called the lyrebird because of its two showy tail feathers which are shaped like a lyre. It is one of the cleverest mockers among birds, for it can imitate laughter, giggling, screeching, the barking of dogs, the tooting of an automobile horn, and the whistle of a locomotive. During his courtship dance the male lyrebird goes through a number of ventriloquist's tricks. At the climax of the dance, the bird tips his lyre tail forward. His whole body then disappears under the torrent of feathers as if he were drawing a silken canopy over himself. Only the great lyres can be seen quivering.

There is another family of birds in Australia who are related to the birds of paradise but who are unique in the animal kingdom in certain courtship practices. These birds not only display their beauty; they also decorate the dance floor on which they will parade themselves. Moreover, some species build veritable bowers for love. The males of the bowerbirds collect twigs, thrust small branches into the ground, and erect structures which look like tiny huts. The floor of these bowers is paved with colored moss or pretty pebbles, the walls tapestried with blades of grass or leaves. The Atlas bowerbirds and two other species actually paint the walls, the males dipping bits of bark or leaves into the blue or dark-green saliva they secrete and applying the fluid to the walls of the bower.

This use of tools is unique among birds. But even such efforts are not enough for the little architects. The male bowerbirds also adorn the dance floors and bowers with snail shells, beetle wings, parrot feathers, leaves, flowers, colored seeds—and even the yellowed skulls of small bats. Near populated areas, they use fragments of glass, bits

The male bower bird builds a decorative nest, like the one above, for courtship purposes only, while the female alone builds a modest brooding nest in a completely different place.

of paper, and other debris of human civilization. Moreover, each of the nineteen species shows its own distinct taste in decor.

The building of these bowers is not the equivalent of nest building. For one thing, they are exclusively the work of the males, while the bowl-shaped and not particularly artistic nests are made by the females alone, and in altogether different places. The males spend weeks and months building their bowers and sometimes change the ornaments almost every day. By whistling, loud calls, and spirited dance steps they invite the females to inspect their work, and sometimes greet them by offering a flower or some other pretty item from their collection of ornaments. Undoubtedly the females are sexually stimulated by the sight of the structures and the precious things they contain.

Among the many variants in the architecture and the courtship habits of these astounding birds is the "dance around the Maypole," which is practiced by the species amblyornis of New Guinea. A German army captain named Karl Detzner, who before the First World War was stationed in what was then German New Guinea, undertook several explorations of the interior, on one of which he was lucky enough to witness this dance. Here is his description:

> The rusty brown bowerbird prepares a dance floor when mating time approaches. He begins by clearing the lush jungle growth from a rectangle about six feet long and three wide. Every plant is removed. With small, dry branches he builds, in the middle of this area, a tiny "tree" whose artistry is amazing. First he inserts a stick about a foot long into the ground, and then brings from the vicinity bits of twig of every imaginable size, which he fits artfully together, tying them to the trunk and shaping his structure in such a manner that it looks like a tiny dead conifer. The bird goes to all this trouble to please his mate. . . . The female comes flying along when the work of art is complete, inspects it, and then joins the architect in a dance around the tree. The cleared ground permits both ample freedom of movement. Their leaps, the beating of their wings, become more and more excited; a game of trying to catch and refusing to be caught begins; after some time the male's courtship accomplishes its purpose.

Why all this effort? Zoologists say that the bowerbird is obeying his instinct, that he is sexually stimulated by the building and the adornment of his structures. But we may also assume that the bird takes pleasure in the beauty of his work, just as we human beings instinctively react to the stimuli of certain colors and shapes and— obeying an innate or learned esthetic pattern—regard such colors and shapes as beautiful.

ENGAGEMENT, FIDELITY, ADULTERY

There is no saying who invented the fable of the storks' tribunal. Probably the story goes back to classical antiquity. Some Greek may have observed storks hacking to death a sick or weak member of their species—this occasionally happens when the birds assemble in late summer for their southward migration. But since the observer applied human attitudes and moralities to the animal world, he concluded that the murdered stork must be a female guilty of adultery and condemned and executed by a council of storks therefor.

The fable was repeated by Gesner and other Renaissance writers, and has persisted down to our own times. To be sure, it is almost impossible to distinguish female from male storks without close examination, but all the same, peasants, journalists, and writers on animals continued to describe every stork found dead, either from natural causes or from the onslaught of its companions, as a female convicted of adultery. The male stork, it is even alleged, smells the female's misdemeanor unless she cleanses herself in water afterward. He thereupon sounds the alarm and at once convokes a tribunal. Those who are somewhat more cautious about their natural history will tell you that the stork abandons his unfaithful mate or drives her away.

Storks are always being cited as examples of what a model marriage should be like and what punishment awaits the sinful spouse. Every spring, country folk would see a single stork arrive at a nest which year after year had been occupied by a pair. One or two weeks later a second stork would apepar, would be greeted by a joyful clattering of the bill, and would enter upon married life with the first. Both would incubate the eggs and raise the young. No one doubted that it was the same pair that faithfully returned to the same nest. It was clear that the marriage of storks was a lifetime affair, as human marriage is supposed to be. And where such fidelity exists, there must also—in keeping with human experience—be infidelity, with suitable punishment following.

Unfortunately, none of this delightful construct is correct. Ever since the Danish schoolteacher Hans Christian Cornelius Mortensen in 1898 introduced the method of banding birds in order to follow their migrations, all such instructive legends about storks have been demolished. It appears that the same pair by no means occupies the same nest every year, and that storks do not lead model monogamous marriages. The first arrival is always a male. He may, indeed, be the same male who nested on the spot the previous year, for the stork has so keen a sense of direction that he is able to find his former breeding territory after his return from the south. But if some younger male stork, who has just come to sexual maturity that spring, discovers the nest first and succeeds in holding it against all comers, the previous owner must give way and seek another nesting place.

The females arrive somewhat later and look around for nests occupied by males. The male stork greets and accepts the first female that comes along, whether or not she is his wife of the previous year. Banding experiments have shown that not all the previous year's couples meet again—far from it. The male stork is not interested in the individual, but in the nest, in incubating the eggs and raising the young. He does not care a hoot who his mate is. And, vice versa, the home-coming female stork is not seeking a particular male, but any male stork who possesses a nest and is willing to sit on the eggs with her.

Quarrels sometimes break out in the nest when a third stork appears before brooding begins and interferes in the marriage. This may have given rise to the fable of the female stork's adultery. The new arrival was taken to be a male, a Casanova attempting to seduce the stork's wife, and the frequently bitter duels which take place on the nest were regarded either as fights between the legitimate husband and the seducer or as chastisement inflicted by the husband upon his flighty wife.

But these were rank misinterpretations. The intruders are never males; they are females who have not yet found a male in possession of a nest. In many cases they may be the wife of the previous year who has sought out the old nesting place and found another female already installed. There then develops a duel for the nest between the two females. The male stork looks on indifferently, for he does not care who wins.

Barn swallows and other birds which nest in large colonies strike the naive observer as particularly promiscuous, for as soon as a pair has raised its young and is about to undertake a new brood, the mates look around among the other pairs to see whether they cannot introduce a little diversion into monogamy. In many cases there is an exchange of partners. The great ornithologist Oskar Heinroth interprets this *changez-les-femmes* correctly:

> The important thing for the species is that eight to ten young are raised every year, for the birds must suffer considerable losses each season from enemies and the weather. The individual barn swallow does not care with whom it mates and rears young, but only that it does it as quickly as possible; the summer is short, and the winter quarters are for molting, not breeding. One reason why the pairs sometimes break up between broods may be that the new breeding cycle of each partner is not quite synchronized with its mate's; it is better that each should choose a new partner in the right stage. At any rate, we know for certain from studies of thousands of banded barn swallows that there is frequently a change of mates.

Nevertheless, we need not abandon all the pretty illusions we have held about birds. There is a large number of birds who do in fact pair permanently. The matter depends upon the habits of life among these species. Two groups may be distinguished. The first consists of the birds faithful to a given place. The pair remains in the breeding area all year round and regards the nest as the center of its territory. Consequently, there is no reason for either of the two partners to look around for other marital prospects. They have one another and are relieved of the necessity of periodically undertaking the troublesome and sometimes vain search for a mate.

The other group consists of those birds which care for their young for almost a full year. The result of such prolonged child care is that the couple is still together in the spring, when the new breeding period begins. As soon as the offspring fly off to independent lives, therefore, the pair can begin mating and nest-building again. In effect, one marriage between the same partners passes without a break into another. Male and female have ended one reproduction cycle and start another immediately. This is the case especially among geese, whose marital life is regarded by men as exemplary. Gray geese and swans sometimes do mate for a lifetime. Even before they reach sexual maturity, the young gray gander approaches a family group in which there are several growing females, and pays court to one of the misses. He casts yearning looks at her, stretches to his full length, dips his neck under water, and with piercing shrieks drives away all sorts of other animals who are no concern of his—solely in order to impress the young female and lure her to his side. For he dare not approach too closely to the goose family; he would be promptly driven away by the parents of the nubile female.

If he succeeds in so enchanting the young lady that she runs away from her family and comes to him, the alliance is sealed for life. Henceforth the parents drop their objections to the suitor. The gander guards and defends his spouse in truly affecting fashion, loyally helps raise one batch of young after another each year, and remains faithful to her unto death. Widowed geese and ganders frequently do not choose a new mate, but spend the rest of their lives as celibates.

"Until death do you part" applies in some cases to the birds who are permanently attached to a given territory. Eagles, ravens, some owls, and many parrots cling to the mate they have once chosen. On this basis, ravens and parrots sometimes become very closely attached to their keepers. The birds regard the human being as a substitute mate, scratch him and let themselves be scratched by him, want to be constantly at his side, and languish away if their owner dies. Some species of parakeets from Africa, noted for their deep attachment to their mates, are called *Agapornides* by zoologists—"lovebirds." They have become extremely popular as pets, for bird fanciers find the tenderness of the parakeets endearing. If a pair of parakeets is separated, or if the mate of one is replaced by another, the lovebird will not pay attention to its new companion until a long period of mourning is over—and sometimes never. These birds are not the only ones who display such fidelity. Other species of parrots will behave similarly; if they lose their mates, they will refuse to accept a substitute for some time.

Many of the birds that form permanent marriages will pass through a regular engagement before they consummate their nuptials. Swans, owls, daws, and parrots form pairs long before sexual maturity, like gray geese. Among daws, the engagement lasts about a year; only then does the couple mate and brood. As Lorenz explains it, what takes place is the falling in love on the part of two biologically immature birds, and often the story is one of typical love at first sight:

> The betrothed pair form a heartfelt mutual defense league, each of the partners supporting the other most loyally. This is essential, because they have to contend with the competition of older and higher-standing couples in the struggle to take and hold a nesting cavity. This militant love is fascinating to behold. Constantly in an attitude of maximum self-display, and hardly ever separated by more than a yard, the two make their way through life. They seem tremendously proud of each other, as they pace ponderously side by side, with their head feathers ruffed to emphasize their black velvet caps and light gray silken necks. And it is really touching to see how affectionate these two wild creatures are with each other. Every delicacy that the male finds is given to his bride and she accepts it with the plaintive begging gestures and notes otherwise typical of baby birds. In fact, the love whispers of the couple consist chiefly of infantile sounds, reserved by adult jackdaws for these occasions.

Nor is this affectionate bond constantly refreshed by sexual intimacy, for the engaged couple must wait a considerable while for that. Lorenz kept watch over many jackdaw engagements, some extending over a period of years, right up to the wedding day. Only one engagement was wrecked right at the beginning. "The cause of the trouble," he writes, "was a young lady jackdaw of unusually vivacious temperament." The same cause, in other words, that leads to the breakup of so many human engagements. But in contrast to many human marital partners, the jackdaw couple's tenderness and displays of affection increase in the course of marriage: "But even after many years, the male still feeds his wife with the same solicitous care, and finds for her the same low tones of love, tremulous with inward emotion, that he whispered in his first spring of betrothal and of life."

Ducks frequently become engaged in the autumn, spend the winter together, and then put on their wedding dress in the spring. But in contrast to the chaste engagements of the jackdaws, the premarital period has distinct sexual overtones among ducks. Although their sex glands are still quite undeveloped in the autumn and winter, the males court; and the females who see members of the opposite sex flying through the air attempt to lure them down by piercing cries. Moreover, among many species of dabbling ducks the engaged couples mate with great eagerness. Such autumn and winter matings have nothing to do with reproduction, since the birds do not yet have sex cells capable of fertilization.

The intimacies of newly engaged dabbling ducks are no mere petting. Drakes possess a penis and during the engagement period perform actual copulation. Heinroth states:

> As early as September many dabbling ducks start to copulate with their legitimate mates. Earlier, sometimes before the drake has completed his display plumage, the female takes the part of the wooer, for such a male is not yet in the mood for love and avoids bodily contact, making up, one might say, all sorts of excuses to repulse the advances of his wife: he has to drive away an enemy (who does not exist), has to take a bath, or has something else that he simply must do.

The females, however, continue to excite the males by rapid, coquettish swimming.

If, come spring, the love affair of the couple at last develops into a proper marriage, the whole situation changes. Now the drake becomes the sexually active partner; in fact, he turns into a thoroughgoing lecher. Male mallards have only one interest in life at this time: they want to rape every female they catch sight of. Yet they have not the slightest inclination to loosen the bonds of their marriage and find a new spouse. The couple remains together, feeding in some pond, but keeping an eye out for other mallards—the female because she fears the violence of strange drakes; the male because he wants to overpower and rape the mates of other drakes. Once he has spied the wife of a neighbor, no matter how invitingly his own mate behaves he pays her no heed; he rises into the air and lands in the water beside the strange female.

From March to May over the ponds of city parks mallards may be seen flying behind one another in groups of three—the female in the van, closely followed by two males. The female utters long-drawn-out cries of alarm. The males persist in their pursuit. It may look as if two rival drakes are chasing an unmated female. But in reality a faithful wife is being pursued by a strange male. The third duck is the rightful husband who joins the chase so that he can find his wife later. Except for staying with her, the husband does not protect his wife from molestation. She, however, does everything in her power to escape the pursuer. She flies faster, hides in the bushes, or strikes out at the stranger until she is utterly exhausted. Some mallard females will sooner let themselves be drowned than yield to the stranger's lust.

When two lovers of our own species are particularly affectionate to one another, they behave, as the phrase has it, "like turtledoves." Actually, doves and pigeons are anything but gentle, loving, faithful spouses. It is a pretty sight to see a pair of pigeons sitting together, cooing, grooming each other's feathers, and rubbing bills. But this sort of thing is reserved for brooding time; otherwise the male is a difficult husband. He follows his wife around, hacks at her if she pauses to eat something, and manifests tenderness only when she is sitting virtuously at home in the cote, not gadding about in the company of others of the species. But then, he has very good reasons for being so mistrustful.

Every cock pigeon automatically courts all females in his vicinity. This is an altogether mechanical reflex; the cock pigeon does not really want anything of her. As Heinroth perceptively remarks, the courting means little more than "Good morning, Mrs. Jones." However, Mrs. Jones will often take advantage of such situations. Heinroth has described what takes place as follows:

> If . . . the male is not quite up to the mark, the female lets another male—often a particular favorite—mount her. Every off-duty female is mildly accosted by almost every off-duty male. . . . If she goes on her way, he does not pester her any more. But if this is just what she wants and she obligingly crouches, the male's politeness turns to embarrassment, for he needs a little time until he comes into the right mood to oblige her. Even then, the mating is without the tenderness usual between married pigeons. The female then goes back contentedly to the nest and is otherwise faithful to her husband, who for his part goes on to raise the family with her as if nothing had happened.

In the sex play of doves and pigeons, incidentally, the female often persuades the cock to crouch and then she mounts him. Other birds also occasionally pair in this manner. For mating they need only press their cloacas together, so that it does not matter whether the male mounts the female or is under her.

The different types of sex play of various species can cause terrible trouble when ornithologists, attempting to produce crosses, house a male and female of unlike species. Lorenz once placed a turtledove with a ringdove and when he saw that the two were beginning to exchange signs of affection, he confidently went away for a day, leaving the lovers to themselves. Then:

> When I returned, the next day, a horrible sight met my eyes. The turtledove lay on the floor of the cage; the top of his head and neck, as also the whole length of his back, was not only plucked bare of feathers, but so flayed as to form a single wound dripping with blood. In the middle of this gory surface, like an eagle on his prey, stood the second harbinger of peace. Wearing that dreamy facial expression that so appeals to our sentimental observer, this charming lady pecked mercilessly with her silver bill in the wounds of her prostrate mate. When the latter gathered his last resources in a final effort to escape, she set on him again, struck him to the floor with a light clap of her wing and continued with her slow pitiless work of destruction. Without my interference she would undoubtedly have finished him off, in spite of the fact that she was already so tired that she could hardly keep her eyes open.

So much for the gentleness of doves.

Indeed, the relations of the sexes among birds may assume widely different forms. One extreme is represented by the woodpeckers, whose males and females, according to Heinroth, are permanently on a war footing with one another. And at the other extreme are the cockatoos, which, save for breeding time, will sit on branches two by two, embracing one another with their wings and billing affectionately.

INFATUATED PENGUINS

The courtship and sex play of the divers takes place on reedy lakes and ponds in the spring. Both sexes have the same coloration; both perform precisely the same actions during the courtship. One diver would seem to be well-nigh the mirror image of the other. Crested grebes swim toward one another, stand opposite one another head to head, then dive down to the bottom of the water, fetch up some bit of plant in their beaks, and show one another the fine nesting materials they have found. As they do so they stretch up, breast to breast, raise their crests and collars, shake their heads, and then glide back into swimming position.

This courtship ceremony of the divers is called the penguin dance. From the point of view of scientific classification, divers have nothing to do with penguins but when they rise out of the water in this way their bearing is surprisingly reminiscent of the droll Antarctic birds.

Diver couples like to be alone and undisturbed at breeding time. Penguins, on the other hand, are sociable creatures who form great breeding colonies comprising many thousands of birds. When man first began invading the coastline and islands of the Antarctic Ocean, the armies of penguins still had no fear of him. Many penguins display no shyness to this day, because on land they have no enemies. Their only dangerous foes, leopard-seals and killer whales, live in water. Consequently, Antarctic explorers can tramp through the breeding colonies and study the intimate life of penguins without upsetting the birds in the least. The result has been a spate of humorous, touching, all-too-human stories about these birds, stories that have on the whole given a false picture of penguin life. Most people are under the delusion that the unfortunate penguins are condemned to live on eternal ice and to raise their offspring under the hardest conditions, in blinding blizzards at temperatures many degrees below zero. This is so only for a few species—the Emperor and King penguins of the Antarctic and the rock penguins which, like the King penguins, inhabit the islands around the continent. The majority of penguins, on the other hand, have migrated far to the north with the cold sea currents. The species which are most frequently seen in zoos come from the coasts and islands of South America, South Africa, Australia, and New Zealand.

The crowded breeding places of a penguin colony have sometimes been compared to a city. Penguins brood, according to species, in holes in the ground, in niches and cracks in rock, frequently on bare crags or swampy soil. Often they mark their nests by a circle of stones or even by the bleached bones of deceased members of the species. The tripping of innumerable feet makes roads and streets from nest to nest and all around the breeding ground, as well as highways down to the sea. Since the penguin streets often cross at right angles, the colony from the air looks like a crude sketch of a human city.

When people or animals are crowded closely in a small space, squabbles easily arise. This is so with many sea birds which assemble in colonies at breeding time. Petrels, gulls, guillemots, auks, gannets, and cormorants, when sitting on their breeding islands and cliffs, are often squeezed together as tight as sardines in a can. They fight and push, and their combined cries drown out the thunder of the waves. There is considerable misappropriation of nests and eggs, all the more so since these breeding communities are formed of a wide variety of species. Even though penguin colonies consist mostly of the members of a single species, bickering and fights are daily occurrences. The birds quarrel at courtship time and fight for nesting places. Strangers from other colonies, who have not respected the borders of the nesting block, are hustled out of the colony by brute force. And if a penguin loses a few feathers in such encounters, the victor complacently upholsters his nest with them.

The Adelie penguins, who are among the southernmost species and breed on barren shores in bitter temperatures, begin collecting stones at breeding time. Each couple diligently gathers stone after stone with which to build a wall around the nest. Since there are frequently not enough stones to satisfy the needs of all the couples, the penguins steal from one another without letup. Louis Bernacchi, who went with an Austrian Antarctic expedition as its naturalist, has described this amusing practice:

> The thief slowly approaches the one he wishes to rob with a most creditable air of nonchalance and disinterestedness, and if, on getting close, the other looks at him suspiciously, he will immediately gaze around with a most childlike and bland air, and appear to be admiring the scenery. The assumption of innocence is perfect; but no sooner does the other look in a different direction than he will dart down upon one of the pebbles of its nest and scamper away with it in his beak as fast as his little short legs will bear his fat body. If the theft is discovered, the injured party will give chase; then all the kind and sympathetic neighbors rush in and rob the unguarded nest to their hearts' desire.

Penguins which breed in caves concentrate on gathering twigs rather than stones. The Southwest African jackass penguins collect bits of brush and use them to line their nesting caves. They can suffer the same misfortune as the Adelie penguins. If, for example, the couple strolls down to the sea for a swim, leaving their cave unguarded, their kind neighbors fall upon the sticks and clean out the nest completely. With unusually bad luck, the couple will find upon its return that the cave has been occupied by another couple who were previously homeless. The thievery can extend even to the eggs. Now and then the colonies of two different species adjoin. It may then happen that the members of one species fall upon the nests of the

A penguin couple relieving one another of the task of brooding.

others and carry the eggs away—not, as is the case with gulls, to eat them, but in order to hatch them themselves.

All Antarctic explorers have extolled the penguins for their devotion to their broods. Both parents regularly relieve one another during incubation. In the case of the Adelie penguin, however, only one relief takes place. During the first half of the incubating period one parent sits uninterruptedly on the eggs; during the second half, its partner. The hatched young scarcely ever leave the nest; they are very awkward, clad in a thick coat of down, and are incapable of getting to their feet. Their eyes do not open until two weeks after hatching. The parents must cross long stretches of very difficult ground in order to reach the sea and catch food for themselves and their offspring. The young, when feeding, thrust their heads deep into the parent's gullet and swallow whatever the mother or father has stored there for them.

As soon as the downy offspring have grown and can leave the nest, they unite in great crowds which the zoologists have called "kindergartens." At this time they are no longer cared for by their own parents, but are tended collectively by the entire colony. They cannot enter the sea until they have exchanged their down for the close-lying plumage of the adults, for the down is highly water-absorbent and would make swimming and diving impossible. In the water the young penguins likewise form great "schools." They fish in common and give one another signals to warn of danger or to inform one another that everything is safe once more.

It takes three to four years for the young penguins to reach reproductive age. Then the period of kindergarten and schooling is over and each young male seeks a mate and a home. The courtship of pen-

This group of young emperor penguins are old enough to have left their parents' nest and are tended collectively in a sort of "penguin kindergarten."

guins likewise has many resemblances to human customs. In his book, *The Island of Penguins*, Cherry Kearton describes this courtship in somewhat facetious terms, but the account agrees in essence with the findings of scientists:

> The young thing on whom he has cast his eye discreetly preens herself, and then still more discreetly becomes absorbed in the scenes immediately around her—taking no notice, of course, of her admirer. But he is not to be put off by that kind of thing; he knows it is all a part of the game. He sidles up, walks around in a circle, so that the object of his growing affection may have every opportunity of noticing the three-quarter view as you stand just behind him, of which he is justly proud, and then edges a little closer.
>
> I imagine that thirty years ago the young lady penguin would have looked at the ground and have murmured: "Oh, but this is so sudden!" Now, however, she does nothing of the sort. She looks up at Master Penguin, and having long ago made up her mind that he would do, she tilts her head on one side, and a few minutes later they walk out together.

Mutual understanding does not always come so swiftly. Certain ceremonial gestures, bows, and calls must precede the awakening of young love in the pair. Moreover, the males are exceedingly belligerent at breeding time. Two young males who have cast their eye upon the same young lady go at one another with bills and flippers until one falls exhausted to the ground. Bernacchi saw the females

> chasing away the less handsome of the warriors. Suddenly the one who had fled rushed his opponent again and the fight began anew. Such duels lasted a quarter of an hour and longer. In fact they did not end until one of the pair was completely overcome. As a rule the defeated bird presents a pitiable sight. He is covered with coagulated blood and has lost a good portion of his plumage. It takes several days for him to regain his normal state.

Engaged and married couples, however, are extremely affectionate. Kearton reports that they actually kiss one another, stretching their necks forward, raising their heads high, and tenderly rubbing beaks for from ten to fifteen seconds. During the kiss they stretch out their flippers, and sometimes the male attempts to embrace the female with them, while she keeps her beak firmly inside his.

All of this is charming enough. Zoologists encountered their greatest surprise, however, in the big King and Emperor penguins, who must endure winter temperatures of sixty degrees below zero. These birds congregate at their breeding areas during the Antarctic winter, of all seasons, under climatic conditions which could scarcely be more hostile to life. From 1872 to 1876 the British research vessel *Challenger*, under the command of the Arctic and Antarctic explorer Sir John Strong Nares, cruised all the oceans of the world, thus instituting systematic deep-sea research. But the scientists on the *Challenger* did more than lower their dragnets into the oceanic trenches. They landed on the Marion Islands in the South Polar zone of drift ice, where they were the first men to encounter a breeding community of King penguins—about one hundred of them.

They saw no signs of nests. But many of the King penguins walked in a strangely crouching position through the snow, and when frightened leaped aside so awkwardly that the explorers first thought they must be sick. Suddenly an egg fell from one of the birds. And when the naturalists looked more closely into the matter, they realized that the King penguin was equipped with a brood pouch between its legs, formed by two folds of skin. The brood pouch held an egg. While one of the two mates fished in the sea, the other incubated the egg in its pouch. Here was something altogether unique in the world of birds—an Antarctic diving bird behaving like a marsupial.

But how did the mates take their turns in the care of the egg? For a long time the accounts of naturalists disagreed because the King and the Emperor penguins had been confused with one another. To-day the matter has been clarified. The King penguins change over every few hours. "When the mate comes back from fishing," Heinroth writes, "the pair approach breast to breast until their toes touch; the penguin who has been guarding the egg rolls it with his beak onto the feet of the other so that the egg never touches the ice. The young, which are at first quite helpless and dependent on their parents for food, are treated in the same way as the eggs: they live like little marsupials." The Emperor penguins, on the other hand, live far from the sea, and the males and females cannot relieve one another so frequently. Consequently, these animals have developed the most amazing capacity to fast. Males and females fast for two full months, until the courtship is over and the egg laid. Then the males take the eggs into their brood pouches and go hungry for another sixty-three days. The females make their way for miles across wastes of ice to the ocean and there eat their fill.

"Shortly after hatching time," writes Gilliard on the basis of modern research, "the female returns, but it no longer remembers its long-suffering mate, and solicits various males for chicks. The chicks are first fed with a special crop secretion which the male produces although it has not taken food for many weeks."

These inhabitants of the South Polar regions outdo all other nest-building birds in solicitude and self-sacrificing care of their brood. Explorers tell us that many Emperor males, when at last they are relieved by their wives, perish of weakness on their way to the sea. There are few parallels to such devotion among the higher animals. The male emu, an Australian cassowary which assumes the task of incubating the eggs alone—as do all ostrichlike birds with the exception of the African ostrich—is said to sit on its eggs for sixty days without taking any nourishment. And the male hornbill is reduced to skin and bones in the incubating period, when he must provide for both wife and fledglings, who are walled up like medieval prisoners.

THE IMMURED PHOENIX

The Egyptians, along with other ancient peoples, held the belief that life renewed itself by passing through death. Their symbol of rejuvenation was the phoenix, the bird that consumes itself in flames and rises newborn from the ashes. According to legend, the home of this bird was India. Now India and Southeast Asia are the habitat of most of those curious-looking birds with huge beaks which are called hornbills because of the horny casques they wear atop their bills. And since the brooding behavior of these birds has probably been known to the natives of these areas from time immemorial, it is possible that the habits of the hornbills first gave rise to the legend of the phoenix.

The building of nests has as its chief function to guard the eggs and the young from danger. Some species accomplish this by making their nests difficult of access, as on the tips of swaying twigs or cemented to vertical walls, or on high, smooth cliffs. The edible nests of the salanganes and other swifts, long esteemed a delicacy by the Chinese, are prized partly because they are difficult to procure. Holes in the ground, crannies in rocks, hollows in trees, and houses supplied by man, are favored by a great many species of birds. Whenever possible, they choose a cavity with an entrance so small that they themselves can slip in only by folding their wings. If in addition the entrance to the hole can be sealed so that it is safe from intruders, mother and offspring enjoy a maximum of security.

That is the principle the hornbills follow. The female moves into a roomy hollow in a tree, lays her eggs, and walls herself in with the aid of her own excrement. The male assists by bringing mud and bits of wood and by pasting resin over the seal. Finally the entrance is completely blocked except for a small opening through which the prisoner can thrust her beak, so that the male can feed her. While she is brooding, the female adds to her difficulties by molting inside her dark cell. During the molt she is half naked and incapable of flight. The cast feathers form a soft bed for the hatched young.

It is hard work for the male to keep providing his wife and the two to five helpless fledglings with fruit. He himself scarcely gets a chance to eat and in the course of his two months of toil grows thinner and thinner. It is a month before the young hatch, and another month before they are half fledged. All that time the father must obtain food for the whole family, single-handed.

Young hornbills look very strange during the first two weeks of their lives. They are quite naked, have a translucent skin, and, as Wallace put it, resemble a sack filled with jelly more than a real bird. When they have acquired their feathers, the wall is broken down. In some species, the mother does this with her powerful bill. She then escapes from her prison and, with the father's aid, walls up the entrance once more. Henceforth the young are fed by both parents through the feeding hole until they are able to fly. Among other hornbills, the young themselves close the entrance again after the mother has left. The female of the South Asian great pied hornbill is said to leave her prison only after the young have been wholly fledged. In each case, however, the parents are a sorry sight after the brooding period is over, "miserable looking, ugly and thin as a rail," as a traveler in India has put it. Thus does the hornbill immure itself, like the phoenix lying down on its funeral pyre, and the next generation emerges from the hornbill's starvation cell like new life from the phoenix's ashes.

But what would become of the female, deprived of her wing feathers, and of the naked offspring, if the father were shot down or lost his life in some other manner? Would the immured female and young starve to death? If that were the case, the hornbill's method of brooding, ingenious as it seems, would represent a miscalculation on the part of nature. For these safety measures would work against the preservation of the species. But other factors are involved. The feeding hole from which a hungry beak protrudes is regarded with interest by young, unpaired males. As soon as the males notice that the provider has vanished, they fly to the hole, feed the widow, and share in the rearing of the young. The impulse to push food into the opening is innate in male hornbills. When the rightful father is present, the other males must keep their distance. But when there is no husband to care for the imprisoned mother, the young males obey their irresistible instinct and substitute for him.

The nest, among almost all birds, is strictly a place to incubate the eggs and raise the young. Only a very few birds (woodpeckers, for example, and a few species of sparrows) build nests as more or less permanent dwelling places. Other birds, outside the brooding period, have no home. When they work as weavers, potters, or carpenters with that almost incomprehensible artistry which both savages and civilized men have imitated as well as admired, when they twine reeds, tie proper knots with their bills and feet, or work the finest plant fibers and spider webs into hanging cradles, they do so solely for the sake of raising their brood.

In the mid-eighteenth century, Pastor Johann Heinrich Zorn published a two-volume study of birds in order "to reinforce men in their admiration, love, and reverence for their almighty, omniscient, and supremely kind Creator." To Zorn it was evident that the nest-building feats of birds rested "neither upon imitation of the parents nor upon their own reasoning nor upon an automatic mechanism. . . . We must seek the explanation of such incomprehensible things in the order and providence of the eternally wise Master who endowed them with the wondrous instinct and conferred upon them sufficient strength and wit."

About a hundred years later, the leading spokesmen for the dawning age of science would no longer accept such supernatural explanations. Alfred Russel Wallace was inclined to regard the instincts of nest-building and caring for the young as rational acts which had become habitual. In 1867, in a treatise on *The Philosophy of Bird Nests*, Wallace proclaimed that he had been unable to trace in the nest-building of birds any shred of proof that forces beyond animal intelligence and imitativeness existed. For God, Wallace substituted tradition:

> It would be very extraordinary if, after they could see, they could neither observe or recollect, and could live for days and weeks in a nest and know nothing of its material and the manner of its construction. . . . Surely young birds before they left the nest had ample opportunity of observing its form, its size, its position, the materials of which it is constructed and the manner in which those materials were arranged.
>
> The great uniformity in the architecture of each species of bird, which has been supposed to prove a nest-building instinct, we may, therefore, fairly impute to the uniformity of conditions under which each species lives. When, however, new conditions do occur they take advantage of them just as freely and wisely as man could do.

But it was with the birds as with the insects. After a brief period of admiration for their rationality and imitative skill, science gradually returned to that almost magical concept of "instinct" which has continued to fascinate behavioral scientists to this day—and to provoke philosophical speculation. This newer doctrine of instinct was promulgated by Lloyd Morgan, professor of zoology at Bristol. In 1896 Morgan published a treatise which took strong issue with Wallace's conclusions. Knowledge of nest-building, Morgan declared, could not possibly be transmitted by tradition from one generation to the next. Birds raised in captivity who had never known their parents would build their nests in the manner typical of their species. However, he admitted that individual birds might indeed introduce certain variations into their structures on the basis of their own experience.

A few years later, a third Englishman—the African explorer Edmund Selous—proposed a most modern-sounding approach to the question of avian sexuality:

> What is the use of knowing that some bird or other goes through "very extraordinary antics in the season of love?" This is not nearly enough. One requires to know what, exactly, these antics are, the exact movements of which they consist—the minutest details, in fact, gathered from a number of observations. When one knows this one may be able to speculate a little, and what interest is there, either in natural history or anything else, if one cannot do that? Mere facts are for children only. As they begin to point towards conclusions they become food for men.

The conclusions that Selous drew from his observations of birds seemed very bold at the time. When a bird courts or builds its nest, Selous decided, it is first yielding to innate blind reflexes. But these in turn evoke a feeling of pleasure in the bird, and this pleasure then gives further stimulus to physical activities and skills. Instead of rigid automatism, of instinct for learning and imitating, Selous set up as guiding principle the pleasure of gratifying instincts.

Today the question of whether Wallace or Morgan was right is no longer debated. A bird that broods for the first time does not know the purpose of its nest-building; it does not know that it is supposed to lay its eggs and raise its offspring. It is slavishly bound to its prescribed mode of building, which is as much a characteristic of its species as its shape and coloring. Hence an ornithologist on seeing an empty nest can in most cases immediately tell what species of bird built it.

Nevertheless, Edmund Selous's idea has not been entirely abandoned by the ornithologists who study the building and brooding mechanisms. As Heinroth says, "The stronger and cleaner the reproductive instinct, the more perfect is the nest." The instinct to build nests and to care for the brood are as insistent as the instinct to copulate. The gratification of these instincts presumably affords the birds similar pleasure. And if the bird builds an especially beautiful nest it may be, as Selous puts it, not extra labor but "extra delight."

ALTRICIAL AND PRECOCIAL BIRDS

At the beginning of the nineteenth century Lorenz Oken suggested that birds could be divided into two great groups according to their state of development after hatching: into altricial and precocial birds. Altricial birds are born helpless and must remain in the nest; precocial birds can run about and feed themselves as soon as they are hatched. Neither of these categories has anything to do with the evolutionary position of the birds, and there are a great number of intermediary stages between the two types. Among mammals, too, there are many species whose young are born blind, helpless, and undeveloped, and others—such as the ruminants—whose newborn can stand on their feet and run about shortly after emerging from the womb.

It has been widely assumed that the length of time each species broods is the determining factor here. Songbirds and woodpeckers, which are extremely altricial, incubate their eggs for only two weeks, whereas hens, ducks, geese, cranes, and ostriches whose chicks are born feathered and are able to run about briskly while pieces of shell are still clinging to their rumps, have an average incubating period of three to four weeks. But there are opposite examples: hornbills sit on their eggs for a month and yet their young emerge as altricial birds, while quail brood barely eighteen days, yet are classed among the precocial birds. There also exists a relationship between the size of the bird and the length of incubation.

Altricial birds obviously require far more intensive care from the parents than precocial birds. The chicks are naked, blind, almost incapable of movement, and very sensitive to cold. They need warmth, protection, and feeding. In order for them to obtain food in sufficient quantity, they have developed a special begging mechanism known as gaping. "The nestling," writes the English zoologist Maurice Burton in his *Infancy in Animals*,

in the early stages of its life is little more than a bag for the reception of food, and the one important action that transcends all others is that the mouth of the bag shall be fully open at the appropriate moment. At first, when the eyes are still unopened, when the other senses are no doubt in their rudimentary stages, vibrations alone suffice to release the reaction. Tapping a twig or the edge of the nest, in imitation of the hen landing with food in her beak, will alone bring the chicks into action. When the eyes are fully opened tapping may bring forth the reaction, but the more certain way to evoke it then is to present some moving object, such as a stick or the finger, about the level of the nest; that is, above the chick's eye level.

It is a simple matter to carry out experiments with nestlings. The infant birds cannot run away, and the experimenter can visit the nest whenever he pleases, without frightening away or harming his subjects. Much has been learned about the mechanism of gaping by means of experiments with decoys similar to those used to test the mechanisms of courting fish. If cardboard circles of different sizes are held in front of a nestling, it will gape toward the circle whose size corresponds with that of the mother's head. The reaction is completely automatic.

Where visibility is poor—if the nest, for instance, is inside a hole— the parents need help in finding the nestling's open beak. Many nestling birds accordingly possess special markings: bright yellow or red gullets, or even phosphorescent spots on the beak. Moreover, it is necessary for the parents to know which nestling is due to be fed next, otherwise the greediest would always receive the most food and the others would starve. This problem, too, is regulated by specific instinctual mechanisms. Immediately after feeding, the nestling relieves itself on the edge of the nest. In so doing it moves one place further on and makes room for the next of the brood. Thus the young keep moving in a circle, so that each receives its just share.

This wise arrangement, however, is not universal. Among some species an intense struggle for existence takes place within the nest. The stronger win; the weaker must give way and are eliminated. Such natural selection operates in the most drastic way among predators. For raptorial birds are in no position to feed their infants between two and four hundred times a day, as do the insect-eating songbirds. They can at best fill the offspring's bellies only once or a few times daily. And any nestling that does not get his share of the spoils and thereby proves itself insufficiently viable is pecked by its brothers and sisters and finally thrown out of the nest. Many of the larger raptorial birds raise only a single nestling. Now and then, however, the females lay two or more eggs. In that case the parents tend only the first-born and kill the others as soon as they hatch.

The parents of precocial offspring have a much easier time of it.

The young chicks get along for their first day of life by using up the supply of yolk in their bodies. On the following day they must learn what is edible and what is inedible. The chick must practice a little before it is able to peck and swallow properly. But the natural gift is there and becomes fully developed after a very brief learning period. As soon as he is able to pick up his own food the parents need only guard the band of chicks, guide them, warn them against danger, and shelter them at night under their feathers.

Young altrices also have an instinct to seek cover the moment they hear the mother's warning cry. The imitation of a hawk's cry, or the sight of a cardboard model of a raptorial bird, will provoke this reaction. Burton writes:

> Even an unhatched chick, cheeping in its shell prior to cracking it open to emerge, is said to go silent on hearing the hen's alarm-call. An incubator-hatched chick is also said to make for cover on hearing the cry of a hawk. If no cover is available it will freeze in a crouching position. . . . The alarm-note of the parent and the responding behaviour of the chicks may differ according to the species, but all have this in common, that neither call nor response have to be learned. Both belong to a fixed and inherited pattern of behaviour.

The same may be said for another instinctive reaction of a protective nature. If a person or animal approaches a bird's nest, the parent often pretends to be lame, flutters away with apparent difficulty, and thus lures the intruder away from the nest. Once it has drawn off the enemy, it hastily flies back to its nestlings. Such behavior is found most frequently in birds that brood on the ground, especially the golden plover, the oyster catcher, the duck, the crane, and the partridge. In the days when anthropomorphizing was more the fashion, it was generally said that the cunning mother knew perfectly well that her sham lameness would deceive the cat, fox, or human being. Rationalists, on the other hand, pooh-poohed that idea and maintained that weeks of brooding had made the bird so stiff that it could only hobble. But as Heinroth points out: "A duck that has been swimming about actively with her young, or up-ending for food, tries the same trick." Moreover, "every member of the species acts in the same manner in the face of the same danger, and you can hardly suppose that a bird which is breeding for the first time spends its time working out what to do if an enemy comes along. The whole business must be inborn."

The most extreme case of precociality is found among certain Australian and Southeast Asian gallinaceous birds (i.e., those related to the domestic fowl). These are called megapods because of their big feet, and mound birds because of their characteristic nests. Young mound birds are completely independent immediately after leaving the egg, and by the third day after birth are able to fly. They have still another quality which makes them remarkable. For these mound birds have emancipated themselves from sitting on their eggs to keep them warm. They build incubators.

Antonio Pigafetta, the chronicler of Magellan's expedition which circumnavigated the globe (1519-22) wrote of having seen in the Philippines "heavy birds the size of a hen which lay tasty and large eggs. We were told that the female lays these eggs in the sand and that the summer heat is sufficient to hatch them." Pigafetta's information was not quite accurate. Three hundred and forty years later Wallace discovered that the birds make a mound of sand, stones, roots, and leaves, usually near the beach. The hen scratches holes in this heap and lays an egg in each hole. She then covers it over once more. The warmth of the decaying vegetation inside the mound suffices to incubate the eggs.

The maleo or brush turkey of Celebes, Indonesia, digs holes in the sand in the vicinity of hot springs, or buries its eggs in volcanic ashes, while South Australian brush turkeys dig a deep pit in the bush. Male and female then work for weeks gathering all sorts of withering and decomposing plant materials until the pit is filled and a yard-high compost heap towers up above it. Part of the fermenting compost is mixed with sand. When the rains have thoroughly soaked the mound and the inside has reached a temperature of 98° F. from fermentation, the birds open an egg chamber which they have prepared beforehand. The hen lays her eggs in several layers, each one strictly separated from all the others.

But their work on the incubator is not yet over. The parents keep watch over the temperature in their compost heap. In cool weather they cover it with sand, in rainstorms with brush; if the sun shines strongly they quickly remove the protective layer and at times dig shafts into the mound so that the sun's heat can penetrate the interior. When the chicks make their presence known—after about six weeks —both father and mother assist the hatching. They open the incubator at the same intervals in which the eggs were laid (every three or four days), help the newborn chicks emerge, and then close the opening once more. The young wander off into the bush, clustering together, and the parents no longer take any interest in them.

Only one East Australian species, the talegallus, cares for its chicks after hatching. In this case it is the cock alone who looks after the little ones. The hen pays no attention to the nest-building or the eggs. Since the work is often too much for a single cock, several cocks frequently cooperate in the construction of the mound. Each then builds a separate incubating chamber for his own female. Such nests, which are entirely above ground, may be sixty feet in circumference and ten feet in height. They are probably the largest nests built by any vertebrate except man.

EGGS IN A STRANGE NEST

As everyone knows, the cuckoo has immensely simplified the matter of infant care by having other birds raise its young. Why it does this, and by what method, turns out to be not so simple as it seems, and only in modern times has the matter been properly investigated.

Even Aristotle was aware of this type of parasitism. As he described it in his *History of Animals:* "The brooding of the cuckoo's egg and the rearing of the hatched chick is undertaken by the bird in whose nest the egg was laid." The medieval authors of natural histories henceforth repeated this saying without pondering the whys and wherefores. But since the cuckoo's parasitism made an unpleasant impression upon them, they credited the bird with other peculiarities. Thus, in a natural history written by the ninth-century Archbishop of Mainz, Hrabanus Maurus, we find the statement: "Cuckoos go south in the winter. They perch on the shoulders of herons, since they are such poor fliers that but for this they would die of exhaustion during the long journey through the air." In other words, the cuckoo's parasitism extends to migration; since the bird is too lazy to build its own nest, it is obviously too lazy to use its own wings. Concerning the cuckoo's habits when laying eggs, Hrabanus writes censoriously: "They devour the eggs of sparrows and lay their own eggs in the sparrows' nests."

Cuckoos do not, as a matter of fact, generally choose sparrows as foster parents for their young. But Hrabanus was right in suspecting that the female cuckoo disposes of the eggs of her involuntary host before she lays her own egg in the nest. The rightful owners of the nest are not aware of the crime. For the eggs of cuckoos amazingly resemble those of their victims in size, color, and markings. This is so strange a phenomenon that zoologists and bird lovers began to study it carefully around the time of the Enlightenment.

To the pious Pastor Johann Heinrich Zorn the question more or less answered itself. For, "God and Nature do nothing in vain. The cuckoo gives its eggs to small birds to brood; and therefore the eggs

*The pipit foster mother of this European cuckoo fledgling looks in dan-
ger of being swallowed by her hungry charge.*

must be small so that the small birds can cover and incubate them."
As for the clever resemblance in coloration, that too was easily ac-
counted for. The Creator ordained that also, so that the host birds
would accept the eggs. In the nineteenth century, however, ornithologists began looking for a more scientific explanation of the phenomenon.

A German ornithologist named Constantin Lambert Gloger spent
the years 1820 to 1830 studying the coloration of birds' eggs. Apparently, however, he was somewhat lax in his observations. For he
decided that in color and markings the cuckoo's eggs struck an average among the eggs of their victims. Otherwise, he wrote, the birds who
were supposed to tend them parentally "would be alarmed and
prompted to abandon the whole nest. Thus cuckoos' eggs, though
highly variable, always vacillate between the extremes, finding a
middle range among all those eggs among which they are usually
placed."

Twenty years later another pastor named Eduard Baldamus took
issue with this. Cuckoos' eggs, he announced, after years of collecting
eggs, do not vacillate between the extremes; they are always identical
in color and markings with the eggs of the bird in whose nest the
cuckoo lays. "Probably," Baldamus argued, "the cuckoo female consistently lays its eggs in the nest of a single species and will lay in
the nests of other birds only if driven by an emergency." Other egg
collectors corroborated this observation. In northern Europe, where

cuckoos are nest parasites of finches, their eggs look like finch eggs; in the Northeast, where they use the nests of redstarts, the eggs are deep blue like the redstart's. In Central Europe, where a number of very different host birds are exploited, the female cuckoo lays all sorts of eggs.

But how do they achieve their counterfeit? For decades ornithologists debated the question. Some contended that the sight of the eggs in the host bird's nest affected the cuckoo female as she was preparing to lay, so that the egg assumed the necessary color and markings during the act of laying itself. Pastor Altum of Münster cited the susceptibility of pregnant mammals to vivid sense impressions—an idea then much in vogue—and reasoned that in the cuckoo such prenatal suggestibility achieved maximum effectiveness.

Other investigators disagreed. They had discovered that the cuckoo's egg did not acquire its coloring and markings at the moment of laying. One faction maintained that the food received by the young cuckoo in the fosterer's nest affected it so that later on it was impelled to lay eggs of the shape and color of the host, and likewise impelled to lay in the nest of this host's species. Another faction held that the female cuckoo made a conscious choice, that she would examine the eggs already in the nest, and would lay only in nests whose eggs resembled her own. In other words, the cuckoo must know exactly what her egg looks like, and she acts accordingly.

On the other hand, cuckoos often make mistaken choices. Cuckoo eggs have been found in the nests of crested grebes where they certainly have no prospect of being brooded. Eggs are deposited with wrens whose own eggs differ in form and color from those of the cuckoos, yet the wren will foster the young changelings as faithfully as other birds whose eggs the cuckoo cunningly duplicates. Darwin may have been right in his suggestion that cuckoos once upon a time laid their eggs in any nest that happened to be available. Where the cuckoos' eggs looked too different from those of the host, they were thrown out; otherwise they were brooded. By the principle of selection, consequently, certain groups of cuckoos came into being, all with the same outward characteristics, but each with a penchant for a special fosterer.

Heinroth calls this type of selection "selection for resemblance of the egg." Wrens and other small songbirds, he holds, are too weak to push a strange egg out of the nest; they must put up with it for good or ill, and brood it along with their own. Stronger songbirds, however, react promptly if the intruded egg does not look right. "I placed a cuckoo's egg under a pair of yellow warblers. After the excitement caused by the disturbance had subsided, one of the parents hastily sat down on the clutch again. Later, however, the cuckoo's egg had vanished, while the pair went on brooding their own eggs."

There are species of cuckoos which have made a point of parasitizing larger birds. The great-spotted cuckoo, whose habitat is the Mediterranean area, Africa, and the Near East, favors the nests of crows, magpies, jays, and glossy starlings. Sometimes it lays several eggs in the fosterer's nest. Its young will fare well, growing up side by side with the offspring of the host birds, since the foster parents are big and strong enough to feed one or more adoptive children.

This is not the case with the European cuckoo, which must depend on very small songbirds, nor with the African gold cuckoo or the Australian and Oceanic glossy cuckoo. For a small bird cannot feed its own four to six young and a voracious cuckoo in addition. Since it has been repeatedly observed that after the hatching of a young cuckoo the host's eggs or nestlings vanished, zoologists long wondered how this came about. All sorts of theories were propounded. John Gould, a contemporary of Darwin and author of many excellent volumes on the birds of remote lands, decided that fosterers of Australian cuckoos expelled their own children in order to stuff food into the insatiable changeling's maw. Other ornithologists wondered whether the female cuckoo might not pay a return visit to the nest in order to destroy the owner's brood.

The mystery has been solved in recent years, through the use of the movie camera. Films of the life of young cuckoos in the nest show plainly that the seemingly helpless infant cuckoo is in fact the unwitting murderer of its stepbrothers and stepsisters. The Heinroths, who succeeded in filming every phase in the life of the baby cuckoo, describe the sequence of events as follows:

A few hours after it is hatched, the completely naked and blind young European cuckoo suddenly acquires the urge to throw out of the nest everything it can find, including, of course, eggs and other young. It pushes sideways and backwards under a nest-mate or under an egg, works the object onto its broad, slightly hollowed back, and supports it with its outstretched wings, which are far stronger and more dexterous than the wings of most small birds. The cuckoo then climbs backwards up the wall of the nest, using its head and neck as a prop. . . . The little blind porter carries his burden to the rim of the nest and has to use all his skill not to fall out himself. When the job is done, he works his way back into the nest to tackle the next load.

After about four days the instinct disappears. By then it is no longer needed, since the cuckoo has the nest all to itself. It is, there-

During the first four days after hatching, the European cuckoo seems to have an irresistible urge to throw out everything in the foster nest, including, of course, any other young or eggs. This series of photographs shows how the young bird (underneath and invisible in the first picture) uses his remarkably strong back and wings to edge another fledgling to the rim of the nest and then push it over. He thereupon moves back into the nest to tackle any other object. After four days this urge seems to disappear, but by that time, there are no rivals left in the nest.

fore, quite untrue that the growing cuckoo gradually forces its host's offspring out of the nest, as books on animal life still teach. Nor is there any evidence that the hoodwinked birds are at all grieved at the loss of their proper family. Rather, they show a definite preference for the young impostor. As Heinroth puts it: "One even gets the impression that the feeding behavior of the foster parents is more strongly aroused by the cuckoo than by their own young; at any rate, they seem quite engrossed in feeding it. One can be sure that if it were not a pleasure to bring up the young cuckoo they would not do so, for birds are not under the compulsion of a moral code."

Nor is it only parents in whom the cuckoo so successfully arouses a protective spirit. Heinroth continues: "When you bring a newly fledged European cuckoo into an aviary you can count on it that the other birds will soon start to feed the stranger—even though they may be hardly able to feed themselves. . . . Small birds that cannot reach up to the mouth of a young cuckoo often perch on its head or hover in front of it in order to put the food in properly."

Not all species of cuckoo are parasites. The American road runner and yellow-billed cuckoos build their own nests and raise their own offspring. On the other hand, cuckoos are not alone in the practice of murderous parasitism. The African honey guide, a member of the woodpecker family whose harsh cry alerts the natives to the fact that it has found a hive of wild bees, lays its eggs in the nests of woodpeckers and of a number of songbirds. Newly hatched honey guides behave much like young cuckoos—with the added advantage that they are equipped during their first days of life with hooklike projections on their bills. Presumably these hooks help them in ejecting their potential rivals from the nest.

According to reports from South American naturalists, the black-headed duck *Heteronetta atricapilla* of Patagonia and southern Chile practices a parasite policy that involves high risks for its eggs. For it not only lays them in the nests of other ducks, gulls, and waterfowl but will also, if need be, lay in the nests of herons and raptorial birds. It is said—though not proved—that the young will flee these dangerous foster parents immediately after hatching and join a family of ducks.

American starlings clearly illustrate the gradual stages from neglect of nest building to parasitism. Some species make pretty pouch-like nests which they hang from twigs; others set up large, disorderly collective nests in which several females brood. Still others have lost the impulse to build, and occupy the abandoned nests of other birds. Another group will seize an occupied nest, throw out the eggs, drive the owners away, and brood in this stolen nursery. Finally there are the cowbirds, which practice the same kind of egg smuggling as the cuckoo. Among them, too, there are variations. In the majority of cases, the changeling cowbirds live at peace with the fosterer's children. In one species, the female pecks open the eggs of the host immediately after laying her own, thus insuring that her offspring will have no rivals.

Among cuckoos a similar trend can be observed. Some of the nest-building species mentioned above occasionally lay an egg in another bird's nest. The South American anis and guira cuckoos practice what Wolfgang von Buddenbrock has called "a kind of nest communism." A number of females gather together, build a communal nest, and brood side by side. Sometimes the birds do not find room in the communal nest for their own eggs. In that case, they deposit the surplus in another ani nest, or in a guira nest.

The nests of the American black-billed and yellow-billed cuckoos are shoddy structures—a mere flooring of twigs through which eggs and fledglings sometimes helplessly tumble. These species sometimes lay an egg in another nest, as has happened here. The young bird in the middle is a yellow-billed cuckoo in a black-bill cuckoo nest. To the left and to the right are two young black-bills, and still another bird is barely seen at the bottom of the nest. The difference between the two black-bills is in their age—the one to the right was hatched earlier.

The common nest of the guira cuckoos is probably one of the shoddiest structures built by any bird. Often the eggs slip through the loose twigs of the bottom and are smashed on the ground. Consequently, the more prudent of the guira females have gradually formed the habit of prematurely abandoning nesting places that are excessively tumbledown and depositing their eggs in the nests of other birds. That is to say, these species are still brooding their own eggs, but have taken the first step toward parasitism.

The truly parasitic cuckoos have broken all familial bonds. The female practices polyandry. She drifts from territory to territory, gives herself to the male in possession of each territory, and after the nuptials steals quietly through thickets seeking a likely looking nest. During the laying period of from five to seven weeks she may lay as many as twenty eggs. But since a cuckoo specializing in redstarts cannot always find a redstart nest, or one specializing in reed warblers a reed warbler's nest, innumerable cuckoo eggs are laid in the wrong places every year, and usually destroyed.

The cuckoo female has earned a bad reputation for her polyandry, as she has for her parasitism, but it too has its significance. It increases egg production and hence furthers the preservation of the species.

CHAPTER SEVEN

■

MAMMALS AND THE ANIMAL IN MAN

In 1905 a book by a Viennese neurologist exploded upon society. Along with Darwin's *Origin of Species* and Karl Marx's *Capital*, it is probably the most revolutionary book of the past century. It unleashed chain reactions and counteractions which have rumbled on to this day. The title of the book was *Three Essays on the Theory of Sexuality*. The author was Sigmund Freud.

Although in the early years of the twentieth century a considerable number of physicians had begun to be cognizant of both the existence of sexuality in children and the connections between sexuality and the neuroses, Freud's revelations nevertheless came as a shock to most of his contemporaries. In fact, Freudian theory was regarded as a criminal attack upon one of the most sacred concepts of humanity—innocent love. And when five years later Sigmund Freud's views were scheduled to be discussed at a scientific congress in Hamburg, the chairman—a distinguished psychiatrist named Wilhelm Weygandt—refused to permit it. "This is no fit subject for a scientific meeting," he declared. "It is an affair for the police."

Freud had broken a number of taboos theretofore considered inviolable. He had asserted that infants and small children were highly responsive to feelings of sexual pleasure. He had designated certain instinctual events which had theretofore been regarded as more or less revolting aberrations as altogether normal. Every man, he had asserted, possessed at least the disposition toward such "aberrations." Freud postulated a number of erogenous zones, as he called them, the

294

stimulation of which yields satisfaction to the libido. He even spoke of the pleasure that the infant feels at its mother's breast, in sucking its fingers, being rocked in the cradle, and being caressed, as a sexual event. "It is only in the rarest instances," he wrote, "that the psychical valuation that is set on the sexual object, as being the goal of the sexual instinct, stops short at its genitals. The appreciation extends to the whole body of the sexual object and tends to involve every sensation derived from it . . . It helps to turn activities connected with other parts of the body into sexual aims."

Freud's theory dealt exclusively with human beings. But among animals, too, actions which have nothing to do with actual copulation become sexual goals, as do actions which appear to offer the opposite of pleasure. In fact, these actions are indispensable to the satisfaction of the libido. The love darts of snails, the love bites of female sea lions and male lizards, martens, and felines, must surely inflict pain upon the mate. The kissing ceremonies of certain species of fish have as little to do with copulation as the billing of birds and the sexual preliminaries of many mammals. Mice, bats, and predators lick one another; cats give one another affectionate blows with their paws. In monkeys mating is often preceded by careful mutual grooming. Man tends to regard a good many of these gestures as obscene, and to equate them with the perversions that crop up among the members of his own species. But among the animals in question they are normal aspects of sexual activity.

Man, who judges the sex act and sexual pleasure by his own standards, finds it hard to imagine that the sexual instinct can be satisfied by a momentary contact of the anus, as is the case in birds. Dr. Alfred C. Kinsey was concerned with this question when, in 1938, he and a large staff of other biologists, as well as physicians, anthropologists, geneticists, chemists, psychiatrists, sociologists, and statisticians, began their now-famous study of sexual behavior in man. The president of this research group was Robert M. Yerkes, known for many years before chiefly as an animal psychologist and student of ape behavior. Kinsey and his associates not only interrogated thousands of men and women; they also compared human sexual behavior with that of animals.

In his two-volume report, published between 1948 and 1953, Kinsey attempted an interpretation of sexual pleasure which may or may not illuminate the origin of the phenomenon:

One of the most characteristic qualities of living matter, plant or animal, is its capacity to respond to touch. The normal, first reaction of an organism is to press against any object with which it may come into contact. One-celled animals mass against objects. Multicellular bodies like cockroaches crowd into corners. . . . If an animal pulls away from the stimulating object, little else may happen to it physiologically. If it responds by pressing against the object, a considerable series of physiologic events may follow. If the tactile stimulation becomes rhythmic, or the pressure is long-continued, the level of response may increase and build up neuromuscular tensions which become recognizable as sexual responses.

The cloaca, portal of the intestines and also of the sexual organs in all vertebrates below the level of mammals, is undoubtedly especially sensitive to those tactile stimuli of which Kinsey speaks. Long ago Bölsche bluntly spoke of the "cloacal loves" of such animals. We may assume that after the requisite preliminaries a union of the cloacas produces sexual reactions which are at least similar to those of mammals. Even in a certain number of human beings, the orifice which serves to discharge the contents of the intestines, and which the ordinary person consequently finds somewhat offensive, must be listed as one of the more or less erogenous zones. For this reason some chroniclers of sex have remarked, half seriously and half ironically, that cloacal sex in animals may cast some light on the origin and development of pederasty.

In female mammals, however, this source of pleasure has generally ceased to function. Aside from the primitive duckbills, mammals have developed a different erogenous zone in that part of the body. A second orifice appeared, devoted exclusively to sexual and reproductive activities, which was henceforth the male's principal sexual goal. And at the anterior end of this orifice the clitoris developed as a morphological counterpart to the male organ of copulation, and the principal source of sexual pleasure in the female. Nevertheless, all mammals up to man remained responsive to a variety of tactile stimuli. As Bölsche has put it:

> . . . you must not picture this localization as confined in too extreme a fashion to one spot; light excitations of sensual pleasure are possible on the entire skin of the body, and they are able to sound along faintly now and again, now here and now there; now as before. The erotically excited kiss as well as the inward feeling of physical well-being, which is so difficult to describe, of a mother nursing her child at her breast, feeds on fare that is both coarse and infinitely fine and becoming finer; but all this in the sense of the primeval evolutionary fact that in the beginning the whole skin was the seat of sensual pleasure.

It therefore seems reasonable to suppose that human aberrations have their roots in the animal kingdom. What was normal in his animal ancestors, the argument runs, becomes in man abnormal and perverse—partly because of his biological evolution, partly because of self-imposed taboos. Freud had the courage to face the consequences of this line of reasoning:

> The conclusion now presents itself to us that there is indeed something innate lying behind the perversions but that it is something innate in *everyone*, though as a disposition it may vary in its intensity and may be increased by the influences of actual life. What is in question is the innate constitutional roots of the sexual instinct. In one class of cases (the perversions) these roots may grow into the actual vehicles of sexual activity, in others they may be submitted to an insufficient suppression . . . while in the most favorable cases, which lie between these two extremes, they may by means of effective restriction and other kinds of modification bring about what is known as normal sexual life.

Zoologists have observed somewhat similar phenomena in the higher animals. Among these, too, there may be individuals who depart from the standards of the species. The satisfaction of the libido by masturbation is by no means rare among young mammals. For male apes, at least in captivity, it represents an almost normal phase of sexual development. Male and female porcupines, as the American naturalist A. R. Shadle has observed, are given to rubbing their genitals on protruding objects. "The females may even seize, straddle, and ride sticks about the cage. Holding the long stick with the forepaws, the animal stands erect as it walks about astride the stick, thus stimulating the genitalia by contact with the stick." The males take an interest in such sticks also: "From the cage floor, sticks which have come in contact with the female's genitals, urine, etc., will also receive attention. If the stick is a foot or two long, the male will often grasp it in his paws, straddle it, and go about the cage riding it as the female did."

In their comprehensive study, *Patterns of Sexual Behavior*, Clellan S. Ford and Frank A. Beach, respectively professors of anthropology and psychology at Yale University, give material on masturbatory activity in elephants, dolphins, carnivores, ruminants, and rodents. The process does not always take place as one might expect. The erogenous zones of various mammals are located in unexpected places. An extremely sensitive erogenous zone, for example, seems to be the antlers of stags at rutting time. The English naturalist F. Fraser Darling describes a very curious case of masturbation among red deer:

This act is accomplished by lowering the head and gently drawing the tips of the antlers to and fro through the herbage. Erection and extrusion of the penis from the sheath follow in five to seven seconds. There is but little protrusion and retraction of the penis and no oscillating movements of the pelvis. Ejaculation follows about five seconds after the penis is erected, so that the whole act takes ten to fifteen seconds. These antlers, used now so delicately, may within a few minutes be used with all the body's force behind them to clash with the antlers of another stag. These mysterious organs are a paradox: at one moment exquisitely sensitive, they can be apparently without feeling the next.

There is an extensive literature on homosexual relationships between male mammals. The primates are notorious for this. Such specialists on apes as H. C. Bingham, C. R. Carpenter, G. V. Hamilton, E. J. Kempf, A. H. Maslow, Robert M. Yerkes, and S. Zuckermann have collected innumerable observations from zoos and apes in the wild indicating that apes indulge in all the practices of human homosexuals. Scientists, however, have by no means come to any agreement on the reasons for animal homosexuality, any more than psychologists can agree on the causation of human homosexuality. Some regard it as merely a substitute activity. Others assume that young apes must pass through a natural homosexual phase before achieving full sexual maturity. Still others attribute it to the complicated dominance patterns among gregarious apes.

According to this latter view, the younger or weaker males demonstrate their submission to the herd sire by offering themselves to him with that famous gesture which Konrad Gesner described four hundred years ago in the classic phrase: "And when he is signed to, he presents his arse." But this is no gesture of derision. "It is a sexual offer," as Grzimek expresses it, "and in addition a general token of humility." In similar fashion the females offer themselves to the herd sire, and the weaker baboon females behave the same way to show humility and respect to stronger females.

In other words, male baboons of lower rank display female mating behavior toward those higher in the social scale. In general it is a mere gesture of politeness, like the gesture of two men who lift their hats by way of greeting. On the other hand, the smaller and younger male can obtain a good many advantages by submitting to a more powerful male. The superior male will protect his favorite against the attacks of other apes. When the stronger partner is about to take food away from the weaker, the young male will frequently offer himself sexually, and in return will be allowed to keep the food.

Among most other mammals the partner of the same sex seems to

The mandrill from Gesner's 16th-century book on mammals. The text beneath the engraving reads: "This animal aroused great wonder when brought to Augsburg and shown there in the year 1551. Is found in the great desert lands of India. Very rare. On his feet he has fingers like a man's, and if one points at him, he presents his arse."

be only an inferior substitute for a missing representative of the other sex. Animal breeders have long known this. They speak of "bulling cows" and "horsing mares," when such females attempt to mount others of their sex in male fashion. To the breeder this is a clear sign that the cows or mares are ready for breeding. But there are exceptions. McBride and Hebb observed two male dolphins kept in a large sea-water tank. These males showed no interest at all in the females that had been placed with them, but instead tried to copulate with one another. When they were separated for a time and then reunited in the same tank, the following behavior was observed:

> No doubt could exist that the two recognized each other, and for several hours they swam side by side rushing frenziedly through the water, and on several occasions they leaped completely out of water. For several days, the two males were inseparable and neither paid any attention to the female. This was in the courting season, and at other times each of the two males seemed bent only on preventing the other's copulation with the female.

Even that practice which all moralities have called the most heinous of the sexual vices—copulation with creatures of other species—

occurs now and then among the higher vertebrates. The human imagination has been intrigued by this particular perversion from time immemorial, and has woven myths around it. Leda's liaison with the swan has been a favorite subject of artists since antiquity. Primitive peoples have created similar myths, the most common of which is that this or that enemy tribe sprang from a union between man and ape, man and predator, or man and snake. The Greenland explorer Knud Rasmussen has reported one such fable common among the Copper Eskimos: "There was once a woman who did not want to have any man. Her family let dogs couple with her. She was taken out to an island where she was made pregnant by the dogs. After that she gave birth to white men. Before that time there were no white men."

Such stories are in part weapons in the campaign of scandalmongering that tribes, nations, and races have waged against one another since the most ancient times. But in part they are also relics of totemistic ideas. Totemism, the belief that certain groups of human beings have descended from certain animals, was once a dominant belief throughout the greater part of the earth. Traces of totemistic ideas can be found to this day among even the most advanced civilizations. But for all these fables, the lawgivers of mankind have always felt a great horror of actual physical contact between men and animals. As late as the eighteenth century in Europe and America it was customary not only to hang people convicted of "bestiality," but also to condemn to death and execute the animal participants.

In a book on the judicial persecution and punishment of animals the American writer E. P. Evans has set forth the case of a certain Jacques Ferron of Vauves (a suburb of Paris), who in the year 1750 was charged with an unnatural relationship with a she ass. Monsieur Ferron went to the gallows, of course. But the ass found a defender in the prioress of the convent of Vauves, who submitted an affidavit attesting to the ass's virtue. The animal, the affidavit stated, had been known to the prioress and other citizens of Vauves for many years as a decent and virtuous animal; it could not possibly have consented of its own free will to the vile desires of Jacques Ferron. The affidavit had the desired effect; the ass was acquitted.

But animals have no objection to copulating with members of other species, if normal mates are lacking. Under natural conditions, of course, such incidents are extremely rare. Nor does a wild animal take the slightest sexual interest in man. There is no basis in reality for Count Buffon's atrocity story, two hundred years old and repeatedly trotted out anew, that the great apes kidnap women and girls and "keep them for the pleasure of their company and always feed them in abundance." Like every wild animal who has had experience with man, apes keep their distance from the lord of creation.

In confinement, however, apes frequently manifest sexual reactions when a human being of the opposite sex approaches their enclosure. Baboons and macaques, according to Hamilton and Kempf, will attempt to couple with all sorts of cage-mates—with apes or monkeys of other species, with dogs, cats, and foxes, even with snakes. Zoo attendants, moreover, report affairs between llamas and goats, mouflons and domestic sheep, elk and cattle, dolphins and marine turtles. "Male rats that have mated with females in a particular observation cage," write Ford and Beach, "attempt copulation with almost any animal of appropriate size that is encountered in the experimental cage."

Birds in captivity quite often conduct affairs with cage-mates of other species. Ibises pair with spoonbills, geese with ducks, parrots even with rails. If American wood ducks and East Asiatic mandarin ducks, which cannot crossbreed, are kept together on a pond, according to Heinroth, "they almost always form mixed wood-mandarin duck pairs. The members of these pairs are extremely fond of each other: they go nest-hunting together and copulate." Heinroth mentions other cases: "For instance, a brightly colored rainbow lorikeet (a parrot) and a European purple gallinule or porphyrio (a rail) have been known to pair. The fact that both have blue feathers may have caused the mutual attraction. Even more bizarre was a white peacock at the Schönbrunn Zoo in Vienna, which was reared with giant Galapagos tortoises and thereafter refused to bestow his affections on anything else." Such matings, aside from those of ibis and spoonbill, are sterile.

Among higher animals, then, everything that psychopathologists consign to the twilight realm of aberrations and perversions apparently exists: masturbation; homosexuality; gratification from all sorts of physical contacts, painful stimuli, and alien or inappropriate sexual objects. But the picture presented by domestic and captive animals can be highly deceptive. In the wild, substitute sexual activities are not necessary. And where innate dispositions of this sort exist, natural selection rapidly and effectively prevents their perpetuation. The variety of sexual possibilities must, in the animal kingdom, pass through the filter of the inexorable struggle for existence. What remains is the classic goal, sexual union with a mate of the same species and different sex, since only this serves to preserve the species. Civilized man, however, is no longer required to pass through the filter of the struggle for existence. The abnormal can survive alongside the normal.

THE PUZZLE OF FEMALE PLEASURE

What constitutes real gratification of the sexual instinct for animals? This seemingly so simple question is in reality difficult to answer. Even if we assume that all male animals feel the ejaculation of semen as pleasurable, there remains the problem of the female animals, in many of whom no corresponding process can be detected.

Does the female fish feel pleasure in ejecting her eggs into the water? Are there pleasure sensations for the female salamander when she has drawn the spermatophore deposited by the male into her cloaca? Does the male frog give the female sexual release when he presses the eggs out of her body? We do not know. Only one aspect of the matter seems to be clear: those female animals which do not engage in genuine copulation are dominated by the same sexual urge as the females of higher vertebrates. And apparently their libidos are gratified by the nuptial play.

There has been considerable discussion of the proposition that the spawning of female fish and amphibians may produce a discharge of tension similar to the orgasm of the male. Among female frogs, who are not exactly treated with tenderness by their mates in the sex act, violent stimulation of the skin of the back may—possibly—evoke spasmic reactions. But it is also possible that sexual pleasure in these animals is not localized at any particular part of the body, nor evoked by a specific event. Perhaps the whole body is charged like a battery during the sexual preliminaries and discharged at the climax of the nuptials.

The overwhelming majority of male birds do not even possess a specific organ of copulation, while female reptiles and birds lack that important female organ of stimulation, the clitoris; this deficiency remains until we reach the mammalia. Yet if these animals felt no pleasure in the sex act, they would not wish to engage in it. Innumerable observations have shown that the females of songbirds, pigeons, plovers, cuckoos, and other species of birds, whose sexual union consists merely of a pressing together of the cloacas, often manifest an astounding sexual craving. And where birds undertake sexual contacts outside their species, the female is frequently the more insistent.

Many biologists maintain to this day that there is no spontaneous climax of sexual pleasure among female mammals. They have produced all sorts of proofs of this theory. Female mammals, they will say, do not manifest that sudden relaxation which marks the end of the sex act in male mammals. What is more, after intercourse females seem to be immediately responsive again. From such observations biologists draw the bold conclusion that the human female occupies a special place in the animal kingdom, since in contrast to all other mammals she is able to reach sexual climax.

If this were really so, it would be hard to account for the fact that female mammals possess any organ of stimulation at all. Why should they be graced with a clitoris, the same organ which in the human female produces an explosive discharge of neuromuscular tensions, but be unable to use it for the same purpose? In animals, as a matter of fact, the clitoris can have an extraordinarily complex structure. Among cats and civet cats it is reinforced by a bony structure. Among certain insectivores and rodents it has a horny tip and protrudes so far from the body that the females may easily be mistaken for males. It is even more difficult to distinguish the sexes among hyenas. The females of some South American species of monkeys, especially the spider monkeys, are equipped with such a large clitoris that it looks just like a male organ.

Female animals cannot tell scientists anything about their reactions, of course, but their curve of excitement can be determined. The American scientists L. M. Pussep and Arthur Weil, for example, have measured the blood pressure of dogs during copulation. Their measurements showed, according to Dr. Kinsey, that "the recession from the peak of response in the female bears a striking resemblance to orgasm in the male." Other scientists have made similar studies of pulse rate and respiration in copulating rats, rabbits, and monkeys. All show that the curves of the females run parallel to those of the males, or at any rate do not deviate significantly. As Kinsey says, it is difficult to see why this should not be taken as evidence of orgasm.

Kinsey adds a number of reports and observations which seem to show that the phenomena of pleasure in cows, female rabbits, cats, and chimpanzees follow much the same course as in the human female. The females of cats, especially, end copulation with characteristic convulsive movements. They twist, writhe, and roll, curvetting their bodies about for seconds or minutes. When experimenters artificially desensitize the sexual parts of female cats, such post-coital reactions disappear.

Orgasm must be viewed as one of the strangest of biological phenomena. Every physiologist and neurologist knows that nervous and muscular tensions can add up until they reach a climax. But sexual biologists still have no idea of the processes involved in the sudden discharge of these tensions in the sex act. Kinsey remarks: "There is only one other phenomenon, namely sneezing, which is physiologically close in its summation and explosive discharge of tension. Sneezing is, however, a localized event, while sexual orgasm involves the whole of the reacting body."

The body can be so violently affected that some mammals subside into a state of exhaustion or total rigidity after mating. This is especially observable in mice and other small rodents, which lie curled up as if they were dead. Cattle stand apathetically in their pasture. Other animals, in a condition of unwonted quietude that is like a half sleep, exchange a variety of gentle caresses. Gazelles allow the bucks to rub them with their horns. Horses nibble one another with their teeth. Even cats, which exhibit such excitement in the immediate postlude of coition, end by licking their mates peacefully. But why this period of quietude occurs in some species and not in others remains one of the many unsolved riddles of sexual gratification.

THE PLATYPUS IS DIFFERENT

In 1799 the zoologists of the British Museum received an animal skin from an Australian supplier in Hawkesbury, New South Wales. The more they examined it, the more they were perplexed. The mysterious animal had a dark-brown, silky skin, four short legs, and a flattened tail. Hence, it must be a mammal. But instead of a mouth it had what looked for all the world like a duck's bill. Was it, then, a bird?

Some naturalists thought the curious creature must be the creation of an overseas jokester. Chinese dealers in rarities were known to sew fishtails to the bodies of monkeys, or to incise human faces on the bodies of rays, mummify these monstrosities and sell them to sailors as mermaids. In Europe, too, taxidermists were wont to adorn stuffed hares with antlers for the amusement of sportsmen. Small wonder that the Australian freak was taken for another such artificial product.

But George Shaw, head of the zoological department of the Museum, eventually realized that the monster was genuine. In the meantime more duck-billed animals had arrived in London, preserved in alcohol. According to the statements of reliable persons in Australia, they were water dwellers and fed in rivers like ducks, probing the bottom with their bills. Shaw noted that the anus of the creatures resembled that of reptiles and birds. The duckbills, or duck-billed platypuses, as he named them, discharged the products of their digestive tracts, kidneys, and sex glands through one and the same opening; they possessed only the well-known cloaca. In the male a copulatory organ was found on the posterior wall of the cloaca. It had a tube-like shape, but was not pierced by a urethra like the penis of other male mammals. In this respect the platypus resembled the reptiles.

In the following decades, two more species of such animals were discovered in the Australian territories—animals likewise four-footed like mammals with bills like birds and a simple intestinal-genital orifice like reptiles. In contrast to the platypus, however, both animals —the Australian echidna or spiny anteater and the New Guinea three-clawed echidna—lived on land and were covered with spines like a hedgehog.

Scientists were much interested in the posteriors of the platypuses and echidnas. For the cloaca was proof that they must be primitive mammals, still half reptile. In fact, they are the most primitive mammals that now inhabit the earth. This characteristic led the French zoologist Etienne Geoffroy de Saint-Hilaire to assign them the scientific name *Monotremata*—Greek for "animal with a single hole." Lorenz Oken baptized them by the popular term "cloacal animals."

For decades zoologists of many lands tried to understand the reproduction of monotremes. Milk glands were found in female platypuses and echidnas, but no nipples. Hence the newborn young could not be sucklings in the proper sense of the word. They must press the mother's milk out of the glands with their own bills, and then lick it up. But how were these young born? Female echidnas possess a pouch like the kangaroo and other marsupials. But the platypus female has no such pouch. Although Australian observers stubbornly maintained that platypuses and echidnas laid eggs, most zoologists were convinced that monotreme offspring must be born alive, possibly in a highly imperfect embryonic state, and that they complete their development either in the pouch or clinging to the mother's body, like marsupials.

At the end of August 1884 these speculations came to a sudden end. Two scientists, the Australian W. H. Caldwell and the German Wilhelm Haacke, each established independently that both platypuses and echidnas laid eggs. As it later developed, so did the New Guinea three-clawed echidna. Monotreme eggs, however, are very peculiar things. They contain only a litle food, so that the growing embryo must be nourished through the parchmentlike shell by secretions from the mother's womb. Although the monotremes are egg layers, they have one of the prime characteristics of mammals: a firm connection between mother and embryo. In contrast to other mammals, however, in platypuses and echidnas only the left ovary functions, exactly as in birds.

Ever since this discovery, monotremes have been favorite subjects for evolutionists wishing to demonstrate their theory. Those first mammals of the Mesozoic Era (who emerged from the saurians called Therapsides) must have looked somewhat like the monotremes: equipped with a cloaca, egg-laying, intermittently warm-blooded, but already covered with fur and able to nurture the still egg-encased embryo through the uterus. Only the interesting bills appear to be, not an archaic relic, but a new acquisition. For the few examples of Mesozoic primitive mammals that have been found, as well as the embryos of platypuses, are provided with teeth.

Monotremes incubate their eggs, after the fashion of birds. Echidnas do so in the maternal pouch, platypuses in holes they dig by the shore of their rivers. During the incubating period the males are not admitted to these structures. Newborn monotremes are as helpless and undeveloped as nestling birds and marsupial young. Echidna babies require about two months before they leave the pouch; platypus young are blind for a full eleven weeks and do not crawl out of the nest until they are all of four months old. Even then they must lick their mother's milk for three weeks more before they go into the water like the adults to hunt for mollusks and insects.

Among the many curious features that distinguish these lowest of all living mammals is one that puzzles zoologists to this day. Male monotremes wear a sharp, hooked, movable spur on the heel of each hind foot. This spur is hollow and contains a channel leading to a gland on the outside of the thigh. Such an apparatus, it would seem, could only serve as a weapon, as a poisoned dagger. For the secretion from the gland in the thigh kills rabbits and other small animals. It produces violent pain and symptoms of poisoning even in men, if they happen to be struck by the spur. But there is an inconsistency, for echidnas never defend themselves with their poisonous spur, and platypuses only occasionally. Moreover, the males produce the poisonous secretion only at mating time. It has therefore been suggested that in the course of sex play the males may run the spur into the female's body in order to stimulate her sexually, "like an injection under the skin with a regular syringe," Bölsche commented, "whose purpose may be to put the female in a state of slight intoxication and so make her more accessible to the male's courtship." The idea could be extended: since female monotremes possess no clitoris to be stimulated, the injection may produce a kind of climax in them.

But no one has ever seen the male give the female such an injection. The real significance of the spur has not yet been determined. The fact remains that monotremes are, aside from a few shrews, the only venom-producing mammals. Poison glands occur among verte-

An engraving from 1825 of a male duck-billed platypus. Note the spur on the hind foot. The spur is hollow and contains a channel leading to a venom-producing gland. Whether the function of the spur is for defense or for sexual stimulation of the female is not known.

brates only in certain fish, amphibians, and reptiles. In this respect, it would seem, the monotremes have retained something of the old reptilian heritage.

FROM POUCH TO PLACENTA

Wilhelm Bölsche compared the yolk in the egg of reptiles and birds with a large piece of thickly buttered bread on which the embryo can live "for the duration of its internment in the little locked chamber of its eggshell." The embryos of monotremes have an additional source of nourishment in the nutritive maternal juices which penetrate the thin shell. It is easy to conceive how this method might come into being when egg laying is discontinued and the young are brought into the world alive:

> The permeable, soft egg skin in there would press as closely as possible against the inner maternal wall, so as to make the most of the good things that were dripping down, like a person who puts his mouth close to the bunghole of a barrel. And the little embryo in the shell would for its part crowd as closely as possible against this covering, so as to suck up the good food stored there as completely as possible.

Young opossums in the mother's pouch. These marsupials are "born" as early as 12 days after conception, when they are still underdeveloped embryos. They attach themselves firmly to the mother's milk glands, where they remain until, after some weeks, they have developed sufficiently to break this intimate contact.

The first marsupial zoologists discovered was the opossum. A fanciful picture of it appeared in Gesner's book on mammals, though he mistakenly called it a baboon. In real life, an opossum family looks quite different. One of the youngsters has wrapped its tail around the mother's nose.

But it would be an inconvenient complication for the embryo to lick the nourishment from the womb with its mouth. The nutritive juices are supposed to reach the intestinal tract as quickly as possible. Thus, in mammals the wall of the uterus is connected directly with the embryo's intestine through the navel cord. This intimate connection between mother and child has a long history. One of its concomitants is experienced by every woman and every mammalian female when it gives birth: birth pangs. Another concomitant is carried on the abdomen of every mammal and every man as a permanent mark: the navel.

Like all vertebrates, mammals form a bag of nourishment in the egg: the yolk sac. In the days before Darwin, many embryologists wondered why there should be this structure in mammalian embryos. For the mammalian egg is rather poorly supplied with nutritive yolk, and the embryos are, after all, nourished directly by the mother. Since Darwin's time, however, zoologists have assumed that mammals descended from reptiles. They have taken over and retained the reptilian yolk sac, but employed it for another function. It ceased to be Bölsche's "thickly buttered bread" and became instead what he calls a "sucking bag" through which the embryo's intestine sucks nourishment from the wall of the uterus as a child drinks at its mother's breast.

The yolk sac still serves its original purpose in marsupials. As monotremes represent the beginnings of mammalian development, the marsupials represent the next stage of evolution. It is of no particular importance whether marsupials were, as was thought in Darwin's day, the immediate predecessors of the higher mammals, or whether the various groups of marsupials should be regarded as branches—blind alleys of evolution. We do, however, know for certain that the earth in Cretaceous times, before the rise of the higher mammals, was populated by marsupials. And it is probable that the embryonic development of the first viviparous mammals followed along the lines of present-day marsupials: kangaroos, dasyures, and opossums.

The chief characteristic of marsupials is, to the mind of most people the pouch in which the young grow. This pouch is generally pictured like that of the kangaroo—a large, roomy sack on the female's belly from which the infant peers merrily out on the world. But there are also marsupials which have very small, insignificant-looking brood pouches, mere folds of skin or even no pouch at all. To the zoologist, marsupials are distinguished from the higher mammals, not by their possession of a built-in cradle but by a number of other anatomical characteristics, and above all by the manner in which their embryos grow.

The embryos in the marsupial womb take nourishment through the transformed yolk sac for a comparatively short time. They are, with some exceptions, not firmly attached in the uterus, like the embryos of other mammals, but connected very lightly.

Parturition among them is a kind of miscarriage. The embryos leave the womb in an almost larval state, singularly undeveloped, for they are "born" as few as twelve days and at most a month after conception. They emerge as tiny, naked, helpless bits of flesh. They seek out the mother's milk glands, attach their mouths firmly to them, and remain attached. Weeks pass before the limbs and sense organs have developed sufficiently for the embryo to break this intimate contact. Thereafter the marsupial baby drinks from the teat at intervals, as do the young of higher mammals.

For almost two hundred years naturalists discussed the question of how the newborn kangaroo reaches the pouch. The way from the birth canal to the pouch is long, and the tiny creature, barely an inch in length, has no functioning senses and barely a speck of a brain. It looks, in Maurice Burton's words, like "an animated haricot bean." Was it conceivable that the kangaroo female could grip this tiny thing in her lips or forepaws, open the pouch and place the embryo with mathematical accuracy at just the right spot, in contact with the almost invisible teat? Or could the animated bean itself creep into the pouch?

The first theory was at least believable. The second seemed fantastic. Yet in 1832 a naval surgeon insisted that he had seen with his own eyes a kangaroo embryo crawl into the mother's pouch of its own accord. No one took him seriously. Only in the past few decades have zookeepers the world over found that the fantastic story of the naval surgeon was absolutely correct. The procedure has been described by Maurice Burton in his book, *Infancy in Animals:*

> As the time for the birth draws near, the female kangaroo takes up a resting position, which is almost a sitting or reclining posture. In this the hind legs are stretched out at full length in front with the tail stretched between them. This brings the exit from the birth-canal into a position where it is directed upwards towards the pouch. In this position, the mother kangaroo grooms the interior of the pouch. Having cleaned it out, she then licks a path in her fur from the exit of the birth-canal to the entrance of the pouch.
>
> As the foetus leaves the birth-canal the mother bends her head to lick it free of the delicate membranes surrounding it. Once free the foetus follows the path licked in the fur, using an overarm movement

of the front legs, which, contrary to what we see in the adult animal, are longer than the hind legs. Throughout the journey the foetus moves its head from side to side in what appears to be a searching movement. Having reached the mouth of the pouch, the newly-born mite enters and travels over the inner wall until its searching mouth touches a nipple. This it grasps and remains attached, suckling until large enough to move about on its own.

The procedure is similar in all marsupials, including those that have no pouch. In these, the newborn crawl directly to the teats and attach themselves.

Behavioral scientists, however, were not content with these observations. They wanted to see what the embryo would do if the mother's position were changed. Since it is rather difficult to make kangaroos in parturition stand on their heads, the scientists decided to experiment with the smaller opossum. They picked up female opossums after delivery and held them head downward. The young promptly crawled in the wrong direction—upward, away from the pouch. Apparently the embryo has a specific instinct which commands it to move upward immediately after it is born.

For a considerable time that first crawl is the only physical activity

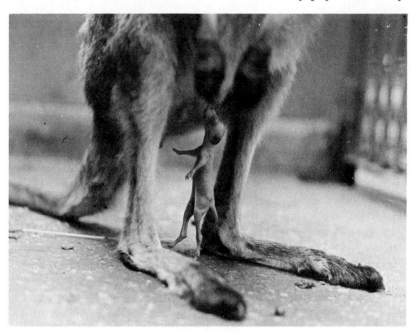

A young kangaroo, accidentally dislodged from its mother's pouch. Note how firmly it holds on to the nipple.

of the marsupial infant. Thereafter it can sleep in the pouch as if it were in a second uterus, its peace disturbed only by experimenting zoologists who roughly remove the little creature from the teat in order to see what happens. That experiment was undertaken a hundred years ago by the English zoologist Richard Owen. The result, in the words of Ludwig Heck, former director of the Berlin zoo, was a sad one:

> The baby moved its limbs violently after it was removed, but made no visible effort to cling with its feet to the mother's skin or to crawl away. Instead, it proved to be completely helpless. It was then laid at the bottom of the pouch. The mother showed decided discomfort; she stooped, scratched at the outer walls of the pouch, opened it with her paws, put her head in, and shifted the baby about. The baby died because the mother did not replace it at the teat and the attendant was unable to do so.

Nevertheless, the experiment was repeated. And it turned out that Owen's kangaroo baby had not been typical. In the majority of cases the baby, after removal from the teat, moved about vigorously in the pouch, sought for the source of milk, and finally took possession of it again. This, too, seems to be innate behavior which is assisted by the tactile sense and possibly by the sense of smell. These instinctive acts and this functioning of senses are amazing. For marsupial infants are not normal mammalian babies, but embryos—the only embryos which can be observed outside the maternal uterus.

The method of the marsupials did not persist. Instead of carrying the undeveloped fetus around in a pouch, a fold of skin, or just clinging to her teats, the mother can just as well retain it somewhat longer in the uterus, until it has reached a more advanced stage of development. Such a procedure, however, requires better nourishment of the embryo in the womb and consequently a more intimate prenatal connection between mother and child.

The first crude placenta arose in the koala, that engaging little marsupial which inhabits the Australian eucalyptus groves, and became even more firmly established in another marsupial—the bandicoot. Called the *allantois*, it is a sac attached to the embryo's abdomen. The koala's allantois sprouts roots into the walls of the uterus in a few places, thus providing for the nourishment and breathing of the fetus. In the bandicoot, the roots or villi which sprout from the allantois grow even more intimately into the uterine wall and absorb all the nutrients and oxygen needed. Thus the first crude placenta arose.

This organ had only to be refined in the higher mammals. The original yolk sac became almost superfluous. Once the embryo has consumed its contents, its function is negligible. In the very primitive scaly anteaters, for example, it still plays a part in an early phase of the embryo's development. But even in these animals, as in all mammals above the level of the marsupials, the placenta has been formed out of the vessels and villi of the allantois. It is a spongy organ, rich in blood, more or less closely attached by the villi to the wall of the uterus. The villi penetrate the mother's blood vessels and float in a constantly renewed lake of blood.

Thanks to the nourishment and oxygen they receive from the placenta, the young of placental animals can be born in a far-advanced stage of their development. But the mother pays a price for this benefit. Henceforth the act of birth becomes a more or less bloody and painful affair—the degree of pain depending on how closely the villi are ingrown and how large a part of the mucous membrane of the uterus is torn off during parturition. Birth is especially difficult for sloths, cats, carnivores, apes, and men.

Zoologists believe that the first genuine placental animals were primitive insectivores resembling shrews or hedgehogs. Perhaps the curious tanrecs of Madagascar, which look partly like hedgehogs, partly like moles, rats, or mice, stand fairly close to the common

Young tanrecs of Madagascar. This curious animal is believed to stand fairly close to the source of all higher mammals.

source of all the higher mammals. From that point on up to the beaver, lion, horse, whale, and man, the newborn of all mammals are alike in one respect: to their navel cord is attached the afterbirth—the expelled placenta which is no longer needed. In the majority of mammals the navel cord tears of its own accord during birth. Some animals bite it off, or worry it until it breaks. In so far as we can determine the behavior of animals in the wild from observations of domestic animals or of animals in zoos, the overwhelming majority of female mammals eat the afterbirth in the course of cleaning the newborn baby.

"The biological significance of this eating," comments the German zoologist Ingo Krummbiegel, "is probably that the afterbirth contains hormones which promote the production of milk. Presumably it is rich in substances whose composition we do not yet know, but whose effects we have often seen."

If this is true, placental hormones might be synthetically produced and fed to dairy animals to increase their milk production. But animals may eat the afterbirth merely for reasons of security, to obliterate all traces of the birth, because water-dwelling mammals—which do not need to practice such precautions—allow the placenta to drift away untouched.

THE INFANT AT THE BREAST

The concept of "mammal" is a product of the age of the Enlightenment. It was introduced into science in the year 1758, replacing the pointless "quadruped," which had been used since the days of Aristotle to designate the most highly organized vertebrates. Aristotle included amphibians and reptiles among the quadrupeds: "All quadrupeds are animals with blood, but some of them bear living young, the others lay eggs. The viviparous ones all have hair; the oviparous animals have scales."

John Ray, the English itinerant preacher and mathematician, had recognized around 1680 that the lower and higher vertebrates should not be lumped together in this way. Ray, the first systematician of modern times, defined the highest quadrupeds as "lung-breathing, viviparous, blooded animals with two separate cardiac chambers." Though somewhat clumsy, this was a considerable improvement over the old definition. But what other name could be given to the haired, warm-blooded organisms which formed the crown of the vertebrate phylum? Many fish, amphibians, and reptiles are also viviparous. And all vertebrates have four extremities, whether these take the form of fins, wings, or legs; at the very least, they have vestiges of four legs.

Linnaeus solved the problem. The females of all haired quadrupeds, he pointed out, are distinguished from other vertebrates by the possession of mammae, milk glands. They use these glands to feed their young for a longer or shorter period after birth. They are the only animal mothers whose children drink from their own bodies. In the fifth edition of his *System of Nature* Linnaeus coined the word Mammalia. And since the human female also has milk glands, *Homo sapiens* must also be a mammal, according to Linnaeus.

Within half a century Linnaeus's terminology became established. His idea of classifying mammals by their methods of reproduction was taken up by the first great zoologists and paleontologists of France. These men—among them Cuvier, Lamarck, Geoffroy de Saint-Hilaire, and Ducrotay de Blainville—proceeded to divide the Mammalia according to the structure of the external and internal organs of embryonic development and the connection between mother and infant. We have already met the three groups they devised: the monotremes, marsupials, and placental animals.

This division was retained by the evolutionists of Darwin's time and is accepted to this day. It has a magnificent clarity and simplicity. No philosopher could construct a more convincing ladder of reproductive evolution. The monotremes still reproduce in the manner of reptiles. The marsupials bear undeveloped larvae. The placental animals, or mammals, have all the equipment for bearing children that are replicas of the parents in form, appearance, mobility, and sense functioning.

Yet if we glance at the higher mammals as a whole, it would seem as if they have not used this advantage to the full. Some small mammals expel their offspring a bare three weeks after fertilization. Consequently, the newborn look almost like embryos. The large cetaceans (whales) and ungulates (hoofed animals), on the other hand, carry their young for a year and sometimes longer in the womb. By the time the offspring is born, it is fully developed, viable, and able to move about freely.

In other words, there are altrices and prococes among mammals as there are among birds. The extremely altricial animals are born naked, blind, and helpless like the nestlings of songbirds. They complete their embryonic development in the nest and need special care during this period. The extremely precocial animals behave like precocial birds. They are equipped with functioning sense organs.

Newborn whales are able swimmers. Newborn ungulates stand firmly on their feet, run about, follow the mother or the herd, and quickly learn to supplement the mother's milk by grazing.

Zoologists have repeatedly attempted to establish a relation between size of body, length of pregnancy, and state of development of the offspring at birth. To some extent such congruencies exist. As a rule, the larger species within a given mammalian order carry their young longer than the smaller species. Similarly, a female bearing precocial young has a longer pregnancy than a female of similar size which bears altricial young. The hamster, for example, bears its immature young only sixteen days after conception, whereas the not much larger guinea pig requires two months before the offspring appear as agile miniature editions of the parents.

The dog and wolf, which like all carnivores are altricial, have a pregnancy of only two months. Hoofed animals of approximately the same size retain their precocial offspring in the womb three or four times as long.

But this rule has exceptions. And among these are the primates— apes and men. Their children are quite undeveloped at birth, although not so helpless as those of predators and most rodents. Nevertheless, pregnancy in the brush monkey, a primate the size of a squirrel, takes four times as long as in the squirrel. The embryonic development of the altricial human child requires almost two months longer than that of the precocial fawn. Perhaps this prolongation of pregnancy in the primates is connected with the advanced development of their brains.

Zoologists were even more baffled by the fact that certain species of animals in the northern hemisphere have much longer pregnancies than closely related species which may be considerably larger. Thus the roe deer has her fawn a full nine and a half months after conception, while the much bigger female of the red deer bears a fawn of equal development after only seven and a half months. Among tropical and subtropical species of marten, the time from mating to birth is barely one and a half months; among species of marten from cold zones between nine and twelve months.

These special cases have been slowly clarified. Among roe deer, northern tree martens, and other inhabitants of cold regions, mating takes place in the spring or summer. The fertilized egg then undergoes a kind of summer or autumn sleep. Its development is checked for months. Otherwise the birth would take place in the depths of winter. Only a few specialists in polar living are hardy enough for that—the most remarkable example being the polar bear. When her time draws near, the female polar bear digs a hole in the snow ten feet deep. There, at the end of November or the beginning of December, protected from the weather in a space warmed by her own body heat, she bears her naked, blind babies, which are no bigger than guinea pigs. Since her body is well supplied with winter fat, she can feed her young for a time without having to emerge to find food.

Roe deer and marten females are unable to do this. Their newborn offspring would suffer severely during the cold season, with its shortage of food, and many would probably die. Even the adult animals often have difficulty surviving the months of snow and frost. A resting period for the ovum is therefore essential for the preservation of the species. The red deer, on the other hand, pair in the autumn, so that the fawns are automatically born in the spring. Consequently, the egg need not pass through any temporary period of arrest in the uterus. And southern breeds of martens can cast their young in any season.

DOTING MOTHERHOOD

Once the young mammal is born, mother and child present a spectacle which human beings find even more affecting than that of birds feeding their nestlings. This intimate mother-child relationship does not cease, in most species, even after weaning. In many cases it continues until the offspring reach sexual maturity. Even the most competent and lively precocial mammal is dependent on its mother for a longer or shorter period.

And among the altricial animals, if the mother does not conceal the young in nests, caves, or tree hollows (as is the case in many species) she must carry it around with her. The story of child transportation begins with the opossum, whose young cling to its teats, and ends with the human mother carrying her infant in her arm, in a sling, or wheeling it in a baby carriage.

In older books on zoology opossums bear the classical-sounding name of "Aeneas rats." For the first discoverers of this American marsupial were struck by the manner in which the mothers carried their young about with them. They were reminded of the Trojan Aeneas, who carried his father on his back out of burning Ilium. Of course, in the opossum, it is the female who performs this feat. Several species of opossum have no pouch. The young attach themselves to the mother's teats and hold on for dear life. When they grow older, they cling anywhere to the mother's skin.

The methods employed by the opossum are common to many mammals. The offspring of some rodents and most bats likewise cling to the teats, except that the young do not cling by sucking, but by biting. Among bats a firm grip on the mother is especially important, since infant bats are not able to fly until from five to eight weeks after birth. Consequently, the females of those species which have little or no hair possess special clinging teats which make the task of holding on easier for the young.

Hairy bats will encourage their offspring to cling to the fur of the chest. "At first they are naked and uncolored," Maurice Burton writes,

> and at birth are delivered into that part of the flying membrane that stretches between the hind-legs of the mother. From this natural pouch—we might almost call it a cradle—the newly-born bat, after having been licked clean by the mother, must at a later date find its way to the teats on the maternal breast. This it does by clinging to the mother's fur, which it does all the time, whether the mother is resting or flying, until it has reached a size too large to be carried about. That is, just before it is weaned.

This is a practical arrangement in so far as the infant can find its way to the teats. For the mother, however, it would seem more comfortable to have the young one firmly on her back. Koalas present a pretty picture when the infant rides on its mother's shoulders, chiefly because the scene corresponds with our own infancy pattern and our conception of the right way to carry infants. When the koala baby has grown too big for the maternal pouch, the mother takes it on her back; it then holds on to her shoulders and waist. For more than a year the koala bear rides its mother's back this way. Meanwhile the next baby has left the pouch and likewise wants to cling. The result is that koala females are frequently seen with two little ones on their backs. The youngest hangs on to the mother's fur; the one born the previous year sits behind it and wraps its arms and legs around its younger brother or sister.

This piggy-back method is particularly suited to arboreal animals; it is used by sloths, small ant bears, scaly anteaters, and lemurs. But ground dwellers also let their young ride on their backs. The great or maned ant bear behaves in this respect just like its smaller, climbing relations. Young Indian sloth bears sit behind their mother's shoulders like jockeys. The elephant shrews, which can run with amazing speed and leap with great agility, have very cleverly arranged to have their teats on their shoulder blades. The young crouch in the fur and hold tightly to the teat with their mouths while the mother darts off in a flash from threatening danger.

The supreme law for the mammal with young is not to lose contact

The koala baby riding pickaback.

with the immature offspring. But sooner or later the day comes for the young ones to emancipate themselves from nest, cave, or the mother's back. Often they are not yet ready to do entirely without maternal care. Disturbing noises, optical and olfactory impressions, sudden changes of temperature or showers of rain, will send the young animals scurrying back to the mother's protection. In the shrew such maternal solicitude takes the form of the "caravan" of children, which has frequently been filmed. As Burton describes it:

> Should the litter, when young, leave the security of the nest, the slightest alarm—a small noise, even a change of temperature or a slight fall of rain—sends the youngsters scuttling behind the mother. One grips the fur of her back near the root of the tail, another grips the fur of that one in a similar way, and so on until the whole litter, numbering eight or more, is lined up in single file. Then all move off, instantly falling into step and keeping in step all the time. If the

mother quickens or retards her pace, the youngsters all do the same. When she leaps a low obstacle, the caravan goes over as one, keeping in step all the time. If a real fear afflicts the mother she stops dead still. Instantly the whole caravan does likewise, without the twitch of a nose or whisker. Sometimes a double row will be formed, or the formation may take other patterns, but always there is this unanimity of action, and the grasp they have of each other is so firm that the mother can be picked up and held with the litter hanging in a string from her.

Young shrews will even try to attach themselves to the mother before their eyes are open and before their milk teeth have grown. With other mammals, too, such as hedgehogs and weasels, similar strings of mother and children have been observed. Probably this caravan formation is an innate thing in these animals, like the clinging instinct of young arboreal animals and the gaping of nestling birds.

Primates can be extremely affectionate and doting mothers.

The Germans have a phrase for the behavior of doting and fatuous mothers who spoil their children. They call it "monkey love." For once, a popular phrase is, within certain limitations, extremely apt. Not that primates spoil their offspring but they are among the most solicitous and devoted of mammalian parents. Such care is necessary, for although primate offspring do not come into the world as naked and blind as many rodents and carnivores, they are remarkably helpless. Only gradually do they learn how to turn their heads, how to grasp things with their hands, how to feed themselves and take their first steps. Anthropoid apes even lead their children by both hands in order to teach them how to walk. And this is but one of the many human gestures in the child-care practices of these closest relatives to our species.

Since all primates have a well-defined family life, whether it takes the form of monogamy, of a family group, or of a collective, herd family, the father often assumes the role of nurse. He picks up his little ones, lets them ride on his back, and self-sacrificingly undertakes to defend and protect his family. It is no easy matter to bring up young apes and monkeys. Because of their keen intelligence, their insatiable curiosity, their playfulness and spirit of enterprise, they can become a veritable torment to anxious parents. Thus the intense affection of grown primates for all the young animals of their family, group, or herd, whether or not these are their own offspring, is dictated by bitter necessity. The parents can never let them out of their sight. Young chimpanzees in confinement, for example, will invent all sorts of acrobatic stunts. They will turn somersaults, spin in circles, dangle from the roof of their cage, climb out to the end of a branch and drop without injury to themselves either to the ground or to another branch. They invent new ways of eating and drinking, will spit out their milk, for example, and then lick it up from the ground. In their playfulness they will find new ways of looking at the world— standing on their heads, or bending over and peering between their legs, or making a hole in a leaf and holding it up to their eyes. They carefully examine every strange object and then try to dismember it.

Undoubtedly this inquisitiveness and play impulse played a large part in the evolution of intelligent, inventive man out of the primate group. Some investigators feel that the primates have developed a distinctive play culture. This is to be found, moreover, not only among the anthropoid apes, who, as is well known, exhibit the signs of true thinking, but also among primates who stand much lower in the intellectual scale. The South African naturalist Eugène Marais has written, in addition to his controversial book on termites, what specialists consider a far sounder book on baboons. For years he studied the repertory of games of baby baboons living under free conditions. Among baboons and many other herd-forming apes, the young of various ages form play groups within the herd. And the members of a baboon kindergarten, like the children of anthropoid apes and men, are highly inventive in their play even without parental supervision.

Marais saw the young baboons throwing themselves from branches in all directions. Others would put their noses into water and try to capture the bubbles they made with their breath. The young ones seemed to think it great fun to launch a sudden attack upon a surly old male baboon. They would climb all over him and prick him with their milk teeth. In their intense curiosity, they would even overcome their fear of human beings. Thus, Marais once discovered a group of wild baboon babies playing with several African children at a clay pit:

> Baboons and Kaffirs pushed one another away from the hole in an attempt to get hold of the clay. From the struggling mass there arose constant laughter mingled with Sesutu curses of the grossest kind, and above it all one could hear the jabbering of the baboons. Neither natives nor baboons ever became really cross and the struggling never degenerated into a real fight.

Under the impact of the nursing instinct, even small primate children will adopt and carry in their arms young animals of every imaginable species. "Those that we kept at the homestead," Marais writes,

> had each a little animal to which it was so attached that when a separation had to take place, as was unavoidable on a farm, it always ended in tragedy. Little goats and lambs, piglets and puppies, kittens, even chickens, ducklings, and goslings, had all been noted by us as favorite playmates of little baboons that grew up at the homestead. This attraction is, of course, similar to that which all small animals have for the human child.

The males of the larger species of apes can devote themselves only sporadically to their offspring. They have other obligations. But among the marmosets of the South American jungles, the brush monkeys and tamarins, for instance, the case is reversed. The father bears the principal burdens of child care—a unique phenomenon among Mammalia. It is astonishing because a young mammal must periodically drink its mother's milk and consequently should become much more closely attached to the mother than to the father. What causes such young marmosets to spend the first months of their lives clinging to the father's back, or fleeing to his fur when in danger, is not known.

While primate mothers in general bear only one child at each birth, South American dwarf monkeys tend to produce twins or triplets. The author of this book has had the rare pleasure of observing how such twins are born, carried, and raised by a pair of marmosets under his care. The species in question are pinchos of the Colombian rain forests; in Germany they are called "Liszt monkeys" because of their mane of white hair.

In this pincho pair, the father took over the care of the young immediately after their birth. The newborn pinchos clung to their father's fur with their hands and feet, and also obtained anchorage with their tails, which can be used as prehensile organs in the first weeks of life. At intervals the father would hand the twins to the mother for nursing. But after they had drunk their fill, he would take them back again. As long as the mother continued to nourish the twins with her milk, she took only a cursory interest in them. Often she was visibly annoyed when a baby wanted to transfer to her at the wrong time. Her chief function was as a supplier of milk. The father, on the other hand, served as a mount and source of warmth, as sentinel and defender. He also prechewed the first solid food for the babies, obtained food for them, and attentively supervised their first timid attempts at climbing. Occasionally he would slap the female if he thought she was neglecting her maternal duties.

The two parents divided the chores only after weaning. By the age of four months the young were independent, but they continued to seek the protecting bodies of their parents at times of imaginary perils or when they were ready for sleep. So far as is known, the Amazonian marmosets are the only mammalian species in the world in which the males thus behave as baby sitters.

THE PASHA AND HIS HAREM

It is an ancient question whether or not mammalian animals have marriages in our sense of the word. A natural historian of the age of Enlightenment once made the ironic observation: "We regard the love life and marriage of birds with pleasure, that of mammals with repugnance, and that of man with peculiar thoughts." This is more than a witticism. If we define marriage in the biological sense as a reproductive community, we must surely speak of marital life among mammals.

It really makes no difference whether the sexual group consists of two individuals, of dozens or even of hundreds of animals. Even the marital relationships of human beings are not unambiguous in this respect. American statisticians examining ethnological literature have made the observation, scarcely a comforting one to upholders of monogamy, that only sixty-one per cent of all peoples have evolved moral and legal injunctions to promote more or less strict monogamy. The British ethnologist and sociologist Bronislaw Malinowski has commented that in many primitive peoples the loosening of marital bonds should not be regarded as a negation of marriage, but rather as a supplementing of it: the function of a less strict conception of marriage is not its destruction but its preservation.

Malinowski's thesis applies to the associations which resemble marriage among many mammals. They are protective alliances. The group seeks food together, defends the family and cares for the children in common. How many wives the herd sire has acquired is a matter of secondary importance. And for the existence of the group it scarcely matters that a female may occasionally consort with a bachelor member of the group. What counts is that the social structure remains intact.

All imaginable reproductive relationships, from complete absence of marriage to distinct monogamy, are to be found among mammals. The solitary species, of which there are many, generally eschew marriages. Digging and burrowing mammals such as the mole and hamster do not even tolerate a member of the opposite sex in their burrows. The mates find one another only at rutting time, copulate, and immediately afterwards go their separate ways.

Predators, too, are largely solitaries. Bears and tigers, for example, are interested in other members of their species only when they are in the grip of their sexual drives. At such times cats sing their love songs; bears and martens follow the scent of their females. Male animals occupy certain territories, marking the boundaries with their urine or with the secretions of certain glands, and defending their ground against intrusive rivals. After mating, each individual goes on living and hunting by itself. The females bring their helpless young into the world in caves or other hiding places, and raise them with the most loving care, as anyone can observe in a zoo.

Zoologists investigating sex and reproduction among wild animals have based their work largely on observations of captive animals. To this day the behavior of most mammals in the wild is not fully known. It is the ambition of every keeper of animals to have his charges reproduce abundantly. In fact, reproduction in captivity is regarded as one criterion of how well the animals are thriving. Moreover, many zoos have undertaken the laudable task of preserving now rare species from extinction. Consequently, zoo animals are frequently bred on a planned basis, much as man has bred his domestic animals since the beginnings of civilization.

The zoo visitor therefore often has the pleasure of observing the varied behavior of animal parents. He sees the mothers affectionately suckling and caring for their young. He watches with delight the amusing play of the young.

All the same, our knowledge of the reproductive behavior of wild animals necessarily leaves much to be desired. For one thing, many species can be persuaded to reproduce in zoos only with great difficulty, if at all. Many animals do not find the conditions in zoos conducive to the full development of their sexual potentialities. Only in recent years have a few zoos succeeded in isolated cases in breeding gorillas, rhinos, okapis, and snow leopards. Even so commonly tamed an animal as the cheetah has reproduced in captivity only a few times; we know virtually nothing about its reproductive habits in liberty. Other species consistently reproduce in zoos, but rarely raise their young. Among these are those zoo favorites, the polar bears. A regular program of breeding polar bears has pretty well become a necessity by now, to save the animals from extinction, for their numbers have shrunk alarmingly since, in the last few decades, men have penetrated to the remotest islands of the Arctic Ocean. But while the cubs of other species of zoo-kept bears are reared without the slightest trouble, the majority of polar bear cubs born in captivity die shortly after birth, or during the first three months of life.

The cause of this high mortality lies in the special living conditions of polar bears, which can scarcely be reproduced in zoos. These bears are on the whole more sociable than others of their species, but they form loose hunting communities rather than coherent packs. On the whole they live, in the wild, on seal meat. A pregnant polar bear stuffs herself on seal blubber. This food decisively affects the fat and vitamin content of her milk. In the depths of the polar winter the she-bear holes up in an ice cave, lets herself be snowed in, and here she drops her cubs (usually two). Alwin Pedersen, the polar explorer, has described polar bear maternity as follows:

> The animal digs into a snowy slope. She makes a tunnel which slants downward and then up again, and finally forks, with one passage leading into the birth chamber proper. Her breath melts the snow of the walls, which then freeze again into solid ice which will not admit drafts. Warmth then begins to accumulate in the dome of the chamber. The cub is kept warm by the bear's breath.

During this period the she-bear lives on her store of fat, and also nourishes the cubs. She emerges from her cave in the spring. The cubs, which are only the size of rats at birth, weighing little more than a pound, are as big as half-grown terriers by the time the family emerges. The mother feeds and cares for them until the following year. And since male polar bears—like all male bears—are anything but fond of their offspring, the she-bear does not mate again until the young no longer need her protection.

Polar bear cubs can be fed artificially, with some difficulty; but the chief problem is how to take the newborn cubs from the mother. "She holds her young," as Alfred Seitz, director of the Nuremberg zoo has reported it, "with her forepaws, pressing them constantly against her chest, where the teats are located. When she lies on her side, she sees to it that her exhalations pass over the little creatures to warm them, for they are keenly sensitive to cold. Even if she has no milk for them and they are dying, she will not let the attendant take them." Thus, the she-bear behaves in captivity exactly as she would in her ice cave. But the same instincts that preserve her young in the arctic delivery room cause them to starve to death in the zoo cage.

Some predators live in packs and are gregarious even during mating time. Among big cats, this is true for the lion; among canines,

Lions mating.

for wolves, jackals and hyena dogs; among the racoon family, for the coatis. Since predators are on the whole armed with far crueler weapons than the normally peaceful hoofed animals, which do, however, inflict severe wounds on one another during rutting time, we can imagine how fierce the sexual struggle of these gregarious predators must be. What battles must sexual rivalries lead to among lions and wolves, for example, when even hares, deer, and gazelles may sometimes kill each other in these combats!

The fact is that clashes among the big predators can sometimes end in death. In 1961 a British photographer in Africa took a number of pictures of a huge lion engaged in a tender tête-à-tête with his mate. Their privacy was disturbed by a rival almost as imposing as himself; the first lion fought the intruder to the ground, and would probably have killed him if the photographer had not startled the threesome.

Nevertheless, such merciless duels are rare exceptions among the gregarious predators. On the whole, animals do not kill each other except by mistake. The weaker rival, as a rule, soon adopts a characteristic posture, such as we have already found among fish and birds. This is the "posture of humility," as Konrad Lorenz has called it. This gesture of submission calls forth an instinctive inhibition in the victor which causes him to abandon the struggle, so that the defeated male can quickly escape. Were it not for this reflex succession of posture of humility and inhibition, there would be much killing among male lions, wolves, and other such fierce predators, with dire effects upon the continuance of the species.

Lorenz has described a battle between two male wolves in the zoo at Whipsnade, England, which clearly exemplified the characteristic gesture and the resultant inhibition:

A gigantic, light-gray old wolf and another, scarcely smaller but visibly younger, stood face to face and circled each other in a narrow circle, with remarkable footwork. The dread fangs darted in lightning alternations of bite and counter, so fast that the eye could not follow. . . . The smaller wolf was driven further and further back, and I guessed that the more experienced of the antagonists intended to maneuver him against the fence. Sure enough, the younger wolf now backed against the wire, stumbled—and instantly the old wolf was on top of him. Then came the most remarkable feature of the duel, exactly the opposite of what one would have expected. Abruptly, the tumbling of the gray bodies stopped. Both animals stood still, perfectly still, shoulder to shoulder. . . . Both growled angrily, the old wolf in a deep bass, the younger one in high falsetto. Observe the precise position of the two predators. The old wolf has his jaws close, very close, to the younger one's throat; and the younger is holding his head turned aside, the curve of his throat, the most vulnerable part of his body, being offered unprotected to the enemy. . . . But the victor does not bite. You can see that he would like to, but that he simply cannot do it. A wolf who offers his throat to the opponent in the manner just described is never seriously bitten.

Because of this natural check on savagery, zoo keepers are able to house sizable packs of wolves, or prides of lions, including several adult males, in the same enclosure. If the rivals have room enough to evade one another at rutting time, and are not constantly in view, such companies of predators are more peaceful than many a human group.

The males are often allowed free run of the enclosure when the young are born. Lions, especially, are unusually amiable and patient fathers. They allow their offspring to tug at them, bite them, pluck their manes and pull their tails, and in general tyrannize over them, without losing their tempers. If the tumbling kittens prove too much of a nuisance after a while, they will stand up quietly, shake themselves, and retreat to a quieter place.

Hoofed animals are usually gregarious. Herd life is a form of safeguard. When many heads are listening, scenting, or keeping a lookout, the danger of being attacked by a predator is reduced to a minimum. Consequently, a number of species gather into groups for purely defensive reasons. Among the bison, wild pig, and various types of deer, the females and their young live in sizable herds outside of rutting season. The adult bulls, boars, and stags form separate male groups in approximately equal numbers. At rutting time these clubs of males break up, and each male must conquer his harem anew, often at the cost of bitter battles with members of his own herd, who have now become his rivals.

The classical example of such behavior is the battle of stags. Perhaps it was these combats that led to the formation of the two-sexed herd out of the original defensive alliance of animals of a single sex. For the male herd sire wielding command of the herd throughout the year would no longer need to conquer his females anew each rutting season; he need only stand guard against potential rivals. Thus the loose association may have developed into the permanent harem. Many hoofed animals form large herds occupying extensive areas. But they do not range the land at will. Modern behavioral research has discovered, on the contrary, that each herd stays within invisible but rigid boundaries in its territory. No individual, moreover, can wander around the herd's domain as it pleases. It must submit to the strict hierarchical order of the herd, and obey the laws and customs of its species. It has superiors and inferiors. Researchers who have studied small herds call the animals at the top of the hierarchy in such a society the *alpha* animal, the next in rank the *beta* animal—and so on down to the lowest in the herd, the *omega* animal.

This herd hierarchy is complicated by the sex life. When, in a herd of mixed sexes, males high in rank mate with females low in rank, the chosen females automatically climb the social ladder. On the other hand, males low in rank have far fewer opportunities for pairing than do their superiors. If they mate with a female higher in rank, it is only a hasty, stolen pleasure which does not at all promote them in the rankings. The part played by herd rank in the sex life is, as we shall see later, more conspicuous among the apes than among the hoofed animals.

The higher-ranking animals in mixed herds are by no means always males. Among deer or cattle, the lead animal may be a female who has won her position in fights with other females. Moreover, the *alpha* animals are by no means secure in their positions at the head of the herd; they must always be prepared for rebellions which may overthrow them. "The ranking is dynamic," says Adolf Remane, the German animal psychologist. "Every individual may rise in it, but also fall. Ascent is attained by contests with near equals in rank, either by pure bluff or by actually fighting and overcoming the next higher animal. The consequence of this social structure is that struggles for rank usually take place between those equal or close to one another in the hierarchy."

Since rankings and struggles for rank play so important a part in the sexual as well as the social life of hoofed animals, zoos afford us a most incomplete picture of the reproductive rituals among these animals. Few species can be kept in zoos in herds large enough to approximate the numbers and structure of free herds. As a rule only a pair or a small family consisting of a male and a few females will be maintained in a zoo enclosure. The reason for this is obvious: many male hoofed animals become bellicose and mean at rutting time. They regard the enclosure as their territory and obstinately defend it against any intruder, just as in liberty they would defend their mating area. But the confined space of a zoo enclosure is not a suitable tournament ground for the battles of horned or antlered ungulates. There is no room for the defeated males to escape, with the result that sooner or later they will be killed. For male hoofed animals testify their inferiority not by a gesture of humility, but by rapid flight. The victor usually abandons the pursuit when the defeated male flees across the invisible boundary of the territory.

Keepers of animals naturally try to avoid casualties. They there-

Fighting wapiti bulls. In wild life, it is very seldom that territorial battles between rivals end in the death of the loser—the loser signifies surrender by rapid flight and is not usually pursued beyond the invisible boundary of the territory in question.

Within the confines of a zoo, however, the loser has no room to escape, and to avoid bloody battles between males in the rutting season, small family groups consisting of a male and several females with their young are customarily kept as a unit. Male calves are separated from the father when they reach sexual maturity.

fore carefully separate the adult males of most species. Thus the animal in captivity has no opportunities to seek, or win by fighting,
suitable partners. Natural and sexual selection scarcely operate in
captivity. In the confined territory the males cannot demonstrate
their strength in the battles of rutting time. In the absence of a large
herd with its natural rankings, many of the animals' rituals and
modes of behavior are reduced to a minimum, or disappear entirely.

Our knowledge of the sexual and societal habits of herd animals
must therefore be based upon our observations of them in the wild.
In recent years behavioral scientists have devoted themselves to
studying species of animals whose patterns had long been thought well
known from observations in zoos. They have discovered that the behavior of these animals in the wild is entirely different from what
they imagined, and some very surprising discoveries have been made.

Among these are the "amatory gardens" of the African waterbucks. Waterbucks are plains-dwelling antelope which are fond of
swampy regions. Like most species of antelope, they reproduce in
zoos, but without betraying the real secrets of their courtship practices and choice of mates. In zoos they are almost always kept in pairs
or small families, so that they have no need of seeking partners. After
long studies in Uganda, however, American zoologists have found
that the waterbucks of the country provide a prime demonstration for
Darwin's theory of sexual selection.

The Uganda waterbucks live in large but not highly organized
herds, with sexes separated. Thus they form one of those monosexual
communities which probably represent the primitive type of herd
formation among ungulates. At rutting time the associations of bachelors break up. The males, however, do not join the females in order
to win themselves wives, the size of the harem depending on their
strength. Instead, they merely go seeking a suitable mating ground.

Each male tries to conquer a small territory, often no more than
fifty square yards in area. The stronger and higher-ranking males
occupy terrain which presumably lies across the paths of the wandering female herd; the bucks lower in rank must be content with territories further away from the regular trails. Soon a large area of the
plains is divided up into a multitude of such "amatory gardens." As
soon as each buck has occupied his "garden," the border disputes
cease; all the rivals respect the conquered territories.

While the male waterbucks stand fast in their places, the female
herd slowly drifts toward the "gardens." Even after the females arrive, the bucks do not leave their territories. They must wait to see
whethei a female deigns to visit them. The females stroll from garden
to garden, making their choices. As soon as a female sets foot inside

a garden, the owner courts and pursues her. Disdained suitors abandon their efforts when the female crosses the border into the neighboring garden. Thus the males fight only for their territory, not for their sexual partners.

Favorably situated gardens seem to exert as strong a spell upon the females as the looks of the owner, for strong bucks generally occupy the best spots. Moreover, the females do not limit themselves to a single garden; many will mate with several of the owners before they rejoin their companions of their own sex, and the whole herd moves on to other pastures.

The fragile beauty of deer and antelope fawns may be seen in many a zoo, likewise the maternal tenderness of giraffes, hippopotamuses, and other such colossal animals. But baby elephants are rarely born in captivity. This seems odd when we consider that Indian elephants have been tamed to labor in Southeast Asia for thousands of years. The African elephant, too, was tamed in early antiquity by the Egyptians and Carthaginians, and figures prominently in Roman history as the "war elephant" of Hannibal's armies.

But the civilized peoples of both Africa and Asia did not multiply their elephants by planned breeding; they added to their stock of animals by regular hunts for elephants born wild. Even the Indians, who amassed great experience with elephants from earliest times, never succeeded in transforming the huge beasts into genuine domestic animals regularly bred from tame stock.

The difficulty centers in a characteristic of male elephants which even the most practiced Indian mahouts have not been able to deal with. Most bull elephants become mean when they reach sexual maturity, so much so that their attendants must fear for their lives. (The onset of sexual maturity and of rut can be detected by the secretion of a large quantity of strong-smelling fluid from two glands near their ears). At rutting time the slightest cause can rouse them to a fury. Sometimes, without warning they will suddenly attack a keeper or driver who has trained them and tended them for years. Bull elephants in rut have taken the lives of a good many zoo attendants.

There are exceptions; some bull elephants never lose their tempers. But keeping a bull always remains a risk. Large zoos have followed the policy of building special bull stalls with automatic doors for feeding and cleaning arrangements, so that the attendant does not have to enter the stall at all. Even such safety measures will not keep furious bulls from breaking their tusks against the bars of their enclosures, or else—despite the affection elephants usually display toward their wives—of injuring the female who is put in with them for mating.

Elephants are dwellers of the jungle and plains. Ordinarily they wander over vast areas. Mature bulls separate from the herds, occupy certain territories, and do not allow any rivals to enter them; they will attack any intruder. Even tamed elephants behave in much the same way in the zoo enclosure. When they are seeking a mate, even the keeper who has raised them becomes an interloper whom they will blindly attack. They regard their enclosure as a mating ground to be defended furiously against all invaders. In this respect they behave like stags and antelope bucks, but their strength, skill, and intelligence makes them far more dangerous than the rutting males of other species. For this reason regular elephant breeding and true, permanent domestication of elephants have never been achieved.

Aggressive though the bull elephants are in maintaining their territory, they can be tender and chivalrous as lovers and husbands. To be sure, we know little about the sex life of elephants in the wild, but couples which have reproduced in captivity behave (by our human standards) in an extremely amiable and affectionate manner toward one another. However, behavioral scientists have long ago learned to drop human value judgments, which are almost always fallacious when applied to animals. Nevertheless, just as man uses his hands for caressing as well as for grasping, the elephant also uses his trunk, which serves him as a hand, for affectionate interchanges. When a pair of elephants stroke each other with intertwined trunks, the human observer cannot help comparing their actions with the caresses of our own species.

The affection of mother elephants for their young also strikes us as familiar and appeals strongly to our feelings. Elephants have the longest pregnancy among animals, twenty months on the average. While the baby elephant is small, it usually stays under the mother's body and between her legs, even when she moves along at a smart pace. In zoo enclosures other female elephants will take an interest in the babies; they will feed them and look after them, warm them with their bodies, and watch over their welfare in the manner of jealous, fussy aunts.

It would seem that childless female elephants also perform other services. Maurice Burton reports the following observations of African elephants living in the wild:

> Three female elephants separated from the herd and wandered slowly toward a thicket. . . . One of the females entered the thicket; the other two remained standing in front of it, and drove away all other elephants who attempted to approach it. After a while the two left their sentinel posts and rejoined the herd. Shortly afterward, the

Both in wild life and in captivity, childless female elephants often act as solicitous "aunts" to young orphans. This African forest elephant in the Bronx Zoo tenderly cared for a young Indian elephant which had been introduced into her enclosure.

third female reappeared out of the thicket, a newborn elephant calf, its hairy hide still moist, following at her heels. Undoubtedly the mother had sought the concealment of the thicket because she knew that the hour of birth was approaching. But the behavior of the two other females is far more astonishing. It was as if they had assumed the role of midwives, as if they knew that their services would be needed even before the pregnant cow-elephant left the herd.

This impulse, Burton thinks, fades away as soon as the "aunt" in question becomes a mother herself: "The mother takes thought for her own calf alone, and loves it exclusively. She will never suckle another calf, and quickly grows mean if other calves are around her." But it is said that mother elephants who have lost their young are quite ready to adopt strange calves. And among some other species the females are quite tolerant. Thus the zoo in Basel, Switzerland, reports that in 1964 a young Indian armored rhinoceros was nursed by both its mother and its grandmother. "Our deer, wild swine, and spectacled bears," a press release from this zoo states, "behave just as generously; they too allow the young of other mothers to suckle them."

Solidungulate (whole-hoofed) animals display a distinctly patriarchal temperament, as compared with other ungulates. Wild stallions and wild he-asses assert themselves at mating time. Like the pasha of the Oriental harem who rules his flock of wives with imperious severity, these herd sires often assume the characteristics of a dictator.

"All the wild stallions I have cared for," Ludwig Heck relates,

> had the habit of rounding up the herd of mares. Many mares were reluctant to obey, especially when they were unfamiliar with herd life and the stallion's rule. But the stallion quickly makes his dominance felt. He does so by lightning-swift bites. Wild stallions usually bite the mane, less often the legs, and occasionally they inflict injuries to the rump by their bites. After biting, or while the stallion is chasing the mare, he may wheel and kick out at her if she persists in her obstinacy.

This sounds distinctly unkind, but it is part of the ceremony. Solidungulates as a rule treat their mates quite roughly. However, the various species differ considerably in the nature of their sex play. All the more remarkable, therefore, are the breeding achievements of the peoples of the Near East—for some three thousand years ago they succeeded in crossing the horse and the donkey. The mules which result from such crosses are usually sterile but their sturdiness has made them prized domestic animals in all warm countries. It is, incidentally, a legend that the mare must have her eyes bandaged before she is led to the male donkey. No mare will resist the fiery he-asses of the large Mediterranean breeds. It is far more difficult for the breeder to persuade a donkey mare to accept a stallion.

The baboon herd is generally considered the most extreme example of pasha behavior among mammals. But the herd sires, who seem to exercise a reign of terror, are not quite so autocratic in freedom, under natural conditions as they are observed to be in captivity. To be sure, they seize the greater part of the food for themselves, and sternly punish all rebels among the many bachelors who attach themselves to the harem. But both types of behavior are essential for the preservation of the hierarchy. Rank must be strictly observed, lest chaos result; and the sires, whose task it is to protect their families from leopards and other dangerous foes, must obtain enough food to keep their strength at its peak. At the feeding place in particular, the pashas scarcely ever need to resort to force. The lower-ranking baboons do not dare to approach the food when the herd sires are nearby.

"It is, incidentally, an interesting fact," writes Adolf Remane, "that in man, too, the order of rank at table is a particularly important problem in social life. It frequently leads to conflicts and a sense of insult. In critical cases a great deal of reflection is necessary at a public dinner to arrange an order which will not give rise to disputes."

Sexual ranking among baboons and macaques is governed much like the order at the feeding place. Among rhesus monkeys the following rule holds, according to C. R. Carpenter:

> Each female derives status from her male consort and accordingly may dominate female relatives to which she was formerly subordinate. Simultaneously she gains degrees of tolerance from animals, including her male consort, which previously would not have tolerated her to an equal extent. Rutting females from one group may gain status in another group and become consorts of the most dominant males.

Here, too, comparisons with human social life come to mind. Almost all human societies are more or less hierarchically constructed; in almost all there is a social ladder from the ruling *alpha* personalities down to the dominated *omega* people. And everywhere in the world attachments which result in love and marriage may raise the social rank of women. In principle, what Carpenter says of the rhesus monkeys applies to human beings and to all social primates: "A kind of social summation of statuses may occur when individuals are closely associated. Also, an individual may derive status from association with another or other individuals."

A large pack of baboons is not really a herd, such as is formed by deer and wild pigs, but a community consisting of several families. Each family has its sire, its wives and children, and in addition a number of bachelors, "friends of the family." These families do not run about in loose groupings, but are arranged in a strictly determined social order. The strongest male has the largest following; the weakest sires can claim only one, at most two or three wives. Consequently the rank-and-file must pay their respects to the chief. They dare not protest if the chief chooses to enjoy one of their wives upon occasion.

In sexual relationships the following law seems to obtain among baboons: males who stand on a higher stage of the hierarchy can indulge themselves freely with the wives of their underlings. But woe betide the underling who casts his eye upon the females of the aristocracy. The attached bachelors, finally, who by far outnumber the

Young fur seal pups. When born, seals cannot swim, and the young must be tended on land.

A bull fur seal guarding his harem.

pashas, keep hoping for a palace revolution. When one of the sires grows too old or too weak to maintain his position, a friend of the family promptly appears to fight with him and dethrone him. The defeated pasha, degraded to the rank of follower, must henceforth hang about the new master's harem, which was formerly his own.

Nevertheless, the bachelors find ample opportunities for sexual gratification. No pasha can have his eyes everywhere at once. In any case the sire is chiefly interested in the females who happen to be in the period of ovulation. Each month the females let him know that their time of fertility has come—and do so in that drastic manner which shocks innocent visitors to zoos or makes them think that the animals are suffering from some disease. For the female sexual parts swell enormously, become flaming red, and look like malignant tumors. Apparently the male baboon finds this sight fetching. Each day he chooses for his principal wife the female who displays the largest swellings. But since baboon females, like all primate females, are also ready for mating at other than the time of highest fertility, the bachelors can have a secret fling with the unswollen females.

If the pasha catches her at such a misdemeanor, the unfaithful wife has only one means of escaping punishment. She must turn the fury of her lord and master against the seducer. Grzimek describes her strategy: "She crouches on the ground, turning her hindquarters to the pasha; she screeches and reviles her seducer with grimaces and by beating her hand rapidly on the rock. Thereupon the pasha rushes at the bachelor, probably not so much on account of the seduction as because he can easily be incited to attack another ape or animal by this behavior on the part of his wives." The wife, meanwhile, takes advantage of the occasion: "Once, while a baboon husband was pursuing a younger male around the whole ape cliff, his wife mated with two other males in succession during the forty seconds in which she was unobserved."

Because of such behavior, the baboon has long been regarded as the symbol of lewdness. A hundred years ago even so noted a scientist as Frédéric Cuvier, son of the founder of zoological research in France, passed the following verdict on the baboon: "It seems as if Nature created it with the intention of displaying vice in all its ugliness." In the meantime scientists have learned that the struggle for existence in the wild imposes extraordinary demands upon the class society of baboons. Natural conditions allow far less leeway for sexuality. But in captivity, excess energy must find an outlet in a confined space. The animals crouch on their rock, close together, and are constantly exposed to the temptation of breaking the unwritten laws of the sexual hierarchy. Thus this unnatural mode of life gives us a false picture of the sexual patterns of baboons.

When zookeepers do not provide for natural social relations among their baboons, the result can be a full-scale sexual and physical disaster. Under conditions of liberty the ranking order gradually develops out of mutual tests of strength, as in all animal groups, and in human society as well. But in the zoo enclosure, terrible battles can spring up if the baboons have not had time to become acquainted with one another and therefore have not yet defined their ranks.

A crisis of this sort erupted at the London zoo in 1927. Until then the baboon enclosure had housed some hundred strong adult males. Unfortunately the zoo director hit on the idea of adding forty females to the group. The result has gone down in the annals of zoo-keeping as the notorious "London battle of the apes." Instantly the enclosure was transformed into a battleground. There was a tremendous free-for-all with every male laying claim to every female. Within a short time sixty males and thirty-three females lay dead. Some of the females actually died from hunger and exhaustion because they were passed along among the males without even a respite to take a morsel of food. Any keeper who had ventured into that inferno would have risked his life.

Dramatic scenes of harem forming can be observed among seals, especially the sea lions and fur seals. Outside of the reproductive period, seals have no particular social ties. They swim about in the sea, climb rocks, fish and play together, and owe no obedience to their pashas. But during the four months of mating, the sea lions and fur seals must go on land and take possession of a definite territory on some coastal strip or island. At this time the young are born, and infant seals must be guarded and nursed on land, since at first they cannot swim.

At mating and bearing time, therefore, a distinct though brief family life develops on the seal islands. "One cannot call such an aggregation either a herd or a pack," Buddenbrock says; "it is almost a nation." First of all, the powerful old bulls appear on the coast. They fight for the best strips of territory and cliffs, forcing younger and weaker males to remoter beaches or even barring them completely. Four weeks later, the females arrive. They seem to do the choosing, for sea lionesses and female fur seals seek out the spots which are occupied by especially sturdy males. But since the other bulls are unwilling to remain wifeless, there is constant kidnaping of females. Again and again a bull will venture into another's territory, grip a female in his teeth and drag her away.

*The first published figure of sea elephants—from Anson's voyage, 1748—
captioned "A Sea Lion of Juan Fernandez."*

The battles which ensue look truly terrifying. Seals have powerful
jaws and teeth and can inflict nasty wounds on one another. Consequently the older males are covered with scars, like medieval mer-
cenaries. The behavior of sea elephants is somewhat more temperate,
according to Beebe:

> The huge masters of harems are three times as large as their mates,
> reaching, it is said, twenty feet in length and a maximum weight of
> perhaps four tons. They have developed a thick, tough breastplate of
> rough hide, a cuirass of corrugated leather which protects them in
> their jealous battles with rivals. The contests are seldom fatal and con-
> sist chiefly of much roaring and rearing, and hurling of themselves at
> each other, striking downward with their short canines.

Nevertheless, Beebe saw "two half-grown welterweight amateurs
each of whom had lost an eye in precocious encounters."

After conquering their harem, the bulls must wait a while before
they celebrate their nuptials. The females they have won must first
give birth to the offspring conceived in the spring, must suckle the
young and gradually accustom them to the water. Thus family life
among these seals is based not on the mating relationship, but on the
requirements of birth and child care. The bulls' sole concern for the
time being is that they do not lose their wives and children. So for
four months the old bulls sit in their places, do not eat a bite, use up
their stock of blubber, and watch over their numerous band of wives
and children. They behave like true fathers of families, although the
children are usually not their own offspring. The females, for their

part, are extraordinarily tender, conscientious mothers who never let their babies out of sight and can distinguish their own child by its smell and sounds from the many other young seals in the harem and the adjacent territories.

When at last the time comes for the harem owners to fulfill their sexual appetites, new complications arise. The wives they have fought for and won can no longer be counted on. The mothers play about in the water with their offspring, teaching them to swim. And here is a chance for all the bachelors, who have hitherto had the worst of it, to make up for lost time. No pasha can stop them from mating with his wives. To do so he would have to leave his territory, and possession of the land is more important to the bulls than the vagaries of their wives.

THE EMBRACE

Much less is known about the sex life of the other great group of marine mammals, the cetaceans, which include the whales and dolphins. Cetaceans, too, form packs and herds, as every sailor knows who has ever watched a school of dolphin following one behind the other and leaping out of the water. Some observations suggest that among the big whales the schools break up at mating time. Males and females then, apparently, seek out one another, form couples, and mate. Thereafter the packs form up again.

Some three hundred years ago John Ray recognized that whales are not fish, but mammals. Ever since, zoologists have wondered how these monstrous animals, which can reach a length of one hundred feet and weigh up to a hundred and fifty tons, manage to copulate. For mammals, as has been known from the most ancient times, all assume a particular mating position. This is so universal as to be almost monotonous. There are some deviations in certain species and groups, but in principle the copulation of mammals is a much more uniform affair, much poorer in variants, than the acrobatic sex acts

The first representation of a dolphin with embryo. From Gesner's book on fish. Even in the 16th century it was suspected that whales were mammals.

of insects and spiders. Most male and land mammals seize the body of their females with their forelegs. They "embrace" their mates, although their embrace is not the human one. "The female," say Ford and Beach describing the normal position,

> flattens or arches her back concavely, thus exposing and elevating her external genitals. The male mounts from the rear, resting his forefeet upon the female or clasping them upon her sides. In most cases penetration is achieved by the male's pelvic movements. Females of most species stand quietly during coitus, although in some cases the female sways to and fro or pushes actively against the male's copulatory thrusts.

The shape of whales, however, would rule out any such position. The large species especially must copulate belly to belly, for otherwise they could not mate at all. Whalers and sailors have often observed two blue whales shoot high out of the water, their bellies pressed tightly together, and remain apparently hovering in air for a brief moment. At first this was thought to be merely sex play. But sharp-eyed zoologists have now determined that in this fraction of a second the actual mating takes place. The male and female circle one another, lash one another with their tail fins, and then leap into the air. The whale's extremely elastic penis is drawn out to a long point. Thus equipped, he can inject his semen into the female in that brief instant.

Since the days of Aristotle, laymen and even serious naturalists have been convinced that there must be other exceptions, other mammals which paired belly to belly. How, for example, could male porcupines or hedgehogs mount the prickly backs of their females? The idea is repeated to this day, with a doggedness that borders on fanaticism. As Ford and Beach comment, "It reflects, one must conclude, the limitations of human imagination or the ubiquitousness of anthropocentrism in human thought." Innumerable observations in laboratories and zoos have left no doubt that spiny mammals pair in the same manner as the other members of their class of the animal kingdom. The female lays her prickles flat and curls her tail upward, so that the male can mount her without impaling himself.

The beaver was the object of a similar controversy, and proved, indeed, to be exceptional. Beaver pairs sit upright in shallow water, embrace one another with their arms like human couples kissing, or drift along on the surface of the water breast to breast. The sexual union of bats is not quite so much like the human. In 1899 Ludwig Wunderlich was the first to observe such behavior in two fox bats or flying foxes:

The two animals hung one behind the other in their usual fashion, in such a manner that the male's belly touched the lower part of the female's back. The male member, a bent tube about two inches long, feels its way behind the female's hind legs into the vagina, while the male's body does not move at all. The penis forms a kind of lever moving about a pivot at its base, and because of its curving shape it can reach its destination.

Among dogs, bears, martens, and their relatives, the method of sexual intercourse does not differ from the standard mammalian pattern, although the duration may. The couples do not finish nearly so quickly as the majority of mammals. The reason is the peculiar character of the male sexual apparatus. The penis is stiffened by a bone, as is the case in some other mammals. In addition it is provided with erectile nodes. These bulbous structures swell after the ejaculation of the semen: they can fill the entire female vagina and so prevent the sperm from flowing out again. This means that the copulating animals may be forced to cling together for several minutes, or even an hour, until the erectile nodes subside. The mink and sable are said to copulate continuously for eight hours at times. It may be assumed that in the course of this period several ejaculations take place.

The final exception concerns the anthropoid apes. As might be expected of these inventive, curious, and highly intelligent animals, sex play among them is enriched by all sorts of variations. Young chimpanzees sometimes embrace sitting or lying down, apparently testing to find out which position they like best. As they grow older their interest in alternative positions visibly diminishes; they fall back on the classic mammalian method. Orang-utans, however, are such acrobats in their sex lives that they can copulate in any conceivable position while performing gymnastics in the branches of trees. If one could speak of any standard behavior among the orang-utans, it would be that described by the German nature writer Paul Eipper:

Making smacking sounds with her tongue, the female loudly greeted the orang male sitting in the bed of straw. She put her arm around his shoulders and caressingly scratched his abdomen. Then she climbed up to the ceiling of the big enclosure and hung with all fours from a crossbeam, her hind legs straddled. The jungle giant straightened up to his full height and looked up longingly. One rapid movement and his hands grasped the beam. Body dangling, he swung toward his mate, who for her part loosened the prehensile toes of her spread legs and affectionately embraced him. He too now clasped her with his thighs and feet twined around her back. Breast to breast they mated, hanging by their hands and rocking back and forth.

As far as we can tell from sparse observations of their behavior in the wild, orang-utans—like gorillas, gibbons, and some species of monkeys—live monogamously. The father, mother, and sexually immature children form a family whose members stay together until the offspring are grown or until one of the mates dies. The male gorilla, who is too heavy for arboreal life, is said to set up camp at the foot of a tree to fend off leopards, while his family make their nest high in the branches.

In contrast to this monogamy on the part of the two largest anthropoid apes, chimpanzees seem to practice polygamy. According to the observations of the German zoologist Alexander Sokolowsky (quoted from Ford and Beach), a chimpanzee family in captivity normally

> consists of one fully adult male, several mature and immature females, and other adolescent males. The mature male copulated freely with all the females, but if he observed a younger male in the act of mounting a female, the dominant individual promptly interrupted the relationship by biting and striking the smaller male. . . . Despite the despot's vigilance, he was not completely successful, for the younger males occasionally succeeded in copulating with the females while he was asleep. In this case, it was obvious that the females were quite willing to receive males other than their mate, when they could safely do so.

It would seem, then, as if the lax morality of the chimpanzee forms the sharpest possible contrast to the fidelity of orang-utans. But this impression is mistaken. Many male chimpanzees in the wild would have to be content with a single female, for lack of opportunity. And, vice versa, there are probably a number of orang and gorilla males who are able to maintain several wives. Only arrant puritans could censure female anthropoid apes for enjoying their occasional adventures with young bachelor apes. If primates make use of their unique ability to mate at all seasons, they are not violating their behavioral standards. A chimpanzee female would be misbehaving only if she ran away from her husband, thus destroying the social bond. But probably such a thing scarcely ever occurs. Moreover, female anthropoid apes are extremely selective in regard to their sexual objects. One of the keenest students of anthropoid psychology, Robert Yerkes, director of the ape station at Orange Park, Florida, believes that emotion plays a role among apes similar to that among men.

The ability of primates to be sexually active throughout the year results from the special cyclical fertility of their females. A majority of other mammals pass through a rutting period only once or a few times each year. This is when the sexual hormones stimulate the fe-

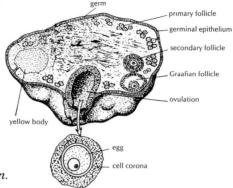

Ovulation in mammals and man.

male ovaries to expel egg cells into the oviduct. During the rest of the year the reproductive apparatus is quiescent. Among primates, however, ovulation takes place every month. The uterus prepares for the reception of an egg by forming special tissues which are supplied with blood and are intended to nourish the placenta. If no conception takes place, these uterine tissues atrophy and are discharged from the body along with the ovum and the blood which has not been availed of.

This periodic alternation of ovulation and menstruation characterizes female apes just as it does human females. In some species the cycle takes three weeks, in others thirty days. Old World apes undergo visible monthly bleedings similar to those of human females; New World apes, on the other hand, have only internal bleeding at the time of menstruation. In principle these physiological processes are the same in apes as in human beings.

Among baboons and some other species of primates, as we have noted, ovulation in the female is accompanied with swelling of the genitalia and sometimes by deep coloration of these parts. But not all varieties of apes have these swellings. In a considerable number of species, the three days of the fertile period are no more conspicuous than in the human female.

ARTIFICIAL INSEMINATION,
NATURAL BIRTH CONTROL

Since the beginnings of civilization men have superimposed their own purposes upon the reproductive life of animals. They have domesticated a great variety of wild animals. They have changed the appearance of animals and developed countless new breeds thousands of years before geneticists discovered the laws of heredity and the surprises of mutation. Many domestic animals nowadays have their sex lives highly restricted. Their reproduction has been extensively mechanized and rationalized. Often natural mating has been replaced by artificial insemination.

Highly bred animals have become living machines, as Robert Jungk concluded after a visit to a station where bull semen is obtained:

> Now the overseer opened the stable door and jumped aside. The bull plunged heavily forward. There was only one direction for him, and only one choice. For he was attached to a chain fastened to a guiding rail above his head. The rail led out into the fresh air, through a long open passage to something dark waiting at the end of it. Was it a cow? From a distance it appeared to be. As the bull leaped upon the dark something, I wondered that there was no sound to be heard except the heavy breathing of the male animal. Suddenly he left off, turned round and trotted slowly back to his pen.
>
> There remained behind a curious thing, which I was now able to look at more closely. It was a hide-covered wire trestle, an artificial cow without a head but with an artificial female sex organ. The bull had leaped upon a dummy, and the extraordinary thing was that this seemed to make no difference to him.

Even more fantastic than artificial insemination are the experiments in the laboratories of avant-garde biologists. By hormone treatments and heat shock, artificial parthenogenesis is induced in rabbits. Or else radiation is used to destroy all the paternal chromosomes in the sperm, so that only the maternal characteristics are inherited when the semen is used for fertilization. Attempts are being made to change sex and to produce twins artificially. Some biologists are even trying to develop the embryos of mammals outside the body of the mother. American and French biologists have already succeeded in keeping the embryos of mice, rats, sheep, and cows alive in the test tube for many days. Experimentation is already going on with human germ cells.

We cannot say as yet to what extent such experiments will prove important to animal breeders and even to the further evolution of man. But already strange visions shimmer upon the horizon of science. According to the American geneticist Joseph Muller, we are approaching the point when man's will can shape the course of evolution in ways so far undreamed of. After all, Muller argues, even the ant can determine which of its larvae will develop into queens, soldiers, or workers. Why then should not *Homo sapiens* also find means of transforming all potential queens and possible soldiers into workers? Or, we might add, could not a dictatorship find biochemical ways to transform all its citizens into soldiers?

The breeders of domestic animals who systematically apply the laws of genetics in order to produce new breeds, and the biologists who try to probe the ultimate secrets of life, have already turned the processes of reproduction far from their natural course and subjected them to the will of man. But even a child does something similar when it mates its white mice, its hamsters, guinea pigs or rabbits. Most domestic breeds would rapidly disappear again by natural selection were they permitted to mate freely under wild conditions. They are creations of man—frequently very handsome, interesting, or useful, but not especially fit for the struggle for existence in the wild. They thrive only under the protection of man.

Konrad Lorenz, who is a great dog lover, upbraids the breeders of fashionable dogs for having shamefully neglected the animals' characterological and spiritual qualities. They have placed more value upon this or that external characteristic than upon producing sturdy, vigorous, loyal, and handsome dogs. Thus in the course of time types of dogs have arisen which are "like cruel caricatures of the original appearance of the breed in question." An intelligent mutt with sound nerves, he maintains, is in the long run a far more gratifying animal to own than an expensive champion.

This complaint against overbreeding in dogs may also be applied to other extremes of breeding among domestic animals—from the albino hamster and the angora cat to the high-performance cow which has become nothing but a milk machine. All such animals are champions from one point of view, but they have lost much of the vitality of their forebears. Lorenz says: "There is not a single breed whose excellent qualities have not been totally destroyed as soon as it became the height of fashion. . . . Breeders with an inordinate sense of honor about their animals' purity of pedigree think there is nothing unethical about breeding physically handsome but psychically defective specimens."

Rabbits are easy animals to keep and can be raised by every child. In the course of time innumerable breeds of rabbits have developed from the wild rabbit. "Breeding like rabbits" has become a stock expression for fecundity. When tame rabbits escape to wild life, the original wild form rapidly emerges again; the breed characteristics induced by man soon disappear by natural selection. Such escaped rabbits can in fact multiply at a tremendous rate, and in regions where their natural enemies are lacking, they become a national plague. The classic example of this is Australia. Starting with a few English rabbits which a Mr. Autin released in Basson Park near Geelong in Victoria in 1859, Australian rabbits have multiplied into millions and thousands of millions. In spite of mass poisoning and artificial mass infection with myxomatosis virus, they continue to hold their own against men, and cause severe damage not only to Australian agriculture, but also to the native wildlife.

The British zoologist Thomas Pennant once calculated that a single pair of rabbits within four years could theoretically multiply into 1,284,840 rabbits. Possibly a breeder with a pair of domestic rabbits might in fact prove that proposition, assuming that all the young lived. But wild rabbits practice a sensible demographic policy; they use birth control to insure that the numbers of rabbits do not become an avalanche. Mice, lemmings, and other rodents likewise have a form of birth control. In fat years their numbers increase rapidly; in lean years they decrease just as rapidly. Here is the explanation for the familiar phenomenon of mouse and lemming years, for mass increase leads to mass migration. This, too, explains the precipitate increase of rabbits in formerly rabbitless Australia. Normally, however, natural birth control restricts the number of individuals so that no dangerous population pressure arises.

Birth control in rabbits and other rodents takes place as follows: Under certain living conditions a more or less high percentage of the embryos in the uteruses of the females do not develop. The cells of the fetuses disintegrate and their substance is absorbed by the mother's body. Environment, weather, and nutrition seem to influence, or perhaps directly to govern, this resorptive process. The process takes place very swiftly, usually within two days. Afterwards, the mother rabbit behaves as if she had given birth in regular fashion. "It has been determined, for example," Burton writes,

> that among the rabbits in North Wales more than ninety per cent of all females were pregnant between the middle of March and the middle of May, and that the majority had already been pregnant once the year before. At the same time it turned out that sixty per cent of the conceived young were never born. Even in litters which did develop, ten per cent of the embryos disappeared before birth. Most of these embryos reached the tenth day of their development and then disintegrated and were resorbed. . . . The little we know of this curious phenomenon throws light upon the close connection between mother and offspring during all stages; in fact, it suggests an intricately connected chain of circumstances which influences the future of the offspring and the living conditions of the mother.

Birth control, then, is no invention of civilized man. Nature, too, fights overpopulation and establishes means for diminishing population pressure as soon as circumstances demand it.

DOG DAYS AND CATCALLS

Everywhere in human society, two animals occupy a special place. The dog and the cat have become the special intimates of man. These predatory animals, which share our homes and our family life, are two very different creatures. The dog has developed the closest possible contact with human beings; he has become something very close to a "human animal." The cat, however, even in house and garden, has preserved much of its wild character; it has remained at bottom an untamed member of the household.

The relationship between man and dog has been a basic component of all civilizations ever since Stone Age man, some twelve thousand years ago, began raising wild cubs or jackals. These tamed wild animals guarded settlements, ate the garbage, gave warning at the approach of enemies; their descendants accompanied the hunters, in later times guarded the flocks, allowed themselves to be hitched to sleds and carts, and gradually became a part of human society. The human family was the dog's substitute for the pack. For thousands of years the poets and thinkers of mankind have paid tribute to the faithful dog. Perhaps the strongest statement of this sort may be found in the *Avesta*, the religious writings of the Zoroastrians. There we may read the blunt, terse claim: "The world exists by the intelligence of the dog." "I think," Lorenz writes,

> that in ability to understand human language the dog is superior even to the anthropoid apes, much as these may surpass him in certain other aspects of intelligence. In one respect the dog unquestionably resembles man more than the most intelligent apes: like man, he is a domesticated being, and like man he owes two significant traits to domestication. This first is *liberation from the rigid paths of instinctive behavior*. This affords him the potentialities for new actions, as it does man. The second is that capacity for *rejuvenescence* which is the root of his lasting sexual desires. In man this takes the form of youthful receptivity, and keeps him a growing personality to advanced age.

But when the natural erotic force is aroused, man too is not free of the rigid paths of instinctive behavior and the dog certainly is not.

Twice a year, when the bitches come into heat, the bonds between master and dog are loosened. The loyal household companion again becomes a creature of instinct, running with his kind in packs, marking out his territory, brawling to establish social rankings, and following the trails of prospective sexual partners. Dog and man live under the same roof; but the dog's instincts call him back to the environment of his wild ancestors. And so at rutting time every dog regards the street as his territory, and as the arena for battles with rivals and encounters with females. Invisible olfactory frontiers divide our residential neighborhoods into canine territories. And even the most placid lapdog will seek to escape his human substitute pack to follow over long distances the scent of bitches in heat. Such runaway dogs often stay away from home for days, laying stubborn siege to the domicile of some desirable female.

Female wolves and the females of wild dogs are frequently *alpha* animals, leading the pack and dominating the males also. In their human environment the bitches can similarly elevate themselves to the rank of queens. They are courted by the males and may play the role of leader in a group of neighborhood dogs, choosing their own partners and jealously suppressing the other bitches. In general, female dogs are anything but coy at rutting time. They leave their scent marks behind to lure the dogs whenever they are taken out, or else they pay calls on the males and go chasing playfully about with them for a while.

This game between male and bitch, with its gestures of threat and flight, gradually becomes serious. "The mouth is slightly opened," Lorenz writes,

> so that the tongue can be seen, and the strongly upturned corners of the mouth, which appears widened almost to the ears, give a look even more distinctly like laughter than before. . . . The male smiles harder and harder, making more and more rapid tripping motions with his forepaws. Suddenly he momentarily knocks against the bitch, nudges her with his forepaws against her chest, whirls around and scurries away in a most curious posture. His back is still submissively bowed, with hindquarters lowered and tail between the legs. But in this posture of anxiety the male performs the oblique leaps of friendly play, and his tail wags, in so far as there is room for it to do so between his legs. Moreover, this pretended retreat ends after a few yards. The male once again whirls around and now stands confronting the bitch with a broad smile on his face. He has also lifted his tail again, so that it can wag unhindered in wide sweeps from side to side. The wagging is not limited to the tail alone; the whole rear half of the dog is pulled back and forth with it. Once again the male jumps forward and col-

lides with the female. And this time his playful gestures indubitably have the note of an erotic proposal.

If the chance offers, a bitch will prefer as sexual partner a male of the large, strong breeds, especially the wolflike "police dogs." Consequently, the most common mongrels are police dog mutts—at least in Central Europe. The bitch, no matter to what breed she herself belongs, is obviously practicing sexual selection. In packs of wild dogs, as among other animals, the rank of the female automatically rises if she mates with a dominant male. And the largest police dogs and wolflike spitzes, which at least in outward appearance come closest to the wild forms, are such dominant types; they easily lord it over other dogs. To the grief of many dog owners, the purest bred terrier or dachshund bitch will prefer any large wolflike street dog to the carefully chosen male of her own breed.

While bitches will often annoy the males, male dogs are remarkably chivalrous toward the females. No normal male will bite a bitch. The bitch, on the other hand, is permitted to tweak and torment the male; and the male can escape such trials only by making the familiar gesture of submission, or by attempting to turn the female's attacks into play. He is not allowed to run away, for that would mean losing face. Male dogs are particularly concerned about preserving their masculine dignity.

The male dog is just as friendly and forbearing toward all pups. Pups can go to any lengths with him without his losing his temper. Such paternal forbearance is another legacy from the wild past. In those days young dogs grew up in the pack and consequently had to be tolerated by all its members. Even today, after twelve thousand years of domestication, the inherited law still holds. To be sure, most pups are born and raised in houses or in kennels but as soon as they make their first acquaintance with adult males, the same poignantly droll thing takes place—which Lorenz describes as follows:

A highly amusing scene may be witnessed if we are cruel enough to present a dignified and somewhat self-important male with a band of playful little whelps. Our old male, named Wolf, was wonderfully suited for this experiment. He was grave and not very playful; consequently, it was extremely embarrassing to him when we forced him to pay a call on the terrace to his own children, who were then about two months old. . . . While bigger pups, from the age of about five months on, have a certain respect for the professorial dignity of an old male, such little ones are totally irreverent. They rush with awkward inconsiderateness at their father, nipping him with their sharp little teeth and biting his feet, so that he lifts one foot after the other, as though he had stepped on a hot surface. At the same time the poor fellow cannot even growl, let alone chastise the naughty pups. Oddly enough, our surly Wolf softened and even began playing with his children after a while. But he never voluntarily went on the terrace as long as the pups were still small.

Nevertheless, although man can only imperfectly control the reproductive life of his most faithful companion, in many matings among dogs, the partners are selected by man, not by the dogs themselves. With cats, he has largely failed to exercise such control. Only a few breeds of cats have been created by planned selection: the bobtailed Manx cat; the short-tailed cats of Japan; the mask-faced Siamese; and the long-haired Persians. But even these differ only slightly from their original form, the so-called Egyptian cat. If we consider the few and uniform breeds of cats, as against the widely differing breeds of dogs, we must recognize that the cat, in spite of five thousand years of domestication, has remained a wild animal which does not permit man to prescribe its sex life.

But then again, man has had no great impulse to remodel the cat by selective breeding. Since the appearance of the first temple cats in Europe and Southeast Asia, we human beings have loved the unadulterated wild animal in the cat. To be sure, we say that the house cat makes itself useful by catching mice; but in reality most people do not keep the little predator out of such utilitarian considerations, but for the pure pleasure of having her. We delight in this playful, highly sensitive animal who has not become our willing slave but who has kept her independence even under our protection and who regards the house and its environs as her territory and hunting grounds, just as her wild ancestors did the forest and the plains.

Female dogs can be locked up when their owners do not wish them to reproduce. But it is far more difficult to prevent cats from fulfilling their sexual instincts. Unless they are given their freedom, they become almost unbearable; they refuse to play or eat, tear about the house, howl incessantly, roll madly on the floor, or leave their scent upon rugs and in corners, in the hope that a sexual partner may succeed in creeping in. And since they are quick to escape through a crack in the door or an open window, they reproduce more frequently than we like. Up to recently, only spaying could prevent a cat from having kittens at least twice a year. Nowadays, a hormone injection is proving to be an effective form of birth control.

A spayed female or altered male is a lovable house pet but essentially it is only half a cat. As Frances and Richard Lockridge point out in their book, *Cats and People:*

One has never known cats until one has lived for the week or ten days it lasts with a female cat in search of a mate. She is revealing then and, to the squeamish, not a little embarrassing. That spinsters should, as so many of them do, associate with cats proves them more tough-minded than the noncontinent habitually suppose them to be. No one who has lived with an unaltered female cat can have any real ignorance of the facts of life.

While females howl and writhe to be let out, locked-up tomcats in the mating season spray doors and walls with their highly odoriferous urine. The whole house soon smells "of cat." And so the "owner" is finally forced to let the lovesick tom go about his concerns in the open air. In short, as the Lockridges put it: "Anyone keeping unaltered cats, whether in country or city, must be prepared for a life in which feline sex plays a considerable, on occasion a major, part. . . . The gentlest and most normal female is . . . determined—she is going to have kittens, or else."

Gardens and roofs are preferred for rendezvous. Here the females utter their wild, banshee cries to call the toms; and the toms respond with hoarse, howling concerts to impress the females. These catcalls are a reminiscence of the nocturnal love life of wildcats in the forests. The cat's sharpest sense is hearing. And those harrowing nocturnal cries obviously do not serve solely to enable the sexes to find one another; they also act as stimulants, increasing sexual desire.

As might be expected of so sensual and sensitive an animal, mating in cats is a highly charged affair. Sexologists therefore are wont to point to the cat when the question arises whether female mammals experience a climax in the sex act similar to the human orgasm. Ford and Beach point out the well-known postlude to intercourse in the female cat. Many females writhe violently and roll convulsively after the tomcat has released them. They repeatedly lick the vulva, and refuse to accept the tom's advances again until the post-coital excitement has died down.

Many feline predators display rather rough sexual habits. Among these is the tom's love bite. Buddenbrock describes it as follows:

A peculiarity which seems to be present only in the large cats, but not in the house cat, is the male's habit of gripping the nape of the female's neck in his jaws during coitus. My own many observations lead me to believe that this is a precautionary measure to prevent the female from slashing the male with her teeth at the decisive moment. On the other hand, eminent specialists maintain that at the moment of ejaculation the male actually bites the neck, and that the scars from such bites may remain visible for a long time. The female part-

In the domestic cat, as well as among the larger feline predators, the "neck bite" during copulation is a common occurrence.

ner takes her revenge for this rather dubious caress by administering several vigorous blows with her paws as soon as the procedure is over. . . . The male seems to know what awaits him, for ordinarily he escapes his just punishment by taking one mighty leap away.

It is curious that Buddenbrock failed to observe exactly the same behavior in domestic cats, for it is quite common.

The consequence of the wild howling of spring and early summer nights is a motley batch of kittens. But for man's intervention, our towns and villages would be periodically flooded with the offspring of cats. The kittens would be abandoned, would go wild, do all kinds of damage, and die miserably after a while. The problem of abandoned and homeless cats is already a grave concern to humane societies among all civilized peoples who have a natural and kindly attitude toward animals. All over the world, innumerable newborn kittens are put to death, innumerable abandoned cats roam about in a semi-starved condition and sooner or later fall victim to the poison, traps, or bullets of gardeners, farmers, and hunters. Most conscientious cat owners, therefore, decide to have their female cats sterilized. It is a simple operation involving severance of the oviduct. The spayed cat remains a lovable animal, but she, and the human family in which she lives, miss the one thing that means much to her: she will never become a mother. And motherhood is the true glory and fulfillment of a female cat's life.

"The cat becomes a kitten with her kittens," Alfred Brehm writes.

> With pretended gravity she sits in the midst of them, but she twitches her tail significantly. The kittens do not yet understand this wordless language, but they are stimulated by the movement. Clumsily, they lash out at the tip of the tail, turn somersaults, try to climb over the mother's back. . . . The mother cat now directs and regulates the hitherto aimless play. Now she lies on her back, tossing the kittens about like balls on her forepaws and hindpaws; now she sits in the midst of the scuffling group, knocks one kit over with a single blow of her paw, draws another in close to her, and teaches the band of kittens the expert use of their taloned paws. Then again she gets up, runs away, and cajoles the children into following her, apparently with the intention of teaching them litheness and agility. . . . When the time comes for the slumbering predator in the children to awaken, the mother brings into the nursery, instead of the toys which have served up to now—pebbles, balls, bits of wool and scraps of paper—a living mouse, as little hurt as possible, or else a small bird, handled with the same caution, or, if the pickings are poor, a grasshopper. General amazement reigns in the little group, but only for a moment. Soon the mania for play is powerfully stirred, and then their predatory instinct.

The methods the mother cat uses to teach her children to catch living prey strike us as cruel. Again and again the victim escapes from the still clumsy kittens; again and again the cat catches it and drops it in front of the litter of kittens. In the wild, young cats must learn the most varied hunting methods from their mothers, if they are to survive in the struggle for existence. And the instincts for teaching and for hunting are as powerful as ever in the domesticated house cat— as irresistible as the sexual and maternal instincts of these self-willed, untamed domestic animals.

In man, too, many such primitive instincts are still alive. In his erotic life and his care of children particularly, domesticated civilized man unconsciously manifests many innate modes of behavior in which he is not so very different from other mammals. Some biologists hold that kissing, for example, is nothing but a relic of those ancient times when mothers fed their children from the mouth, after weaning. This tender gesture was then imitated by lovers when they wanted to demonstrate that they were as intimately united as mother and child.

In general, as Georg Kleemann, the German writer and psychologist, has put it:

> In the erotic relationships of vertebrates, including man, the general similarity of infantile movements and sounds among lovers is quite embarrassing. Human lovers always act as if the beloved woman or the beloved man were a tiny infant. Not a word that is whispered into the baby's basket is lacking in the vocabulary of love. Is it any wonder, then, that the feeding movements of the parents have been taken over into the ritual of love?

Certainly close connections exist between maternal love and eroticism, in animals as well as man. "In this matter the emotions flow into one another," as Kleemann puts it. "Giving the breast and feeding the child are linked with erotic sensations in the woman. If we consider this, we will realize our close ties with our house cat when, at some affectionate moment, she comes to us purring and making the kneading motion of a kitten pressing out the milk."

SEX AND MORALITY

In 1951 the American scientists Clellan S. Ford and Frank A. Beach published the most complete and comprehensive study of sexual behavior among mammals and man that had been made up to that time. They had of course to face the question of the need for such a work—and prefaced their book with a justification in which they addressed five groups of potential readers: biologists, psychologists, sociologists, moral philosophers, and the general public.

The first three groups could be expected to approach the subject objectively:

> The biologist considers sexual behavior to be of fundamental significance because it leads to perpetuation of the species and thus to the continuity of life itself. The psychologist finds in the sexual impulse wellsprings of human conduct, deep reservoirs of motivation that impel men and women to action and furnish the driving force for many of their day-to-day activities. Sociologists recognize the integrating, cohesive functioning of sex as contributing to the stability of the family unit and thus to the entire structure of the social group.

This statement clearly delimits the functions of sexuality. But civilized man has not let the matter rest there. He has tried to shift the natural foundations of sexuality, has at once elevated and debased the sexual instinct. In human societies sexuality has assumed a far greater importance than it possesses anywhere in the realm of nature. It has entered into religion, art, and daily life; it has nourished literature, humor, and advertising. Even politics has been sexually determined and the mightiest decisions forged in the bedchambers of rulers. Detached from its primary purpose, sexuality has become an inexhaustible topic of conversation and food for thought of the normal human being. But civilized man has not only fostered this universal power; he has also hedged it round with rules and regulations, and has denounced everything that goes against his self-created prohibitions as wickedness or sin.

As a result, sexuality has become a field of dangerously high tension. Dominated by it, man has found it necessary to try to dominate it. And he has not succeeded, to this day. This is why the sexual behavior of animal and man is of grave concern to the last two groups Ford and Beach mention. "For the moralist, man's perpetual attempt to reconcile his basic sexual tendencies with the ethical standards and ideal demands of his social group presents a primary problem." Moreover, a broad understanding of the subject of sex "is useful for anyone who conceives of his own life as worthy of intelligent direction and management." Such understanding, Ford and Beach stress, cannot be attained by introspection, nor solely "by learning how other members of the same society feel, believe, and act with respect to sex." It is also essential to study the sexual feelings, conceptions, actions, and habits of primitive peoples and animals.

Civilized man has only gradually and reluctantly accepted the necessity for such study. The habits of animals were partly despised, partly anthropomorphized; and the customs of primitive peoples would be described by explorers as late as the last century as "atrocious rites." Standards of the Western Christian world were projected upon the lives of animals and alien peoples. It represents one of the most significant intellectual triumphs of our age that scientists have reversed this tendency, looking to the animal kingdom and primitive peoples for the roots and foundations of our own behavior. Only such study has taught us to what extent inherited dispositions and modes of behavior change in the course of evolution. Our standards, we have recognized, have not existed for all eternity; they are the result of historical growth. And they are subject to the same processes of growth, flourishing, and decay as any other historical phenomenon.

In the days when allegory and fable were favorite didactic methods, naturalists and philosophers devoted considerable effort to the task of dividing the animal kingdom into moral and immoral species.

The elephant ranked high among the good animals. The Roman writer Pliny credited the pachyderm with every possible virtue: sense of honor, righteousness, conscientiousness, and above all a distinct sense of shame: "Out of shame elephants copulate only in hidden places. . . . Afterwards they bathe in a river. Nor is there any adultery among them, nor cruel battles for the females."

Medieval writers embellished this legend with further details. Albertus Magnus stated that the elephant had no sexual instinct, but conceived and bore in paradisiac innocence in an animal Garden of Eden. In the fourteenth century one of the first popular zoologists, Konrad von Megenberg, contrasted the frivolous morals of those animals which "live for their lust without divine worship" with the sobriety of the elephants who copulate only in order to beget offspring and who after achieving this purpose "do not touch the female for a space of three years." Even Konrad Gesner, two hundred years later, held up the virtue of the elephant to his fellow men: "Chaste and pure they lead their lives, giving way to no luxurie, offending never against their wedded state, and are of speciall shamefulness, for they engage not in such thinges unless before they have enclosed them in thicke shrubberie and dense undergrowthe."

The fable persists in modern books on animals, although zoologists have known for at least one hundred and fifty years that sexual shame does not exist for animals and that they have no concept of marital fidelity. If animals copulate in hidden places, they do so from caution and not from prudery. And in the rare cases in which couples remain united for life (which scarcely happens among elephants), they are not practicing fidelity in our moralistic sense, but conforming to the behavioristic law of their particular species.

As more and more was learned about zoology, it became patent that animals would not serve as moral examples for men. But the impulse to moralize from nature died hard, and lessons began to be read from the imaginary patterns of primitive man. The hunting nomads of the Old Stone Age were held up as examples of the restraint innate to humankind. Unfortunately, nothing very definite can be said about the sexual habits of paleolithic man. Prehistoric bones, tools, cave paintings, and figurines tell us little. Nevertheless, some anthropologists ventured to assert that paleolithic man must have lived monogamously like the first human pair in the Bible, and that his sexual life was probably governed by strict taboos.

There is one thing we do know about ancient man: he confronted the whole problem of sexuality with far less embarrassment than his civilized descendants. For evidence, there are numerous cave drawings representing initiation rites and fertility cults. Further proof is the candid manner in which, ten to twenty thousand years ago, male and female sexual parts were drawn, and even coitus pictured. Strangely enough, some students of prehistory continue to be embarrassed by this frankness on the part of their paleolithic subjects. Thus, we will come upon estimable books on Ice Age art in which the drawings depicting sexual intercourse are cautiously and overmodestly interpreted as "interments" or "duels."

The impact of Western morality upon primitive peoples who still inhabit the globe has been particularly unfortunate. Until the twentieth century, small and isolated ethnic groups whose customs diverge from those of the European colonizers were labeled savages and were mercilessly punished for their adherence to their traditional codes. Ethnological literature records countless cases where thoughtless interference with the ethical and social patterns of primitive tribes all but brought about their destruction. The material and hygienic benefits which these groups drew from contact with a higher civilization have scarcely recompensed them for the damage done.

On the other hand, Europe's apparently so sturdy moral structure was rocked by these encounters with bizarre moralities. The explorers, colonizers, and missionaries seemed to have stumbled upon a veritable witches' sabbath: polygamy and polyandry, guest and temple prostitution, group marriage, institutionalized rape and purchase of women, incest, male childbed practices, and the burning of widows. Among some peoples religious celebrations passed over into sexual orgies. Others had sexual intercourse on freshly sowed fields in order to assure good crops. Among still others, religion prescribed a specific kind of embrace. In many parts of the world initiation rites included circumcision of the adolescent girls as well as youths. Instead of carefully concealing the sexual organs, some peoples exposed them, or exhibitionistically emphasized them by all sorts of adornments.

A large number of primitive peoples had no prejudice against adultery. Some tribes regarded the lending of wives or direct exchange of wives as actions pleasing to the gods. Nearly half the world outside Europe looked upon homosexuality as a private affair, not especially desirable but not a matter to be forbidden. And only that portion of humanity valued premarital virginity who lived—as the ethnologists phrase it—in a patrilineal social order. Many peoples considered it desirable for the bride to prove her fruitfulness before marriage.

On the other hand, there were tribes and groups whose marital patterns should have been heartily approved by the white-skinned apostles of morality. They lived monogamously and more or less chastely. Sad to say, their behavior offended the civilizers and missionaries in other respects. Dwarf races such as the Pygmies of the

Congo jungles, South African Bushmen, the Negritos of the Philippines, the Veddas of Ceylon, the Semang in Malaya, and the inhabitants of the Andaman Islands in the Indian Ocean were numbered among these, as well as some of the aboriginals of Australia and various Indian tribes of Tierra del Fuego. Since these races could not be regarded as models for European humanity, not too much was made of their monogamous habits.

One of the finest of present-day ethnologists, Margaret Mead, conducted an extensive study of one of these monogamous peoples: the Arapesh of New Guinea. In many respects the morality of the Arapesh is astonishingly close to the standard morality of the Occident:

The Arapesh do not seriously conceive of sex outside of the marriage bond. The casual encounter, the liaison, a sudden stirring of desire that must be satisfied quickly—these mean nothing to them. Their ideal is essentially a domestic one, not a romantic one. Sex is a serious matter, a matter that must be surrounded with precautions. . . . It is least dangerous when it occurs within the protective circle of long betrothal, when one's young, inexperienced wife is almost a part of one's own family, when one has seen her every day for years. . . . Therefore if a man permits himself to be seduced by a woman whom he encounters casually . . . it is reasonable for him to conclude that she seduced him with intent to sorcerize him, as an enemy and a stranger. Only with marriage—long-established, comfortable, friendly marriage—is sex safe and valuable.

Other Papuan tribes behave similarly. What congenial people, the European might exclaim. But the inhabitants of the mountainous New Guinean jungles are also head hunters. It is simply not possible to measure the ethical worth of a given people by our own standards, for we can only do so by isolating this or that aspect of their moral and social lives. Students of manners and customs have learned over the centuries, often from painful experience, that the different peoples of the human race cannot be divided into sheep and goats according to their attitude toward sex at any given time. Every people in the course of its history has created a moral world of its own, with its own standards and taboos. The very variety and complexity of human cultures, laws, and principles are what place man far above all species of animals, no matter how like human beings these may be. "Man," Margaret Mead writes,

became not merely one of the beasts that mated, fought for its food, and died, but a human being, with a name, a position, and a god. Each people makes this fabric differently, selects some clues and ignores others, emphasizes a different sector of the whole arc of human potentialities. . . . Each simple, homogeneous culture can give scope to only a few of the varied human endowments, disallowing or penalizing others too antithetical or too unrelated to its major emphases to find room within its walls. . . . And each new generation is shaped, firmly and definitely, to the dominant trends.

But there is still another respect in which man has reached the top rung in the ladder of sex and reproduction. No matter what attitudes, principles, and values the various peoples and cultures have created in the long course of their moral history, one trait is common to all of them: Human mates are attached not only by mutual sexual interest, but also by emotions which go far beyond physical need. For all human beings, the sexual relationship developed into love.

A TABLE OF CLASSIFICATION

including all the phyla and typical examples of each subdivision

(Blanks occur because, for example, there is sometimes no need to assign a "family" name when the "order" consists of only one family.)

PHYLUM	CLASS	ORDER	FAMILY	GENUS	SPECIES	COMMON NAME
I. PROTOZOA ("first living things")	Sarcodina ("flesh-ones") *Subclass:* Rhizopoda ("whip-bearers")	Amoebina		Amoeba	Amoeba proteus	amoeba
II. PORIFERA ("hole bearers")	Calcarea ("lime-ones")	Homocoela		Leucoselenia	Leucoselenia primordialis	sponge
III. COELENTERATA ("hollow-guts")	Hydrozoa ("water-livers")	Siphonophora		Physalia	Physalia arethusa	Portuguese man of war
IV. CTENOPHORA ("comb bearers")	Tentaculata ("feeler-equipped ones")	Cestida		Cestus	Cestus pectinalis	Venus's-girdle
V. PLATYHELMINTHES ("flatworms")	Trematoda ("hole-shaped ones")	Digenea	Fasciolidae	Fasciola	Fasciola hepatica	liver fluke
VI. NEMATHELMINTHES ("threadworms")	Nematoda ("thread-shaped ones")	Telogonia		Ancyclostoma	Ancyclostoma duodenale	hookworm
VII. TROCHELMINTHES ("wheel worms")	Rotifera ("wheel bearers")	Seisonidea		Utricularia	Utricularia vulgaris	bladderwort

Phylum / Subphylum / Class	Order	Family	Genus	Species	Common name
VIII. ECHINODERMATA ("spiny-skins")					
Subphylum: ECHINOZOA ("spiny-livers")					
Echinoidea ("spiny ones")	Cidaroida	Cidaridae	*Echinocardium*	*Echinocardium cordatum*	sea urchin
IX. ANNELIDA ("little rings")					
Subphylum: CHAETOPODA ("hair-foots")					
Oligochaeta ("sparse-hairs")	Megadrili	Lumbricidae	*Lumbricus*	*Lumbricus terrestris*	earthworm
X. ARTHROPODA					
Crustacea ("shelled ones")	Decopoda	Homaridae	*Homarus*	*Homarus americanus*	lobster
Insecta ("cut-in ones")	Orthoptera	Mantidae	*Mantis*	*Mantis religiosa*	praying mantis
XI. MOLLUSCA ("soft-ones")					
Gastropoda ("stomach-foots")	Pulmonata	Helicidae	*Haplotrema*	*Haplotrema concava*	snail
Cephalopoda ("head-foots")	Dibranchiata	Loliginidae	*Loligo*	*Loligo pealii*	squid
XII. CHORDATA ("stringed-ones")					
Subphylum: VERTEBRATA ("turners")					
Amphibia ("dual-livers")	Anura	Ranidae	*Rana*	*Rana pipiens*	leopard frog
Mammalia ("breasted ones")	Carnivora	Canidae	*Canus*	*Canis familiaris*	dog
	Primates	Hominidae	*Homo*	*Homo sapiens*	man

GLOSSARY

CAUDAL: Having to do with the tail, or with the hind end of a body.

CHITINOUS: Having the character of the horny outer integument (chitin) of certain invertebrates, including insects, crustaceans, etc.

CHROMOSOMES: Complex structures, parts of plant and animal cell nuclei, which bear, in a fixed order, the factors of inheritance (genes).

CILIA: Hairlike processes capable of vibratory or lashing movement, serving for locomotion or to produce currents in a fluid medium.

CLASSIFICATION: The systematic arrangement of the forms of life. The largest divisions are the Animal and Vegetable Kingdoms. After them come phylum, (subphylum), class, order, family, genus, species. The earliest systems were based on shared physical features; later classifiers have made modifications designed to reflect evolutionary relationships. (For a sample Table of Classification *see* p. 362.)

CLOACA: The passage, or, often, the end of the passage, through which, in birds, reptiles, amphibians, some fishes, and some mammals, the intestinal, urinary, and generative canals discharge.

CYTOLOGY: Branch of biology dealing with individual cells in terms of structure, function, life history, etc.

GENES: The basic units of inheritance, which replicate at each cell division and determine the characteristics of the offspring organism.

GONAPOD: An appendage, found in certain crustaceans, which has been adapted as an organ of copulation; a pseudo penis.

MOTILE: Capable of self-movement (opposed to SESSILE).

OVIPOSITOR: Organ, frequently found in insects, for placing eggs in a location suitable for their development.

PARTHENOGENESIS: Reproduction, as in certain insects, worms, etc., by the development of an unfertilized egg, without the participation of male sperm.

PHYLUM: Primary, major division of the animal or vegetable kingdom. *See* CLASSIFICATION.

PLANKTON: Animal and plant organisms, mainly of minute size, found floating or weakly swimming in a body of water, usually near the surface. They constitute the major food of many forms of marine animals.

RAPTORIAL: In general, living on prey; the term is used most particularly in the classification of birds according as their beaks and claws are adapted to predatory habits.

SESSILE: Permanently attached; not capable of self-movement (opposed to MOTILE).

SOMATIC: Pertaining to the soma, i.e., all of an organism except the germ cells.

SPORE: A reproductive body, generally minute and primitive, found in plants and protozoans, and formed asexually, by simple division of cell.

SYMBIOSIS: The living together of two dissimilar organisms in more or less intimate union, whether advantageous or necessary to either or both, or harmful to either or both.

VENTRAL: Abdominal; in most vertebrates and arthropods, pertaining to the lower surface.

VIVIPAROUS: Producing living young within the parent's body, as mammals and certain fish distinguished from *oviparous:* producing eggs which hatch outside the parent's body.

BIBLIOGRAPHY

ALTUM, BERNARD: *Der Vogel und sein Leben.* Münster, W. Niemann, 1868

AQUINAS, SAINT THOMAS: *Basic Writings of Saint Thomas Aquinas.* New York, Random House, 1945

ARISTOTLE: *History of Animals.* London, H. G. Bohn, 1862

BAER, KARL ERNST VON: *Welche Auffassung der lebenden Natur ist die richtige?* Berlin, A. Hirschwald, 1862

BALDAMUS, AUGUST K. E.: *Baldamus illustriertes Handbuch der Federviehzucht.* Berlin, R. C. Schmidt & Co., 1908

BALLAUF, THEODOR: *Probleme des Lebendigen.* Bonn, Humboldt, 1950

————: *Die Wissenschaft vom Leben.* Freiburg, K. Alber, 1954

BEACH, FRANK A.: *Hormones and Behavior.* New York, 1948

BEACH, FRANK A. and FORD, C. S.: Patterns of Sexual Behavior. New York, Harper and Brothers and Paul Schoeber, Inc., 1951

BECHSTEIN, JOHANN MATTHAUS: *Cage and Chamberbirds, Their Natural History,* London, G. Bell & Sons, 1905

BEDDARD, FRANK EVERS: *Mammalia.* London, Macmillan & Co., 1902

BEEBE, WILLIAM: *Book of Bays.* New York, Harcourt, Brace and World, 1942

————: *High Jungle.* New York, Duell, Sloan & Pearce, 1949

BENECKE, BERTHOLD: *Fische, Fischerei und Fischzucht in Ost-und-West-Preussen.* Königsberg, Hartung, 1887

BERNACCHI, LOUIS CHARLES, F.R.G.S.: *To the South Polar Regions: Expedition of 1898–1900.* London, Hurst & Blackett Ltd., 1901

BERRILL, NORMAN JOHN: *The Living Tide.* New York: Dodd, Mead & Co., 1951

BILHARZ, THEODOR: *Ein Deutsches Forscherleben in Ägypten von Ernst Senn.* Stuttgart, Ausland und Heimat Verlags-Aktien Gesellschaft, 1931

BLAINVILLE, HENRI MARIE DUCROTAY DE: *Prodrome d'une Nouvelle Distribution Systematique Du Règne Animal.* Bulletin de la Science Philomathique de Paris, 1816

BLANCHARD, ÉMILE: *Histoire Des Insects*. Paris, 1945

BÖLSCHE, WILHELM: *Love Life in Nature: The Story of the Evolution of Love*. London, J. Cape, 1931

————: *Der Termitenstaat: Schilderung eines geheimnisvollen Volkes*. Stuttgart, Kosmos, Gesellschaft Der Naturfreunde, 1931

BONNET, CHARLES: *Contemplation de la Nature*. Hambourg, Chez J. G. Virehaux & Compagnie, 1782

BRAUN, MAXIMILIAN G. CH. K.: *Auf welche Weise infiziert sich der Mensch mit Parasiten?*: Hamburg, J. F. Richter, 1892

BREHM, ALFRED EDMUND: *Tierleben*. 13 vol., Leipzig und Wien, Bibliographisches Institut, 1925

BREUIL, HENRY: *Four Hundred Centuries of Cave Art*. Montignac, Dordogne, Centre d'études et de Documentation Préhistoriques, 1952

————: *Les Cavernes du Volp: Trois Frères*. Paris, Arts Et Métiers, 1958

BRONSARD: *Zeugungswunder*. Dresden, 1954

BUCHSBAUM, RALPH: *The Life in the Sea*. Eugene, Oregon State System of Higher Education, 1954

————: *Animals Without Backbones*. Chicago, The University of Chicago Press, 1947

BUDDENBROCK, WOLFGANG VON: *The Love-Life of Animals*. New York, Crowell, 1958

BUECHNER, LUDWIG: *Mind in Animals*. London, A. and H. B. Bonner, 1903

BUFFON, GEORGES LOUIS LECLERC, CONTE DE: *Buffon's Natural History of Man, The Globe and of Quadrupeds*. New York, Leavitt & Co., 1852

BURTON, MAURICE: *Infancy in Animals*. New York, Roy Publishers, 1956

BUSCH, WILHELM: *Sämtliche Werke*. Gütersloh, C. Bertelsmann, 1959

BUTENANDT, ADOLF: *Untersuchungen über das weibliche Sexualhormon*. Berlin, Weidmannsche Verlagsbuchhandlung, 1931

BUYTENDIJK, FREDERIC J. J.: *Wege zum Verständnis der Tiere*. Zürich-Leipzig, M. Nichans, 1938

————: *The Mind of the Dog*. Boston and New York, Houghton Mifflin Co., 1936

CARSON, RACHEL L.: *The Sea Around Us*. New York, Oxford University Press, 1961

CHAMISSO, ADALBERT VON: *Reise um die Welt*. Berlin, G. Hempel, 1879

COCHRAN, DORIS MABEL: *Living Amphibians of the World*. Garden City, New York, Doubleday, 1961

COLBERG, EDWIN HARRIS: *The Dinosaur Book: The Ruling Reptiles and Their Relatives*. New York, McGraw-Hill Book Co., 1951

COPE, EDWARD DRINKER: *On the Hypothesis of Evolution, Physical and Metaphysical*. New Haven, C. C. Chatfield & Co., 1870

CORRENS, KARL: *Deutsche atlantische Expedition auf dem Forschungs-und Vermessungschiff "Meteor."* Wissenschaftliche Ergebnisse, 1925–27

CRANE, JOCELYN: *Book of Bays*, by William Beebe (Chapter XXII with Jocelyn Crane.) New York, Harcourt, Brace & Co., 1942

CUVIER, GEORGES: *The Animal Kingdom Arranged After Its Organization, Forming a Natural History of Animals and an Introduction to Com-*

parative Anatomy. London and Edinburgh, A. Fullarton & Co., 1859

DARLING, FRANK FRASER: *A Herd of Red Deer: A Study in Animal Behaviour*. London, Oxford University Press, 1937

DARLINGTON, CYRILL DEAN: *The Facts of Life*. London, G. Allen & Unwin, 1953

DARWIN, CHARLES ROBERT: *The Descent of Man in Relation to Sex*. New York, D. Appleton & Co., 1930

————: *The Formation of Vegetable Mould Through the Action of Erd Worms*. New York, Appleton, 1896

————: *The Voyage of the Beagle*. New York, Doubleday & Co., 1962

————: *The Origin of Species*. New York, Mentor Book, 1958

DECKERT, KURT and GÜNTHER, KLAUS: *Creatures of the Deep Sea*. New York, Scribner's, 1956

DETZNER, HERMANN: *Vier Jahre unter Kannibalen*. Berlin, A. Scherl, 1920

DICKINSON, R. L.: *Human Sex Anatomy*. Baltimore, The William & Wilkins Co., 1933

DUFOUR, LEON: *Recherches anatomiques et physiologiques sur les Hémiptères*. Paris, Impre. de Bachelier, 1833

EHLERS, ERNST HEINRICH: *Die Borstenwürmer*. Leipzig, W. Engelmann, 1864

EHRENBERG, CHRISTIAN GOTTFRIED: *Die Infusionstierchen als vollkommene Organismen*. Leipzig, L. Voss, 1838

EIPPER, PAUL: *Animals Looking at You*. New York, The Viking Press, 1929

————: *In My Zoo*. New York, The Viking Press, 1932

EISELEY, LOREN: *The Immense Journey*. New York, Random House, 1957

EMPEDOCLES: *The Fragments of Empedocles*. Chicago, The Open Court Publishing Co., 1908

ESCHERICH, KARL: *Die Termiten oder weissen Ameisen*. Leipzig, W. Klinkhardt, 1909

EVANS, EDWARD PAYSON: *The Criminal Prosecution and Capital Punishment of Animals*. London, W. Heinemann, 1906

FABRE, JEAN HENRI CASIMIR: *The Glow Worm and Other Beetles*, 1919

————: *Fabre's Book of Insects*, 1921

————: *Bramble Bees and Others*, 1915

————: *The Hunting Wasps*, 1915

————: *The Life of the Caterpillar*, 1916

————: *The Life of the Fly*, 1913

————: *The Life of the Grasshopper*, 1917

————: *The Life of the Scorpion*, 1923

————: *The Life of the Spider*, 1913

————: *The Life of the Weevil*, 1922

————: *The Mason Bees*, 1914

————: *The Mason Wasps*, 1919

————: *More Beetles*, 1922

————: *The Sacred Beetle and Others*, 1918

(All published by Dodd, Mead & Co., New York)

————: *Insect Adventures*. New York, World Book Co., 1918

————: *The Life and Love of the Insect*. London, A. C. Black Ltd., 1918

————: *Animal Life in Field and Garden*. N.Y., The Century Co., 1921

————: *Social Life in the Insect World*. London, T. F. Unwin, 1922

————: *Souvenirs entomologiques*. Paris, Librairie Delagrave, 1914–24

FENTON, CAROL LANE: *Our Amazing Earth*. New York, Doubleday Doran & Co., Inc., 1938

FLEMING, JOHN: *On a Submarine Forest in the Firth of Tay: with Observations on the Formation of Submarine Forests in General*. Royal Society of Edinbourgh, 1823

FOREL, AUGUST: *Ants and Some Other Insects*. Chicago, The Open Court Publishing Co., 1904

FRANCE, RAOUL HENRI: *Das Liebesleben der Pflanzen*. Stuttgart, Franckh-'sche Verlagsbuchhandlung, 1923

FRANZ, VICTOR: *Zur Anatomie Histologie und funktionellen Gestaltung des Selachierauges*. Jena, G. Fischer, 1905

FREUD, SIGMUND: *Three Contributions to the Theory of Sex*. New York and Washington, Nervous and Mental Disease Publishing Co., 1930

FRIELING, HEINRICH: *Liebes-und Brutleben der Tiere*. Stuttgart, Kosmosgesellschaft der Naturfreunde, 1940.

FRISCH, KARL VON: *The Language of Bees*. Washington, Smithsonian Institution Annual Report, 1938–39

GALILEI, GALILEO: *Le Opere di Galilei*. Firenze, G. Barbera, 1929

GEOFFROY SAINT-HILAIRE, ETIENNE: *Histoire Naturelle des Mammifères*. Paris, A. Belin, 1847

GERHARDT, ULRICH: *Biologie der Fortpflanzung im Tierreich*. Berlin, J. Springer, 1934

GESNER, KONRAD: *Historia Animalium*. Zürich, C. Froschower, 1551–58

GILLIARD, E. THOMAS: *Living Birds of the World*. Doubleday & Co., 1958

GLOGER, CONSTANTIN LAMBERT: *Die Hegung der Höhlenbrüter*. Berlin, Allgemeine Deutsch Verlags-Anstalt, 1865

GOLDSCHMIDT RICHARD BENEDICT: *Portraits from Memory: Recollections of a Zoologist*. Seattle, University of Washington, 1956

GRAAF, REGNIER DE: *Regeneri de Graaf Opera Omnia*. Logduni, Batavorum ex Offizina Hackiana, 1677

GRAUPNER, HEINZ: *Sie erforschten das Leben*. Oldenburg, Hamburg, Stalling, 1960

GRZIMEK, BERNHARD: *Wir Tiere sind ja gar nicht so*. Stuttgart, Frankh, 1941

————: *Affen im Haus*. Stuttgart, Frankh, 1951

————: *Wolf Dschingis*. Stuttgart, Frankh, 1943

GUENTHER, KONRAD: *A Naturalist in Brazil*. Boston & New York, Houghton Mifflin Co., 1931

————: *Natur als Offenbarung*. Stuttgart, I. F. Steinkopf, 1935

GUMPERT, MARTIN: "Kaspar Friedrich Wolff: Founder of the Evolutionary History of Mankind," in *Trail Blazers of Science*. New York, Funk & Wagnalls

HAECKEL, ERNST: *The Evolution of Man*. New York, G. P. Putnam's Sons, 1910

———: *The Riddle of the Universe*. New York and London, Harper & Brothers, 1901

———: *History of Creation: or The Development of the Earth and Its Inhabitants by the Action of Natural Causes*. London, Kegan Paul, Trench, Trubner & Co., Ltd., 1906

———: *Die Kalk-Schwämme*. Berlin, G. Reimer, 1872

HAGBERG, KNUT HJALMAR: *Carl Linnaeus*. New York, Dutton, 1953

HAGEN, HERMANN: *Bibliotheca Entomologica*. Leipzig, W. Engelmann, 1862–63

HALLER, ALBRECHT VON: *Elementa Physiologiae Corporis Humani*. Lausanne, M.-M. Bousquet, 1766

———: *Dr. A. Haller's Physiology*. London, G. Robinson, 1772

HÄMMERLING, JOACHIM: *Fortpflanzung im Tier-und Pflanzenreich*. Berlin, 1951

HARTMANN, MAX: *Geschlecht und Geschlechtsbestimmung im Tier-und Pflanzenreich*. Berlin, W. de Gruyter & Co., 1939

HARTSOEKER, NICOLAAS: *Conjectures Physiques*. Amsterdam, H. Desbordes, 1706

HARVEY, WILLIAM: *The Works of William Harvey*. London. Printed for the Sydenham Society, 1847

HECK, LUDWIG: *Living Pictures of the Animal Kingdom*. New York, Akron, The Saalfield Publishing Co., 1900

———: *Tiere wie sie wirklich sind*. Berlin, P. Parey, 1934

HEINROTH, OSKAR and KATHARINA: *The Birds*. Ann Arbor, University of Michigan Press, 1958

———: *Die Vögel Mitteleuropas*. Berlin, H. Bermüher, 1926–28

———: *Aus dem Leben der Vögel*. Berlin, J. Springer, 1938

HEMPELMANN, FRIEDRICH: *Der Bauplan des Tierkörpers im Zusammenhang mit der Umwelt*. Leipzig, E. A. Seemann, 1922

HERNÁNDEZ, FRANCISCO: *Quatro Libros de la Naturaleza y Virtudes de las Plantas y Animales de uso Medicinal en la Nuova Hispania*. Mexico, Officina Tip. de la Secretaria de Fomento, 1888

HERTWIG, OSCAR: *Textbook of the Embryology of Man and Mammals*. New York, The Macmillan Co., 1899

HESSE, RICHARD and DOFLEIN, FRANZ: *Tierbau und Tierleben in ihrem Zusammenhang betrachtet*. Leipzig and Berlin, B. G. Teubner, 1910–14

HIPPOCRATES: *Hippocrates*, with an English translation by W. H. S. Jones, New York, G. P. Putnam's Sons, 1923

HOFFMEISTER, WERNER: *Die bis jetzt bekannten Arten aus der Familie der Regenwürmer*. Braunschweig, F. Vieweg und Sohn, 1845

HOLMGREN, NILS FRITIOF: *Neu-Guinea Termiten*. Mitteilungen des Zoologischenmuseums, Berlin, 1911

KAESTNER, PAUL: *Die Tierpathogenen Protozoen*. Berlin, R. Schoetz, 1906

KAHN, FRITZ: *Buch der Natur, das Weltbild der modernen Wissenschaft*. Zürich, A. Müller, 1952

KAMMERER, PAUL: *Geschlecht, Fortpflanzung und Fruchtbarkeit: eine Biologie der Zeugung.* München, Dreimasken Verlag, 1927

KEARTON, CHERRY: *The Island of Penguins.* London, New York and Toronto, Longmans, Green & Co., 1930

KINSEY, ALFRED CHARLES, and OTHERS: *Sexual Behavior in the Human Male.* Philadelphia, W. B. Saunders Co., 1948

————: *Sexual Behavior in the Human Female.* Philadelphia, W. B. Saunders Co., 1953

KLOTS, ALEXANDER B.: *Living Insects of the World.* New York, Doubleday & Co., 1959

Knaurs Tierreich in Farben. 6 vol., München, Droemersche Verlagsanstalt Th. Knaur Nachf., 1956–62

KOELREUTER, JOSEPH GOTTLIEB: *Vorläufige Nachricht von einigen das Geschlecht der Pflanzen betreffenden Versuchen.* Leipzig, W. Engelmann, 1893

KRUMBIEGEL, INGO: *Biologie der Säugetiere.* Krefeld, 1960

KÜCHENMEISTER, FRIEDRICH: *On Animal and Vegetable Parasites of the Human Body.* London. Printed for the Sydenham Society, 1857

LAMARCK, JEAN BAPTISTE: *Zoological Philosophy: An Exposition with Regard to the Natural History of Animals.* London, Macmillan, 1914

LEEUWENHOEK, ANTONY VAN: *The Select Works, Parts I and II.* Henry Fry, London, 1798

————: *Part III.* Philanthropic Society, London, 1807

LEUCKART, RUDOLF: *Über die Morphologie und die Verwandtschaftsverhältnisse der wirbellosen Tiere.* Braunschweig, Friedrich Vieweg, 1888

LINNAEUS, CAROLUS: *A General System of Nature Through the Three Grand Kingdoms of Animals, Vegetables and Minerals.* London, 1806

————: *New Illustrations of the Sexual System of Carolus Linnaeus* by R. J. Thornton. London, T. Bensley, 1807

LORENZ, KONRAD: *King Solomon's Ring: New Light on Animal Ways.* New York, T. Y. Crowell Co., 1952

MAETERLINCK, MAURICE: *The Life of the Bee.* New York, Dodd, Mead & Co., 1936

————: *The Life of the Ant.* New York, The John Day Co., 1930

MAGNUS, ALBERTUS, BISHOP OF RATISBONE: *Albertus Magnus.* Chicago, De Laurence, Scott & Co., 1910

MALPIGHI, MARCELLO: *Opera Omnia.* Lugduni, Batavorum Petrum Vander A. S., 1687

MARAIS, EUGÈNE: *The Soul of the White Ant.* London, Methuen & Co., Ltd., 1937

MARSHAL, WILLIAM: *Der Bau der Vögel.* Leipzig, J. J. Weber, 1895

MEAD, MARGARET: *Sex and Temperament in Three Primitive Societies.* New York, W. Morrow & Co., 1935

MELL, RUDOLF: *Biologie und Systematik der Südchinesischen Sphingiden.* Berlin, W. Friedländer & Sohn, 1922

MELLERSH, HAROLD E. L.: *The Story of Man: Human Evolution to the End of the Stone Age.* London, Hutchinson, 1959

372 BIBLIOGRAPHY

MENDEL, GREGOR: *Experiments in Plant-hybridisation.* Cambridge, Harvard University Press, 1925

MERIAN, MARIA SIBYLLA (Frau J. A. Graff): *Dissertatio de Generatione et Metamorphosibus Surinamensium.* Hagaecomitum, Petrus Grosse, 1726

MEYER, ARTHUR WILLIAM: *Human Generation & Conclusions of Burdach Düllinger and von Baer.* Stanford, Stanford University Press, 1956

MIDDENDORF, ALEXANDER THEODOROVICH VON: *Die Barabá.* Mémoires de L'Académie Impériale des Sciences de St. Pétersbourg. St. Pétersbourg, 1870

MILLER, STANLEY: *A Production of Organic Compounds under Possible Primitive Earth Conditions.* Chicago, University of Chicago Press, 1954

MORGAN, THOMAS HUNT: *The Genetics of Drosophila.* In *Bibliographia Genetica.* 's Gravenhage, 1925

MORUS: *A History of Sexual Customs.* New York, Harper & Row, 1960

MÜLLER, JOHANNES: *Elements of Physiology.* Philadelphia, Lea and Blanchard, 1843

NARES, SIR GEORG STRONG: *Narrative of a Voyage in the Polar Sea During 1875–76.* London, S. Low, Marston Searle and Rivington, 1878

NAUMANN, JOHANN ANDREAS: *Naturgeschichte der Vögel Deutschlands.* Leipzig, E. Fleischer, 1820–60

NISSEN, HENRY W.: *A Field Study of the Chimpanzee: Observations of Chimpanzee Behavior and Environment in Western French Guinea.* Baltimore, Johns Hopkins Press, 1931

NOLL, F. C. *Beiträge zur Naturgeschichte der Kieselschwämme.* Frankfurt, Abhandlungen der Naturforscher Ges., 1888

NORDENSKJÖLD, ERIK: *A History of Biology.* New York, A. A. Knopf, 1928

NOWIKOFF, MICHAEL: *Grundzüge der Geschichte der biologischen Theorien: Werdegang der abendländischen Lebensbegriffe.* München, Hanser, 1949

OKEN, LORENZ: *Allgemeine Naturgeschichte für alle Stände.* Stuttgart, Hoffman, 1833

PASTEUR, LOUIS: *Die in der Atmosphäre vorhandenen organisierten Körperchen: Prüfung der Lehre von der Urzeugung.* Leipzig, W. Engelmann, 1892

PERON, FRANÇOIS: *A Voyage of Discovery to the Southern Hemisphere.* London, R. Phillips, 1809

PEYER, BERNHARD: *Geschichte der Tierwelt.* Büchergilde Gutenberg, Zürich, 1950

PIGAFETTA, ANTONIO: *Magellan's Voyage Around the World.* Cleveland, The A. H. Clark Co., 1906

PLINIUS, SECUNDUS: *Natural History.* Cambridge, Harvard University Press, 1938

POOTMANN, FRANZ: *Wie im Paradies: Die Sitten der Tiere.* Frankfurt, Verlag der Frankfurter Bücher, 1958

PORTMANN, ADOLF: *Animals As Social Beings.* New York, Viking Press, 1961

PRATT, J. B.: *Sex Functions in Men.* Baltimore, 1939

RASMUSSEN, KNUD JOHAN VICTOR: *Intellectual Culture of the Copper Eskimos.* Copenhagen, Gyldendal, 1932

REDI, FRANCESCO: *Experiments of the Generation of Insects.* Chicago, The Open Court Publishing Company, 1909

REMANE, ADOLF: *Das soziale Leben der Tiere.* Hamburg, Rowohlt, 1960

ROESEL, ROSENHOF AUGUST JOHANN VON: *De Naturlyke Historie der Insekten.* Amsterdam by C. H. Bohnen, H. DeWitt, 1764–68

ROSTAND, JEAN: *Life, the Great Adventure.* New York, Scribner's, 1956

SAVAGE, THOMAS S.: *A Description of the Characters and Habits of Troglodytes-Gorilla.* Boston, Freeman and Bolles, 1847

SCHMIDT, JOHANNES: *Über die Fortpflanzung des Aals und seine Laichplätze.* Hamburg, Klindworth & Neuhaus, 1912

SCHOMBURGK, SIR ROBERT HERMANN: *Travels in British Guiana, 1840–44.* British Guiana. Published by Authority Georgetown *Daily Chronicle* Office, 1922–23

SCHWANN, THEODOR: *Microscopical Researches into the Accordance in the Structure and Growth of Animals and Plants.* London, The Sydenham Society, 1847

SELIOUS, EDMUND: *Realities of Birdlife.* London, Constable & Co. Ltd., 1927

SHADLE, ALBERT RAY: *The Sex Relations of the Porcupine.* Journal of Mammalogy, 1946

SILVESTRI, FILIPPO: *Contribuzione alla Conoscenza dei Termitidi e Termitofili dell' America Meridionale.* Portici, Premiato Stab. Tip. Vesuviano, 1903

SOKOLOWSKY, ALEXANDER: *Beobachtungen über die Psyche der Menschenaffen.* Frankfurt a. M., Neuer Frankfurter Verlag, 1908

SPALLANZANI, LAZZARO: *Dissertations Relative to the Natural History of Animals and Vegetables.* London, Murray, 1784

SPENGEL, JOHANN WILHELM: *Studien über die Enteropneusten der Siboga Expedition.* Leiden, E. J. Brill, 1907

SPENGLER, OSWALD: *The Decline of the West.* N.Y., Alfred A. Knopf, 1934

SPRENGEL, CHRISTIAN KONRAD: *Das entdeckte Geheimnis der Natur.* Leipzig, Wien, Grelmann, 1894

STEENSTRUP, JOHANNES: *On the Alternation of Generations.* London. George Busk printed for the Ray Society, 1845

STRESEMAN, N. ERWIN: *Die Entwicklung der Ornithologie von Aristoteles bis zur Gegenwart.* Berlin, Scherz & Groverts, 1951

SWAMMERDAM, JAN: *The Book of Nature; or, The History of Insects.* London. Printed for C. G. Seyffert, 1758

TASCHENBERG, ERNST LUDWIG: *Die Insekten.* Leipzig, P. Reclam Jun., 1929

TEMBROCK, GÜNTER: *Verhaltensforschung.* Jena, G. Fischer, 1961

———: *Tierpsychologie.* Wittenberg Lutherstadt, A. Ziemsen, 1956

THESING, CURT: *Wunder der Fortpflanzung.* München, Weismann, 1948

———: *Geheimnisse des Lebens.* München, Weismann, 1947

TINBERGEN, NIKOLAAS: *Social Behavior in Animals with Special Reference to Vertebrates.* New York, Wiley, 1953

TREMBLEY, ABRAHAM: *Mémoires pour servir à l'histoire d'un Genre Polypes d'eau douce à bras en forme de cornes.* Leiden, Jean and Herman Verbeck, 1744

TSCHERMAK-SEISENEGG, ERICH VON: *Versuche über Pflanzenhybriden.* Leipzig, W. Engelmann, 1901

UEXKÜLL, JAKOB VON and KRISZAT, GEORG: *Streifzüge durch die Umwelten der Tiere und Menschen.* Hamburg, Rowohlt Verlag, 1961

UREY, HAROLD CLAYTON: *Distribution of Electrons in the Various Orbits of the Hydrogen Atom; The Best Capacities and Entropies of Diatomic and Poly-atomic Gases.* Berkeley, University of California Press, 1924

VALLISNIERI, ANTONIO: *Dialoghi del Signor Dottor Antonio Vallisnieri.* Venezia, G. Albrizzi, 1700

VESALIUS, ANDREAS: *Des Andreas Vesalius sechs anatomische Tafeln.* Leipzig, J. A. Barth, 1920

VINCI, LEONARDO DA: *The Notebooks of Leonardo da Vinci.* New York, Reynal & Hitchcock, 1939

———: *The Literary Works of Leonardo da Vinci.* London, New York, Oxford University Press, 1939

VOGT, KARL: *The Natural History of Animals in Word and Picture.* London, Blackie and Son Ltd., 1890

VRIES, HUGO DE: *The Mutation Theory: Experiments and Observations on the Origin of Species in the Vegetable Kingdom.* Chicago, The Open Court Publishing Co., 1909

WALLACE, ALFRED RUSSEL: *The Malay Archipelago, the Land of the Orang-utan and the Bird of Paradise.* London and New York, The Macmillan Co., 1894

WALTON, IZAAK and COTTON, CHARLES: *The Complete Angler.* Privately Printed for the Navarro Society, 1925

WEIL, ARTHUR: *The Internal Secretions.* New York, The Macmillan Co., 1914

WESENBERG-LUND, CURT JURGEN: *Anatomical Description of the Larva of Mansonia.* Richardii Odense, 1918

WEYGANDT, WALTER: *Lehrbuch der Nerven und Geisteskrankheiten.* Halle a. S., Marhold, 1935

WILLIAMS, TENNESSEE: *Suddenly Last Summer.* New York, The New American Library, 1960

YERKES, ROBERT M. and YERKES, ADA: *The Great Apes.* New Haven, Yale University Press, 1929

ZIMMERMANN, RUDOLF: *Das Liebesleben der Vögel.* Dresden, E. Reissner, 1922

ZUCKERMAN, SOLLY: *The Social Life of Monkeys and Apes.* London, Kegan Paul, Trench, Trubner & Co., Ltd., 1932

INDEX

375